A ROOM OF ONE'S OWN

THE VOYAGE OUT

A Room of One's Own

The Voyage Out

◆

VIRGINIA WOOLF

with Introductions and Notes by
SALLY MINOGUE

WORDSWORTH CLASSICS

For my husband
ANTHONY JOHN RANSON
with love from your wife, the publisher.
Eternally grateful for your unconditional love.

Readers who are interested in other titles from
Wordsworth Editions are invited to visit our website at
www.wordsworth-editions.com

For our latest list and a full mail-order service, contact
Bibliophile Books, 5 Datapoint, South Crescent, London E16 4TL
TEL: +44 (0)20 7474 2474 FAX: +44 (0)20 7474 8589
ORDERS: orders@bibliophilebooks.com
WEBSITE: www.bibliophilebooks.com

First published in 2012 by Wordsworth Editions Limited
8B East Street, Ware, Hertfordshire SG12 9HJ

ISBN 978 1 84022 679 9

Text © Wordsworth Editions Limited 2012
Introduction and Notes © Sally Minogue 2012

Wordsworth® is a registered trade mark of
Wordsworth Editions Limited

Wordsworth Editions
is the company founded in 1987 by
MICHAEL TRAYLER

Typeset in Great Britain by Antony Gray
Printed and bound by Clays Ltd, St Ives plc

CONTENTS

GENERAL INTRODUCTION

Wordsworth Classics are inexpensive editions designed to appeal to the general reader and students. We commission teachers and specialists to write wide-ranging, jargon-free introductions and in some cases to provide notes that will assist the understanding of our readers rather than interpret the stories for them. In the same spirit, because the pleasures of reading are inseparable from the surprises, secrets and revelations that all narratives contain, we strongly advise you to enjoy this book before turning to the Introduction.

General Adviser: KEITH CARABINE
Rutherford College, University of Kent at Canterbury

A ROOM OF ONE'S OWN

A Room
of One's Own

◆

VIRGINIA WOOLF

This essay is based upon two papers presented by
VIRGINIA WOOLF
*to the Arts Society at Newnham and
the Odtaa at Girton in October 1928.
The papers were too long to be read in full
and have since been altered and expanded.*

INTRODUCTION TO
A Room of One's Own

A Room of One's Own is an iconic text of the twentieth century. Many people will think they have read it when they have not; and even when they have not read it, they might have some idea of what it is about. Virginia Woolf's title is in that way a stroke of genius, since it announces something we can all understand. A room of one's own: privacy, independence, security, shelter, but not necessarily separated from the lives of others in the same house or building, and therefore not inherently signifying isolation or loneliness. The chance to be alone, to be oneself in one's own room, to do what one wills and wishes without the thought or intervention of others: this is the ultimate desire of the social animal, the human being, only because s/he is both hemmed about by and can always resort to the company of others.

But Woolf's clever pronoun, 'one', disguises the fact that her essay does not apply to us all. This is a piece emphatically *parti pris*, addressed by a woman to women, about women. Naturally, men figure largely in such a piece of writing; and if men are not the original intended audience, this essay is surely required reading for them, especially here in the twenty-first century where we can come to these matters more equally and coolly. Women and men will, however, read this essay differently; and this is the nub of Woolf's argument. With a grammatical nicety which is almost lost to us, Woolf uses 'one' to apply to herself whilst avoiding an over-personalisation; it is, as it were, the royal use of 'one', where the gender of the speaker infects the pronoun whilst keeping its impersonality. Key to this is the fact that this essay has its origin in a couple of lectures which Woolf gave to female undergraduate audiences at Cambridge, at Newnham and Girton colleges respectively. There is a deliberate complicity with her female audience at times, a teasing 'dare we?' about literary references to same-sex love, a crude irony about the male Oxbridge academic, which certainly derive from the original delivery as lectures.

These elements can be a touch trying. Woolf's irony in particular can hang heavy, the more so when it deliberately obscures a more complex set of responses. Her style, too, can be meandering, to the point of perplexing the reader. Yet suddenly, in the midst of apparently gentle reflections, probing and finding her way, she delivers a number of poniard thrusts which make me frankly glad to be a woman. And indeed this is the real function of the essay, to provide a turning point for the woman reader where even as she reads and understands how she has been systematically robbed of power, she is given power by that understanding. She is given the tools for the job. For today's male reader, while it sometimes makes uncomfortable reading, the interest and importance of the piece lie in the way it lays bare a historical inequality which, Woolf shows, was perhaps as damaging for men as for women. And both men and women can read it today from the vantage point of having achieved at least a measure of redress of the unequal relations of power which Woolf so elegantly lays bare.

The writer of this essay and its original Cambridge audience had both escaped already some of the structural inequalities that it analyses. Woolf, from the age of twenty-two, had not only a room of her own, but her own sitting room;[1] the female undergraduates she addresses would also enjoy the college luxury of a private bed and study room, even if they had not experienced that before. But the strength of this for Woolf is that she knows whereof she speaks; she understands, from her own privileged position, exactly how important her advantages have been to her, and to that extent how exceptional she is in being able to pursue the freedom necessary to an artist.

Woolf's understanding of the necessity of that freedom lies at the heart of *A Room of One's Own*, for she is interested predominantly not in women as a class but in the woman artist; it is almost by the by that she comments on the lot of women in general. The central, and best remembered, passage of the essay (it occurs in the third of six chapters), is that in which Woolf conjures up the shade of a woman who never existed, and yet who exists powerfully in our imagination after reading this essay: Shakespeare's sister.[2] Woolf notes that '[it] was a bishop, I

---

1 See Virginia Woolf, 'Old Bloomsbury', in *Moments of Being: Unpublished Autobiographical Writings*, edited by Jeanne Schulkind, p. 187. For full details of this and of all other works cited, please turn to the Bibliography which follows the Introduction.

2 Tillie Olsen points out that Woolf's argument and example are prefigured by Olive Schreiner in *From Man to Man* (1883); the relevant passage from Schreiner is quoted in Olsen's *Silences*, p. 151.

think, who declared that it was impossible for any woman, past, present, or to come, to have the genius of Shakespeare' (p. 60). In a clever subversion of his argument, Woolf concurs that 'the bishop was right at least in this: it would have been impossible, completely and entirely, for any woman to have written the plays of Shakespeare in the age of Shakespeare' (p. 60), going on to show that economic, social and cultural circumstances would have made that impossible. The bishop's point, of course, is that women are inherently inferior and so could not have the imaginative capability to produce such works. Woolf's brilliant stroke is to see that women's inferiority in this respect was culturally determined, and that the very bishop's opinion remains in her own time part of that cultural determination.

Who would have put Virginia Woolf down as a cultural materialist? (By cultural materialism, I mean a set of explanations of the relations of power as being determined by the social and economic circumstances in which people find themselves living, and which also underlie the production of culture.) Well before we had even heard of the term she crisply reveals the way in which socio-economics has shaped the role of women in society and in culture. The age of Shakespeare is apt for her analysis (as indeed it has proved to be for contemporary critics in that field). With the example of Shakespeare's sister, she brings the theory down to the level of the individual:

> She had the quickest fancy, a gift like her brother's, for the tune of words. Like him, she had a taste for the theatre. She stood at the stage door; she wanted to act, she said. Men laughed in her face. The manager – a fat, loose-lipped man – guffawed. He bellowed something about poodles dancing and women acting – no woman, he said, could possibly be an actress. He hinted – you can imagine what. She could get no training in her craft. Could she even seek her dinner in a tavern or roam the streets at midnight? Yet her genius was for fiction and lusted to feed abundantly upon the lives of men and women and the study of their ways.   [pp. 61–2]

Judith Shakespeare ends badly: 'killed herself one winter's night and lies buried at some crossroads where the omnibuses now stop outside the Elephant and Castle' (p. 62). But the harsher the story becomes, the more Woolf distances herself from the patronising bishop. Her point is that Shakespeare's sister – the symbol of any woman writer or artist of his period – could not but fail, even with a gift equal to Shakespeare's, because she had neither the imaginative nor the physical freedom that come from economic freedom, that ability to 'seek her dinner in a tavern or roam the streets at midnight'.

Furthermore there is a vulnerability added to the woman in earlier societies, that if she avails herself of social and economic freedom, she risks being therefore seen as sexually available. This is why Judith Shakespeare, in Woolf's scenario, ends as she does. For 'who shall measure the heat and violence of the poet's heart when caught and tangled in a woman's body?' (p. 62). Woolf distances the twentieth-century woman from the imagined Judith in this respect of sexual risk, but we are still aware of its spectre for women, and of the converse but linked suspicion of women's powers. Woolf is spot on when she says:

> When, however, one reads of a witch being ducked, of a woman possessed by devils, of a wise woman selling herbs, or even of a very remarkable man who had a mother, then I think we are on the track of a lost novelist, a suppressed poet, of some mute and inglorious Jane Austen, some Emily Brontë who dashed her brains out on the moor . . .   [p. 62] [3]

In this brief but eloquent description lie the tragedies of many women, even up to and including the present day in certain societies.

Woolf's is not then a text of the past; but it is of its moment. Only ten years before Woolf gave her lectures to the young women of Newnham and Girton, no woman had the vote. It had taken a bitter, and sometimes bitterly divided, campaign to achieve the vote for women in January 1918, and only then with the qualification that they must be over thirty (to avoid the inflammatory notion of universal suffrage). In November 1918 women were granted the right to stand as Members of Parliament, catching up with the right of women to vote for the same. The lectures were delivered in 1928, another landmark year, with women over twenty-one granted the vote, and the achievement of universal suffrage. Yet Virginia Woolf specifies that achieving the vote in that year was far less important than having an independent income.

It has been conveniently forgotten in the remarkable history of Woolf's influential feminist essay that she consistently places money alongside a room of one's own as a prerequisite for female independence. Indeed it comes first. Here she is on the very first page of her essay: 'a woman must have money and a room of her own if she

---

3 Woolf here draws on Thomas Gray's 'Elegy Written in a Country Church-yard', where he imagines 'some mute inglorious Milton' buried in anonymity. Gray's point is about class; Woolf neatly turns it to one about gender.

is to write fiction' (p. 29). It is an uncompromising statement. Later it becomes more specific:

> My aunt, Mary Beton, I must tell you, died by a fall from her horse when she was riding out to take the air in Bombay. The news of my legacy reached me one night about the same time that the act was passed that gave votes to women. A solicitor's letter fell into the postbox and when I opened it I found that she had left me five hundred pounds a year for ever. Of the two – the vote and the money – the money, I own, seemed infinitely the more important . . . No force in the world can take from me my five hundred pounds. Food, house and clothing are mine for ever. Therefore not merely do effort and labour cease, but also hatred and bitterness. I need not hate any man; he cannot hurt me. I need not flatter any man; he has nothing to give me. [pp. 53–4]

Allowing both for the captious tone of this and for the fictional framework (Woolf adopts an alter ego for much of her essay: 'call me Mary Beton, Mary Seton, Mary Carmichael or by any name you please' [p. 30]), the point made is deadly serious. Woolf sees financial independence as of equal importance to the woman artist as the 'room of one's own', not because it can provide that room (which can be got by other means), but because in itself it entirely alters the woman's relationship with men. Her device of the legacy of course calls up nineteenth-century fiction. Charlotte Brontë's Jane Eyre is freed by a legacy both to refuse marriage with her cousin St John Rivers and to seek it on a now equal footing with Rochester. Elizabeth Gaskell's Margaret Hale (in North and South) uses hers to lend money to the man who will become her husband, thus establishing a sort of equality before marriage.[4] But these are legacies mired in the old relations of men and women. For the twentieth-century woman the money is to be used for true independence; it buys the freedom of the artist.

In Chapter 4, when Woolf is giving a quick historical run-through of known English women writers, she commends Aphra Behn as the first woman to earn her living with her pen. Behn, she notes, circumvented the need of a legacy, or being born with private means; she got the money by her own labour. But Woolf, without specifying, implies that there was a cost in terms of her personal life; the implication is that

---

4 See respectively Charlotte Brontë, *Jane Eyre*, and Elizabeth Gaskell, *North and South*.

though Behn's was an excellent model in terms of financial independence through writing, it was a model which was also used as a warning to women of the risks of that independence. Woolf is perhaps making the mistake here of conflating the bawdy nature of Behn's plays with her personal circumstances.[5] And it is an interesting mistake. For in *The Cambridge History of English Literature* current with Woolf's time – a deeply masculinist history on the whole – Behn is given equal page space with other dramatists of her time. Moreover, F. E. Schelling, in the relevant volume and chapter, published in 1911, defends her against the implied charge Woolf makes:

> Mrs Behn was a very gifted woman, compelled to write for bread in an age in which literature, and especially comedy, catered habitually to the lowest and most depraved of human inclinations. Her success depended on her ability to write like a man. On the score of morality, she is again and again more daring and *risquée* than any of her male competitors . . . But as has been well said, it remains difficult for us to believe that a woman whose literary talents commended her to the friendship and association of Dryden could have been degraded in her personal life.[6]

Even allowing for a certain patriarchal slant in Schelling's comment, he is nevertheless fairer to Behn than is Woolf in the matter of confusing her life with her art.[7]

Woolf redeems herself, however, in her full and admiring recognition of the historical importance of Behn's example:

> All women together ought to let flowers fall on the tomb of Aphra Behn . . . for it was she who earned them the right to speak their minds. It is she – shady and amorous as she was – who makes it not

---

5 Woolf would undoubtedly have been influenced by Vita Sackville-West's account of Aphra Behn. Sackville-West's book, *Aphra Behn: The Incomparable Astrea*, was published in 1927; although she does make a creditable attempt to distinguish Behn's life from her work, and commends her for being the first woman to make her living from writing, she does also to some extent perpetuate Behn's reputation for sexual availability.

6 *Cambridge History*, Vol. VIII, p. 142

7 Sue Wiseman, in *Aphra Behn*, points out how very little fact is known of Behn's life, and how much has been speculatively suggested, based on the content of her work. She does note that 'when she was alive ... she had a reputation for sexual freedom', p. 5. Wiseman's book gives a recent, balanced account of Behn's work and importance.

quite fantastic for me to say to you tonight: Earn five hundred a year
by your wits.   [p. 74]

The specificity of £500 a year is a rhetorical device, but it is striking
how often it is repeated through the essay, calling us back to the simple
and singular importance of money. And here something needs to be
said about the value of money in 1928 relative to the present day. I am
indebted to Alan Carruth for pointing out the distinction between the
calculation for the relative values as income, and the calculation for
those values as spending power. He notes that 'one of the well-
documented and defining economic trends of the twentieth century
was the much faster rate of increase of consumer prices compared to
previous centuries ... This huge increase in the price level ... means
that the price levels recorded in [1928] bear no relation to current values
for roughly similar goods and services.'[8] Carruth has kindly provided me
with the equivalent values today of £500 in 1928, using the calculation
both for income and for spending power. These are staggeringly
different, as is explained by the aforementioned huge growth in consumer
prices. In terms of income, then, £500 a year would today be £86,089,
which sounds an extraordinarily large amount for a writer to need to
survive, or a woman to need to be fully independent of a man – surely a
smaller sum would suffice for either? However, the equivalent today of
£500 a year in terms of spending power would be £19,000; while this is
still a large sum, and would be adequate to live on independently today, it
is by no means generous. Another way of looking at the figures is to look
at average incomes for various groups in the 1920s. In 1920 an unskilled
worker earned £80 a year; a civil servant earned £240; and a doctor
earned £450 (all average figures). So Woolf is pitching the required
income at around the level of income of a higher professional in her day.

Interestingly, £500 is precisely the sum that Vera Brittain was granted
in 1932 as an annuity by her father, after her marriage and the birth
of her two children, to ensure that she was freed from household
responsibilities. The decision by Brittain's father was to counter her
husband's suggestion that they save money by her assuming more
household responsibilities rather than employing servants. The
alternative if her father had not settled this money on her would have
been to earn an equivalent sum by day-to-day journalism. The annuity

8 Carruth in Keith Carabine and Alan Carruth, *Conradiana*, Vol. 40, Summer
   2008, No. 2, p. 202; my general figures about earnings in 1920 are also
   taken from this review.

thus freed her both from 'women's work' and hack work, and allowed her to bring to fruition the book which made her reputation, *Testament of Youth* (1933).[9]

Brittain makes an interesting counterpoint to Woolf. They are not exact contemporaries (Brittain was eleven years younger), and Woolf's background was both more intellectual and more of the upper-class social world than Brittain's (which she herself describes, with much distaste, as one of 'provincial young-ladyhood', the title of Chapter 2 of *Testament of Youth*). Yet it was Brittain who fought her way to Oxford against the initial wishes of her parents; Woolf never received that formal education, and there are times in *A Room of One's Own* where one feels a pull of resentment at that lack. Talking about the fictional Shakespeare's sister, she notes:

> She was as adventurous, as imaginative, as agog to see the world as he was. But she was not sent to school. She had no chance of learning grammar and logic, let alone of reading Horace and Virgil. She picked up a book now and then, one of her brother's perhaps, and read a few pages. But then her parents came in and told her to mend the stockings or mind the stew and not moon about with books and papers.   [p. 61]

True, Woolf would never have been told to mend stockings or mind the stew; that was what servants were for (of which more later). But, though given the run of her father's library, and her father's guidance and encouragement in reading, and a private tutor, and availing herself of lessons in Greek and History at King's College London at the age of fifteen, Woolf, along with her sister Vanessa, was treated differently from her brothers Thoby and Adrian in the matter of public formal education and its attendant expectations:

> Father laid enormous stress upon schoolmasters' reports, upon scholarships, triposes[10] and fellowships . . . Every one of our male relations was shot into that [patriarchal machinery] and came out at the other end, at the age of sixty or so, a Headmaster, an Admiral, a Cabinet Minister, a Judge. It is as impossible to think of them as natural human beings as it is to think of a plough horse galloping wild and unshod in the street.   [*Moments of Being*, p. 154]

9 Paul Berry and Mark Bostridge, *Vera Brittain: A Life*, p. 244. *Testament of Youth* remains a classic text of World War I and its aftermath.
10 Cambridge degree examinations

The final image suggests dismay at the constraint of her male relations within the social machine; but where did it leave her and Vanessa? Horses galloping wild and unshod in the street? Certainly they were not that, and Virginia was wonderfully well read and schooled in the Classics. But they were never in the club, never accepted as the winners of prizes. While, in their own milieu, this gave them a certain freedom, it also left its mark. Recounting their father going through the account books with Vanessa (as the elder daughter, the female appointed to answer to him in and for the household), while she looked on, Virginia depicts Leslie Stephen's terrifying rages:

> Even now I can find nothing to say of his behaviour save that it was brutal. If, instead of words, he had used a whip the brutality would have been no greater . . . These scenes were never indulged in before men . . . If Thoby had presented those books or George, the explosion would have been suppressed. Why had he no shame in front of women? Partly of course because the woman was his slave – being the most typical of Victorians. [*Moments of Being*, pp. 145–6]

By comparison, Vera Brittain's father, in spite of his initial discouragement of Brittain's educational ambitions, comes out rather well; and her brother Edward encouraged her to try for the Somerville Scholarship (rather than just the Entrance) examinations, and was delighted when he learnt that she would join him at Oxford. After Oxford, both Brittain and her lifelong companion and colleague Winifred Holtby devoted themselves to political work on behalf of women, through the Six Point Group which campaigned for social justice for women in areas such as pensions, the rights of the unmarried mother, and equal pay in the public sector. Brittain's first non-fiction book, published in July 1928 a few months before Woolf's Cambridge lectures, was *Women's Work in Modern England*, inspired in part by Olive Schreiner's feminist work, *Woman and Labour* (1911). Brittain and Holtby were part of a well-established women's movement which went beyond the issue of suffrage into areas of social justice and equality for all women.

This was not Woolf's way. Although she did and could write politically, and in support of feminism, her diaries reveal a certain suspicion of political activism. She admired *Testament of Youth*, and allowed rather than encouraged Holtby's book on her own work;[11] but,

---

11 Holtby's *Virginia Woolf: A Critical Memoir* was published in 1932.

in personal terms, she was unpleasantly contemptuous of both women. Brittain's was 'a stringy metallic mind, with, I suppose, the sort of taste I should dislike in real life' (*Diary*, Vol. IV, 2 September 1933, p. 177). Holtby she characterised as 'a Yorkshire farmer's daughter, rather uncouth, and shapeless' (letter to Vanessa Bell, 14 May 1931, *Letters*, Vol. IV, p. 331) who 'learnt to read, I'm told, while minding the pigs' (letter to Hugh Walpole, 26 October 1932, *Letters*, Vol. V, p. 114). This casual, cruel snobbery runs through her writing, but here perhaps it veils a deep-seated jealousy; Holtby, after all, had an Oxford degree, one of the men's prizes.[12] Whatever Woolf's view of Brittain and Holtby, *A Room of One's Own* needs to be seen in its proper relation to the long and well-established feminist movement to which they belonged, which devoted itself to the rights of all women, and which was in certain of its manifestations embedded in socialism and the rights of man.

Woolf sets herself against these models, and it is important to note that she does so in part because writing is her forte. Brittain's and Holtby's writings are leaden in comparison. Woolf sees, rightly, that it is through her strength and elegance as a writer that she can make a difference. Perhaps this is why she devotes her essay to a certain sort of woman, the artist, and in particular the writer. The 'witch being ducked . . . the wise woman selling herbs' she sees only as the frustrated writer; but might not that witch, that wise woman, simply have been a frustrated woman? Woolf implies that it is the special gift of creativity that necessitates 'money and a room of one's own'. In fact, any woman would flourish with those provisions, and any woman deserves them, including the women of the working class who underpinned the life-styles of both Woolf and Brittain. Both writers had ample rooms of their own in which to advance feminist principles, without much genuine thought about whether their female servants had the conditions they were advocating. Brittain's £500 a year allowed her to buy the services of household staff, and thus buy her own intellectual freedom; Woolf comments in her *Diary* of 21 September 1929 (Vol. IV, p. 255), just before the publication of *A Room of One's Own*, that her housemaid Annie has to manage on 15s. a week (the princely sum of £39 a year).[13] And Woolf's arguments about money and a room

12 Holtby and Brittain were in the first year of women to receive degrees at Oxford, which changed its Statutes in 1920 to allow women full membership of the university.

13 To be fair to Woolf, at Annie's request she purchased the cottage Annie was living in, which she then occupied rent-free in exchange for the full-time

could equally apply to working-class men. She briefly and tangentially mentions such men, but without a thought of their hidden writing lives – or even just their hidden lives.

And yet, and yet; we must allow Woolf the canvas she has chosen, and we should be glad of the concentration, the eloquence, the analytic intelligence and the grace and wit that she brings to her subject. For all the apparent hypocrisies and contradictions, Woolf (and Brittain too in her different way) made huge contributions to the advancement of all women. Even if we accept that Woolf's argument in her essay is devoted to the woman writer, she at the same time exposes ruthlessly the structural inequalities which mean that women, including herself, have been excluded from positions of power, even at the simple individual level of power over their own lives. To point it out was to begin to address it. Woolf's gift is as a writer, and she uses all her considerable writerly skills to show to both men and women what needs to be changed in the material circumstances of society to bring about women's equality with men. Part of her technique in the essay is to take the reader with her through the vagaries of her researches, to show the enormousness and impenetrability of her topic 'women and fiction', and to stand us alongside her in her mind, as her train of thought develops with her wanderings from lunch to river or street to library and to lunch again. The constraints of time are forgotten and the researches are shown as seamless, again to reflect the continuous pattern of her thought. In Chapter 2, now in the British Museum Reading Room, she sits haplessly, achieving little except to produce a caricature of Professor von X who she imagines is writing 'his monumental work entitled *The Mental, Moral and Physical Inferiority of the Female Sex*' (p. 49). Looking idly at a newspaper as she breaks her researches for lunch, and noting the various news stories, from murders and film actresses at one end to politics and sport at the other (cricket has the biggest headline), she concludes:

> The most transient visitor to this planet, I thought, who picked up this paper could not fail to be aware . . . that England is under the rule of a patriarchy. Nobody in their senses could fail to detect the dominance of the professor. His was the power and the money and the influence. He was the proprietor of the paper and its editor and

---

commitment of her labour to the Woolfs at Monks House. Patriarchal as this exchange might itself be seen to be, it saved Annie from poverty and gave her a cottage, if not of her own, then leased to her for her labour.

> sub-editor. He was the Foreign Secretary and the judge. He was the cricketer; he owned the racehorses and the yachts. He was the director of the company that pays two hundred per cent to its shareholders. He left millions to charities and colleges that were ruled by himself. He suspended the film actress in midair. He will decide if the hair on the meat axe is human; he it is who will acquit or convict the murderer . . . With the exception of the fog he seemed to control everything. [p. 51]

In this rhetoric the professor may remain a caricature; but the patriarchal control which Woolf sees through the lens of the newspaper is no caricature.

Earlier, in Chapter 1, she has traced a path through 'Oxbridge', seeking inspiration for her subject. Beside the river 'Thought . . . had let its line down into the stream' and caught something, 'the little tug' of an idea which 'however small it was, it had, nevertheless, the mysterious property of its kind – put back into the mind, it became at once very exciting, and important; and as it darted and sank, and flashed hither and thither, set up such a wash and tumult of ideas that it was impossible to sit still' (pp. 30–1). Woolf here captures wonderfully the thrill of intellectual discovery; and for her it is so great that she jumps to her feet:

> I found myself walking with extreme rapidity across a grass plot. Instantly a man's figure rose to intercept me. Nor did I at first understand that the gesticulations of a curious-looking object, in a cut-away coat and evening shirt, were aimed at me. His face expressed horror and indignation. Instinct rather than reason came to my help; he was a beadle; I was a woman. This was the turf; there was the path. Only the Fellows and Scholars are allowed here; the gravel is the place for me. [p. 31]

Woolf's use of apposition (' . . . he was a beadle; I was a woman. This was the turf; there was the path') neatly places the relation of power here; and meanwhile, her idea has fled. None the less, she resumes her thinking as she wanders through the courts and quadrangles; and now she bethinks herself, via Charles Lamb, of Milton's poem *Lycidas* and of Thackeray's novel *Henry Esmond* (*The History of Henry Esmond, Esq.*, 1852) and realises that she is near the library that contains their respective manuscripts. Again, she captures very cleverly the patterns of thought in her own mind, the series of connections so quickly made, unfettered, free ranging, while also demonstrating her own wide knowledge and curiosity of mind. These carry her, as naturally as walking, to the library:

> ... here I was actually at the door which leads into the library itself. I must have opened it, for instantly there issued, like a guardian angel barring the way with a flutter of black gown instead of white wings, a deprecating, silvery, kindly gentleman, who regretted in a low voice as he waved me back that ladies are only admitted to the library if accompanied by a Fellow of the College or furnished with a letter of introduction. [p. 32]

The two examples are, it is true, particular to Oxbridge, and redolent of the assured exclusivity of that institution. But the writing itself enacts the way such exclusions and barrings of the way to women act as an abrupt stop on the very freedom of thought itself, even to as established a writer and thinker as Virginia Woolf herself.

Woolf's response is first anger, and then self-restriction, or anyway self-exclusion; seeing the college chapel and the door open for service, she now recoils: 'I had no wish to enter had I the right, and this time the verger might have stopped me, demanding perhaps my baptismal certificate, or a letter of introduction from the Dean. But the outside of these magnificent buildings is often as beautiful as the inside' (p. 32). Thus she enacts the way women have been led to censor themselves, to assume exclusion even before they are excluded. Yet at the same time we feel here emerging in Woolf a sort of pride in being on the outside. Watching the university members entering the chapel, 'one was reminded of those giant crabs and crayfish who heave with difficulty across the sand of an aquarium. As I leant against the wall the university indeed seemed a sanctuary in which are preserved rare types which would soon be obsolete if left to fight for existence on the pavement of the Strand' (p. 33). At the end of this first chapter, setting the scene for the essay by revisiting the manner in which she investigated her topic of 'women and fiction', she reflects, 'I thought how unpleasant it is to be locked out; and I thought how it is worse perhaps to be locked in ...' (p. 44). This calls to mind the machine into which the boys are fed and spat out as men – successful, powerful men certainly, and not really aware of how they have been shaped to be so, but still shaped always into a certain mould. Women escape that fate, as Woolf shows; in this respect they have the advantage over men. But always men's power and superiority hold the day, benefiting, in respect of pure power, the weakest of men, and holding back the strongest of women.

Woolf thus makes clear the material nature of women's

disadvantage. She also proposes ways to combat it. This is where 'a room of one's own' comes to the fore. In Woolf's first novel, *The Voyage Out* (1915), the central character, Rachel, is persuaded to leave her father's voyage up the Amazon, and instead accompany her aunt to a South American port:

> Among the promises which Mrs Ambrose had made her niece should she stay was a room cut off from the rest of the house, large, private – a room in which she could play, read, think, defy the world, a fortress as well as a sanctuary. Rooms, she knew, became more like worlds than rooms at the age of twenty-four. Her judgment was correct, and when she shut the door Rachel entered an enchanted place, where the poets sang and things fell into their right proportions.   [*The Voyage Out*, p. 244]

This is the sort of room Woolf has in mind when she proposes that every woman artist needs a room of her own. One would not mind being locked into such a room. And this is perhaps the difference between what men are locked into and what women might aspire to. For a woman, that singular room opens out into a large mental space. A man has always had that space and he has taken it for granted; but it is closed down for him by the constraints and expectations of society. Yes, he has power, always; but the rooms within which he can wield that power are predetermined. Just because a woman hasn't characteristically had that power, when a space opens up for her, it expands beyond itself into something greater. This is the optimistic message of Woolf's essay.

A Room of One's Own and Feminism

A Room of One's Own has a special place in the development of feminist thought and action in the twentieth century (and continuing into the twenty-first century). As I reread it now I am astonished by the extent to which Woolf prefigures so many of the arguments of the women's movement and of feminist theory from the 1960s onwards. One is tempted to say that the movement and the theory could not have happened without this extraordinary precursor, though Woolf's determinedly materialist position would argue against that. She begins with an analysis of patriarchy, of the ways in which women's lack of power is written into the structures of society; she complements that with a reading of the way women's sexuality became part of the structures of her subjection. She takes a clearly historicist position, showing the ways in which women's power gradually increased over time (while always remaining subjugated to that of men) as her socio-economic position improved. She links this to the extent to which the woman artist could flourish, showing that initially only women of a higher social class and private means could even think of taking up the pen. She shows, using the unusual model of Aphra Behn, that it was possible to earn one's own living by that pen, but in Behn's time only to the detriment of her personal reputation. None the less, Behn set the example, and thereafter it became possible for women to make their living by writing (but not probable, and not common). The great period of emancipation for the female writer comes in the nineteenth century; for Woolf this is because women then had a sitting-room to write in – Jane Austen, the Brontës, George Eliot. But as she points out, who knows what they might have written if they had had a private rather than a public space to operate in?

All of this seems very well known to us now. But Woolf said what had never been said. We are familiar with it only because her cry was taken up by feminists who came after her. No better exemplar could itself be adduced for the female role model, the very argument Woolf puts forward when she says that we should all lay flowers on Aphra Behn's tomb. And Woolf goes further. She anticipates the importance of early models of female writing (the idea that gave the impetus to the publishing house Virago, which in turn opened up a mass of women's writing to a mass audience). She gives a thorough and persuasive Marxist (materialist) analysis of women's subjection. Same sex love enters her frame, as it did her life. While she does not go so far as separatism, *écriture feminine* can be spotted in her account of male and female difference.[14] One must bow before the full frame of her reference, and before her prescience.

One other thing Woolf understands which was important to later feminists: anger. Storm Jameson, also a contemporary of Woolf, recounts her mother's 'fits of rage when she jerked the Venetian blinds in her room up and down, up and down, for the relief of hearing the crash'.[15] We will all think of our mothers when we read this. Jameson's mother, a housewife in Hull, is the sort of person who is outside Woolf's

---

14 *Écriture feminine* is a writing which is seen by certain twentieth-century feminist theorists, most notably Hélène Cixous, as distinctively female in its form as well as in its concerns.

15 Storm Jameson, *Journey from the North*, Vol. 1, p. 33, quoted in Anthea Trodd, *Women's Writing in English: Britain 1900–1945*, p. 11

remit. But the rage Jameson identifies is of the same kilter as that which Woolf feels when excluded from the college turf and the college library. They may derive from entirely different experiences and be framed by entirely different backgrounds, but the feeling is the same, and the reason for the feeling is the same.

Woolf looks at that anger, and admits to it in herself; yet she doesn't like it when it breaks through into women's writing. Her ideal (exemplified by Shakespeare) is of the writer freed from extraneous pressures into a purified writer's medium where true writing comes forth. This is odd given her understanding of the effects of the material on the creative – clearly Shakespeare was as subject to those effects as the rest of us. Woolf has been criticised by feminists for this ideal of creative androgyny, with women writers escaping any emotional under-tow to float into free creative air – alongside Shakespeare, presumably. On these grounds Woolf excoriates Charlotte Brontë for putting her own anger into the mouth of Jane Eyre, exemplifying this with one of the finest passages from Brontë's eponymous novel:

> It is in vain to say human beings ought to be satisfied with tranquillity: they must have action . . . women feel just as men feel; they need exercise for their faculties, and a field for their efforts just as their brothers do . . . it is narrow-minded in their more privileged fellow-creatures to say that they ought to confine themselves to making puddings and knitting stockings, to playing on the piano and embroidering bags. [*Jane Eyre*, p. 95]

Is this not just what Woolf has been saying in her essay (even mentioning the same stockings)? But she sees this as proselytising rather than good fiction.

She develops her theory of the androgynous artist more fully later in the essay (Chapter 6); and my goodness, how she has been made to suffer by feminist critics for this, most notably by Elaine Showalter in her formative work *A Literature of Their Own*.[16] Certainly, I part company from Woolf when she sees Jane Eyre's anger as purely Charlotte Brontë's rather than her own; and even where Brontë's own anger surfaces through the fictional and narrative frameworks of her novels, I would argue that this is not necessarily a bad thing. It moved the novel as a form in a different and interesting direction. But I don't necessarily expect Woolf to see that. I am the beneficiary of a whole raft of ideas, set in motion partly by Woolf's own extraordinary essay, and

16 See the Bibliography for a range of feminist responses to Woolf's essay.

developed in the 1960s onwards, which have informed my more complex state of knowledge. Woolf interrupts her own narrative interestingly when she quotes Jane's long cry of injustice, which culminates with Jane's hearing Grace Poole's laugh. 'That is an awkward break, I thought. It is upsetting to come upon Grace Poole all of a sudden. The continuity is disturbed' (p. 77). Actually, Woolf was on to something; but it took the feminist critics Sandra Gilbert and Susan Gubar to see what it was: 'that jerk in them [Brontë's pages], that indignation' (p. 77) became the basis for their brilliant if flawed analysis of the suppressed anger in female writing, *The Madwoman in the Attic* (1979). If Woolf does not fully recognise her own anger, either in this essay or in her novels, that may have been a self-protection, since she had to contend always with her bouts of depression and possible psychosis. It is well to remember, too, that as a young adolescent her own bedroom was not in fact her own, being regularly entered by her half brother George from whom she had to endure unwanted sexual advances (see *Moments of Being*, p. 180). This may have produced an ingrained habit of emotional suppression, and may also underlie her particular emphasis on a room of one's *own*. But Woolf does see and reveal the roots of righteous anger in women; it is only anger that surfaces inappropriately (as she sees it) in fiction that she condemns.

But – to use the marvellously provisional conjunction with which Woolf opens her essay – let us allow Woolf her small, and even her big, slips. Hers is a brilliant diagnosis of male supremacy and a prescription for the cure. As I said before, she gives women the tools for the job. Not everyone can get £500 a year and a room of one's own. But a room of one's own is in the end not, in spite of Woolf's stress on materialism, an actual space but a mental one. Here I disagree strongly with Showalter who sees Woolf's desire for a 'private room' as equivalent to digging one's own (i.e. woman's own) grave, since that is the ultimate private space (Showalter, p. 297). I see Woolf's idea as going in the opposite direction, opening out rather than closing in, and recognising a community of women rather than a privatised space. At one time the mental space might have required the physical one. Today that is not the case. But having that 'room' in which to imagine, perhaps to write, but in the first place just to be, remains the need and right not just of all women but of all men. The great strength, for me, of *A Room of One's Own* is that it is still able to make me reflect on myself (as a woman), and to understand myself afresh, and to think of my place in society and my relation to other human beings. In that respect, I commend the text to today's young women: it still speaks feelingly to them. It encourages, it uplifts, it reminds us that ours is an ongoing struggle, but one that can be talked of with wit, elegance and confidence – yes, and practicality. I hope and believe it may also speak feelingly to a man; but it, and he, will do it differently. In this we are at once together as human beings and apart in our gender: it remains a fact for us all, in Woolf's closing words, 'that there is no arm to cling to, but that we go alone and that our relation is to the world of reality and not only to the world of men and women' (p. 108). We should all, then, let flowers fall on the tomb of Virginia Woolf; but perhaps we should do it on separate visits.

SALLY MINOGUE

BIBLIOGRAPHY

PRIMARY SOURCES

The first edition of *A Room of One's Own* was published by the Woolfs' own Hogarth Press, London, 1929.

Virginia Woolf, *The Voyage Out* (1915), Oxford University Press, Oxford, 1992

Virginia Woolf, *Moments of Being: Unpublished Autobiographical Writings* (1976), ed. Jeanne Schulkind, Triad/Granada, London, 1978

Anne Olivier Bell, assisted by Andrew McNeillie (eds), *The Diary of Virginia Woolf*, 5 vols, Hogarth Press, London, 1977–84

Nigel Nicolson and Joanne Trautmann (eds), *The Letters of Virginia Woolf*, 6 vols, Hogarth Press, London, 1975–84

Leonard Woolf, *Autobiography*, 5 vols, Hogarth Press, London, 1960–9

Elinor McNees (ed.), *Virginia Woolf: Critical Assessments*, 4 vols, Helm Information, Robertsbridge, 1994. Vol. II relates to *A Room of One's Own*.

Biography

Quentin Bell, *Virginia Woolf: A Biography*, 2 vols, Hogarth Press, London, 1972

Lyndall Gordon, *Virginia Woolf: A Writer's Life*, Oxford University Press, Oxford, 1984

Hermione Lee, *Virginia Woolf*, Chatto and Windus, London, 1996

FEMINIST CRITICISM

Books

Rachel Bowlby, *Feminist Destinations and Further Essays on Virginia Woolf*, Edinburgh University Press, Edinburgh, 1997 (an extended version of Bowlby's *Feminist Destinations*, Blackwell, Oxford, 1988)

Sandra M. Gilbert and Susan Gubar, *The Madwoman in the Attic:The Woman Writer and the Nineteenth-Century Literary Imagination*, Yale University Press, New Haven, 1979

Jane Marcus (ed.), *Virginia Woolf: A Feminist Slant*, University of Nebraska Press, Lincoln and London, 1983

Jane Marcus, *Virginia Woolf and the Languages of Patriarchy*, Indiana University Press, Bloomington and Indianapolis, 1987

Jane Marcus, *Art and Anger: Reading Like a Woman*, Ohio University Press, Columbus, 1988

Toril Moi, *Sexual/Textual Politics: Feminist Literary Theory*, Methuen, London and New York, 1985

Tillie Olsen, *Silences*, Virago Press, London, 1980

Elaine Showalter, *A Literature of Their Own* (1977), revised edition, Virago, London, 1999. This edition has a new Introduction looking at the range of feminist responses to it since its first publication.

Janet Todd, *Feminist Literary History*, Routledge, London and New York, 1988

Anthea Trodd, *Women's Writing in English: Britain 1940–1945*, Longman, London and New York, 1998

Articles

Margaret J. M. Ezell, 'The Myth of Judith Shakespeare: Creating the Canon of Women's Literature', *New Literary History*, Vol. 21, No. 3, Spring 1990, pp. 579–92

Alex Zwerdling, 'Anger and Conciliation in Woolf's Feminism', *Representations*, No. 3, Summer 1983, pp. 68–89

General Criticism

Gillian Beer, *Virginia Woolf: The Common Ground*, Edinburgh University Press, Edinburgh, 1996

Julia Briggs (ed.), *Virginia Woolf: Introductions to the Major Works*, Virago Press, London, 1984

Winifred Holtby, *Virginia Woolf: A Critical Memoir* (1932), Continuum, London, 2007

Laura Marcus, *Virginia Woolf*, Northcote House/British Council, Tavistock, 1997; 2nd edition, 2004

Keith Williams and Steven Matthews, *Rewriting the Thirties: Modernism and After*, Longman, London and New York, 1997. (See especially the chapter: ' "Alien Experiences": Virginia Woolf, Winifred Holtby and Vera Brittain in the Thirties'.)

OTHER WORKS CITED

Vera Brittain, *Women's Work in Modern England*, Noel Douglas, 1928

Vera Brittain, *Testament of Youth* (Gollancz, 1933), Virago Press, London, 1978

Paul Berry and Mark Bostridge, *Vera Brittain: A Life*, Chatto and Windus, London, 1995

Charlotte Brontë, *Jane Eyre*, Wordsworth Editions, Ware, 1999

Keith Carabine and Alan Carruth, Review of Laurence Davies and J. H. Stape (eds), *The Collected Letters of Joseph Conrad: Volume 7, 1920–22*, in *Conradiana*, Vol. 40, Summer 2008, No. 2, pp. 198–210

Elizabeth Gaskell, *North and South*, Wordsworth Editions, Ware, 1994

Storm Jameson, *Journey from the North*, 2 vols (Collins, 1969), Virago Press, 1984

Elaine Marks and Isabelle de Courtivron (eds), *New French Feminisms: An Anthology*, Harvester Press, Brighton, 1982 (for translations of Hélène Cixous, Luce Irigaray *et al.*)

Vita Sackville-West, *Aphra Behn: The Incomparable Astrea*, Howe, London, 1927

Olive Schreiner, *Woman and Labour* (Unwin, 1911), Virago, London, 1978

A. W. Ward and A. R. Waller (eds), *The Cambridge History of English Literature*, Vol. VIII, Cambridge University Press, Cambridge, 1911

S. J. Wiseman, *Aphra Behn*, Northcote House/British Council, Tavistock, 1996; 2nd edition, 2007

A ROOM OF ONE'S OWN

Chapter 1

But, you may say, we asked you to speak about women and fiction –
what has that got to do with a room of one's own? I will try to explain.
When you asked me to speak about women and fiction I sat down on the
banks of a river and began to wonder what the words meant. They
might mean simply a few remarks about Fanny Burney;[1] a few more
about Jane Austen; a tribute to the Brontës and a sketch of Haworth
Parsonage [2] under snow; some witticisms if possible about Miss Mitford;[3]
a respectful allusion to George Eliot; a reference to Mrs Gaskell and one
would have done. But at second sight the words seemed not so simple.
The title women and fiction might mean, and you may have meant it to
mean, women and what they are like, or it might mean women and the
fiction that they write; or it might mean women and the fiction that is
written about them, or it might mean that somehow all three are
inextricably mixed together and you want me to consider them in that
light. But when I began to consider the subject in this last way, which
seemed the most interesting, I soon saw that it had one fatal drawback.
I should never be able to come to a conclusion. I should never be able
to fulfil what is, I understand, the first duty of a lecturer – to hand you
after an hour's discourse a nugget of pure truth to wrap up between the
pages of your notebooks and keep on the mantelpiece for ever. All I
could do was to offer you an opinion upon one minor point – a woman
must have money and a room of her own if she is to write fiction; and
that, as you will see, leaves the great problem of the true nature of
woman and the true nature of fiction unsolved. I have shirked the duty
of coming to a conclusion upon these two questions – women and
fiction remain, so far as I am concerned, unsolved problems. But in
order to make some amends I am going to do what I can to show you
how I arrived at this opinion about the room and the money. I am
going to develop in your presence as fully and freely as I can the train
of thought which led me to think this. Perhaps if I lay bare the ideas,
the prejudices, that lie behind this statement you will find that they
have some bearing upon women and some upon fiction. At any rate,
when a subject is highly controversial – and any question about sex is

that – one cannot hope to tell the truth. One can only show how one came to hold whatever opinion one does hold. One can only give one's audience the chance of drawing their own conclusions as they observe the limitations, the prejudices, the idiosyncrasies of the speaker. Fiction here is likely to contain more truth than fact. Therefore I propose, making use of all the liberties and licences of a novelist, to tell you the story of the two days that preceded my coming here – how, bowed down by the weight of the subject which you have laid upon my shoulders, I pondered it, and made it work in and out of my daily life. I need not say that what I am about to describe has no existence; Oxbridge is an invention; so is Fernham; 'I' is only a convenient term for somebody who has no real being. Lies will flow from my lips, but there may perhaps be some truth mixed up with them; it is for you to seek out this truth and to decide whether any part of it is worth keeping. If not, you will of course throw the whole of it into the wastepaper basket and forget all about it.

Here then was I (call me Mary Beton, Mary Seton, Mary Carmichael[4] or by any name you please – it is not a matter of any importance) sitting on the banks of a river a week or two ago in fine October weather, lost in thought. That collar[5] I have spoken of, women and fiction, the need of coming to some conclusion on a subject that raises all sorts of prejudices and passions, bowed my head to the ground. To the right and left bushes of some sort, golden and crimson, glowed with the colour, even it seemed burnt with the heat, of fire. On the farther bank the willows wept in perpetual lamentation, their hair about their shoulders. The river reflected whatever it chose of sky and bridge and burning tree, and when the undergraduate had oared his boat through the reflections they closed again, completely, as if he had never been. There one might have sat the clock round lost in thought. Thought – to call it by a prouder name than it deserved – had let its line down into the stream. It swayed, minute after minute, hither and thither among the reflections and the weeds, letting the water lift it and sink it until – you know the little tug – the sudden conglomeration of an idea at the end of one's line: and then the cautious hauling of it in, and the careful laying of it out? Alas, laid on the grass how small, how insignificant this thought of mine looked; the sort of fish that a good fisherman puts back into the water so that it may grow fatter and be one day worth cooking and eating. I will not trouble you with that thought now, though if you look carefully you may find it for yourselves in the course of what I am going to say.

But however small it was, it had, nevertheless, the mysterious property of its kind – put back into the mind, it became at once very exciting, and important; and as it darted and sank, and flashed hither and thither, set up such a wash and tumult of ideas that it was impossible to sit still. It was thus that I found myself walking with extreme rapidity across a grass plot. Instantly a man's figure rose to intercept me. Nor did I at first understand that the gesticulations of a curious-looking object, in a cut-away coat and evening shirt, were aimed at me. His face expressed horror and indignation. Instinct rather than reason came to my help; he was a beadle;[6] I was a woman. This was the turf; there was the path. Only the Fellows and Scholars are allowed here; the gravel is the place for me. Such thoughts were the work of a moment. As I regained the path the arms of the beadle sank, his face assumed its usual repose, and though turf is better walking than gravel, no very great harm was done. The only charge I could bring against the Fellows and Scholars of whatever the college might happen to be was that in protection of their turf, which has been rolled for three hundred years in succession, they had sent my little fish into hiding.

What idea it had been that had sent me so audaciously trespassing I could not now remember. The spirit of peace descended like a cloud from heaven, for if the spirit of peace dwells anywhere, it is in the courts and quadrangles of Oxbridge[7] on a fine October morning. Strolling through those colleges past those ancient halls the roughness of the present seemed smoothed away; the body seemed contained in a miraculous glass cabinet through which no sound could penetrate, and the mind, freed from any contact with facts (unless one trespassed on the turf again), was at liberty to settle down upon whatever meditation was in harmony with the moment. As chance would have it, some stray memory of some old essay about revisiting Oxbridge in the long vacation brought Charles Lamb[8] to mind – Saint Charles, said Thackeray, putting a letter of Lamb's to his forehead. Indeed, among all the dead (I give you my thoughts as they came to me), Lamb is one of the most congenial; one to whom one would have liked to say, Tell me then how you wrote your essays? For his essays are superior even to Max Beerbohm's,[9] I thought, with all their perfection, because of that wild flash of imagination, that lightning crack of genius in the middle of them which leaves them flawed and imperfect, but starred with poetry. Lamb then came to Oxbridge perhaps a hundred years ago. Certainly he wrote an essay – the name escapes me – about the manuscript of one of Milton's poems which he saw here. It was Lycidas[10] perhaps, and Lamb wrote how it shocked him to think it possible that any word in Lycidas could have been different from what it is. To think of Milton changing the words in that poem seemed to him a sort of sacrilege. This led me to remember what I could of *Lycidas* and to amuse myself with guessing which word it could have been that Milton had altered, and why. It then occurred to me that the very manuscript itself which Lamb had looked at was only a few hundred yards away, so that one could follow Lamb's footsteps across the quadrangle to that famous library where the treasure is kept. Moreover, I recollected, as I put this plan into execution, it is in this famous library that the manuscript of Thackeray's[11] *Esmond* is also preserved. The critics often say that *Esmond* is Thackeray's most perfect novel. But the affectation of the style, with its imitation of the eighteenth century, hampers one, so far as I can remember; unless indeed the eighteenth-century style was natural to Thackeray – a fact that one might prove by looking at the manuscript and seeing whether the alterations were for the benefit of the style or of the sense. But then one would have to decide what is style and what is meaning, a question which – but here I was actually at the door which leads into the library itself. I must have opened it, for instantly there issued, like a guardian angel barring the way with a flutter of black gown instead of white wings, a deprecating, silvery, kindly gentleman, who regretted in a low voice as he waved me back that ladies are only admitted to the library if accompanied by a Fellow of the College or furnished with a letter of introduction.

That a famous library has been cursed by a woman is a matter of complete indifference to a famous library. Venerable and calm, with all its treasures safe locked within its breast, it sleeps complacently and will, so far as I am concerned, so sleep for ever. Never will I wake those echoes, never will I ask for that hospitality again, I vowed as I descended the steps in anger. Still an hour remained before luncheon, and what was one to do? Stroll on the meadows? sit by the river? Certainly it was a lovely autumn morning; the leaves were fluttering red to the ground; there was no great hardship in doing either. But the sound of music reached my ear. Some service or celebration was going forward. The organ complained magnificently as I passed the chapel door. Even the sorrow of Christianity sounded in that serene air more like the recollection of sorrow than sorrow itself; even the groanings of the ancient organ seemed lapped in peace. I had no wish to enter had I the right, and this time the verger might have stopped me, demanding perhaps my baptismal certificate, or a letter of introduction from the Dean. But the outside of these magnificent buildings is often as beautiful as the inside. Moreover, it was amusing enough to watch the congregation assembling, coming in and going out again, busying themselves at the door of the chapel like bees at the mouth of a hive. Many were in cap and gown; some had tufts of fur on their shoulders; others were wheeled in bath-chairs; others, though not past middle age, seemed creased and crushed into shapes so singular that one was reminded of those giant crabs and crayfish who heave with difficulty across the sand of an aquarium. As I leant against the wall the university indeed seemed a sanctuary in which are preserved rare types which would soon be obsolete if left to fight for existence on the pavement of the Strand. Old stories of old deans and old dons came back to mind, but before I had summoned up courage to whistle – it used to be said that at the sound of a whistle old Professor — instantly broke into a gallop – the venerable congregation had gone inside. The outside of the chapel remained. As you know, its high domes and pinnacles can be seen, like a sailing-ship always voyaging never arriving, lit up at night and visible for miles, far away across the hills. Once, presumably, this quadrangle with its smooth lawns, its massive buildings and the chapel itself was marsh too, where the grasses waved and the swine rooted. Teams of horses and oxen, I thought, must have hauled the stone in wagons from far countries, and then with infinite labour the grey blocks in whose shade I was now standing were poised in order one on top of another, and then the painters brought their glass for the windows, and the masons were busy for centuries up on that roof with putty and cement, spade and trowel. Every Saturday somebody must have poured gold and silver out of a leathern purse into their ancient fists, for they had their beer and skittles presumably of an evening. An unending stream of gold and silver, I thought, must have flowed into this court perpetually to keep the stones coming and the masons working; to level, to ditch, to dig and to drain. But it was then the age of faith, and money was poured liberally to set these stones on a deep foundation, and when the stones were raised, still more money was poured in from the coffers of kings and queens and great nobles to ensure that hymns should be sung here and scholars taught. Lands were granted; tithes were paid. And when the age of faith was over and the age of reason had come, still the same flow of gold and silver went on; fellowships were founded; lectureships endowed; only the gold and silver flowed now not from the coffers of the king but from the chests of merchants and manufacturers, from the purses of men who had made, say, a fortune from industry, and returned, in their wills, a bounteous share of it to endow more chairs, more lectureships, more fellowships in the university where they had learnt their craft. Hence the libraries and laboratories; the observatories; the splendid equipment of costly and delicate instruments which now stands on glass shelves, where centuries ago the grasses waved and the swine rootled. Certainly, as I strolled round the court, the foundation of gold and silver seemed deep enough; the pavement laid solidly over the wild grasses. Men with trays on their heads went busily from staircase to staircase. Gaudy blossoms flowered in window-boxes. The strains of the gramophone blared out from the rooms within. It was impossible not to reflect – the reflection whatever it may have been was cut short. The clock struck. It was time to find one's way to luncheon.

It is a curious fact that novelists have a way of making us believe that luncheon parties are invariably memorable for something very witty that was said, or for something very wise that was done. But they seldom spare a word for what was eaten. It is part of the novelist's convention not to mention soup and salmon and ducklings, as if soup and salmon and ducklings were of no importance whatsoever, as if nobody ever smoked a cigar or drank a glass of wine. Here, however, I shall take the liberty to defy that convention and to tell you that the lunch on this occasion began with soles, sunk in a deep dish, over which the college cook had spread a counterpane of the whitest cream, save that it was branded here and there with brown spots like the spots on the flanks of a doe. After that came the partridges, but if this suggests a couple of bald, brown birds on a plate you are mistaken. The partridges, many and various, came with all their retinue of sauces and salads, the sharp and the sweet, each in its order; their potatoes, thin as coins but not so hard; their sprouts, foliated as rosebuds but more succulent. And no sooner had the roast and its retinue been done with than the silent servingman, the beadle himself perhaps in a milder manifestation, set before us, wreathed in napkins, a confection which rose all sugar from the waves. To call it pudding and so relate it to rice and tapioca would be an insult. Meanwhile the wine glasses had flushed yellow and flushed crimson; had been emptied; had been filled. And thus by degrees was lit, halfway down the spine, which is the seat of the soul, not that hard little electric light which we call brilliance, as it pops in and out upon our lips, but the more profound, subtle and subterranean glow which is the rich yellow flame of rational intercourse. No need to hurry. No need to sparkle. No need to be anybody but oneself. We are all going to heaven and Van Dyck[12] is of the company – in other words, how good life seemed, how sweet its rewards, how trivial this grudge or that grievance, how admirable friendship and the society of one's kind, as, lighting a good cigarette, one sank among the cushions in the window-seat.

If by good luck there had been an ashtray handy, if one had not knocked the ash out of the window in default, if things had been a little different from what they were, one would not have seen, presumably, a cat without a tail. The sight of that abrupt and truncated animal padding softly across the quadrangle changed by some fluke of the subconscious intelligence the emotional light for me. It was as if someone had let fall a shade. Perhaps the excellent hock was relinquishing its hold. Certainly, as I watched the Manx cat pause in the middle of the lawn as if it too questioned the universe, something seemed lacking, something seemed different. But what was lacking, what was different, I asked myself, listening to the talk? And to answer that question I had to think myself out of the room, back into the past, before the war indeed, and to set before my eyes the model of another luncheon party held in rooms not very far distant from these; but different. Everything was different. Meanwhile the talk went on among the guests, who were many and young, some of this sex, some of that; it went on swimmingly, it went on agreeably, freely, amusingly. And as it went on I set it against the background of that other talk, and as I matched the two together I had no doubt that one was the descendant, the legitimate heir of the other. Nothing was changed; nothing was different save only here I listened with all my ears not entirely to what was being said, but to the murmur or current behind it. Yes, that was it – the change was there. Before the war at a luncheon party like this people would have said precisely the same things but they would have sounded different, because in those days they were accompanied by a sort of humming noise, not articulate, but musical, exciting, which changed the value of the words themselves. Could one set that humming noise to words? Perhaps with the help of the poets one could. A book lay beside me and, opening it, I turned casually enough to Tennyson. And here I found Tennyson was singing:

> There has fallen a splendid tear
>   From the passion-flower at the gate.
> She is coming, my dove, my dear;
>   She is coming, my life, my fate;
> The red rose cries, 'She is near, she is near';
>   And the white rose weeps, 'She is late';
> The larkspur listens, 'I hear, I hear';
>   And the lily whispers, 'I wait.'[13]

Was that what men hummed at luncheon parties before the war? And the women?

> My heart is like a singing bird
>> Whose nest is in a water'd shoot;
> My heart is like an apple tree
>> Whose boughs are bent with thick-set fruit;
> My heart is like a rainbow shell
>> That paddles in a halcyon sea;
> My heart is gladder than all these
>> Because my love is come to me.[14]

Was that what women hummed at luncheon parties before the war? There was something so ludicrous in thinking of people humming such things even under their breath at luncheon parties before the war that I burst out laughing, and had to explain my laughter by pointing at the Manx cat, who did look a little absurd, poor beast, without a tail, in the middle of the lawn. Was he really born so, or had he lost his tail in an accident? The tailless cat, though some are said to exist in the Isle of Man, is rarer than one thinks. It is a queer animal, quaint rather than beautiful. It is strange what a difference a tail makes – you know the sort of things one says as a lunch party breaks up and people are finding their coats and hats.

This one, thanks to the hospitality of the host, had lasted far into the afternoon. The beautiful October day was fading and the leaves were falling from the trees in the avenue as I walked through it. Gate after gate seemed to close with gentle finality behind me. Innumerable beadles were fitting innumerable keys into well-oiled locks; the treasure-house was being made secure for another night. After the avenue one comes out upon a road – I forget its name – which leads you, if you take the right turning, along to Fernham.[15] But there was plenty of time. Dinner was not till half-past seven. One could almost do without dinner after such a luncheon. It is strange how a scrap of poetry works in the mind and makes the legs move in time to it along the road. Those words –

> There has fallen a splendid tear
>> From the passion-flower at the gate.
> She is coming, my dove, my dear –

sang in my blood as I stepped quickly along towards Headingley. And then, switching off into the other measure, I sang, where the waters are churned up by the weir:

> My heart is like a singing bird
>> Whose nest is in a water'd shoot;
> My heart is like an apple tree . . .

What poets, I cried aloud, as one does in the dusk, what poets they were!

In a sort of jealousy, I suppose, for our own age, silly and absurd though these comparisons are, I went on to wonder if honestly one could name two living poets now as great as Tennyson and Christina Rossetti were then. Obviously it is impossible, I thought, looking into those foaming waters, to compare them. The very reason why that poetry excites one to such abandonment, such rapture, is that it celebrates some feeling that one used to have (at luncheon parties before the war perhaps), so that one responds easily, familiarly, without troubling to check the feeling, or to compare it with any that one has now. But the living poets express a feeling that is actually being made and torn out of us at the moment. One does not recognise it in the first place; often for some reason one fears it; one watches it with keenness and compares it jealously and suspiciously with the old feeling that one knew. Hence the difficulty of modern poetry; and it is because of this difficulty that one cannot remember more than two consecutive lines of any good modern poet. For this reason – that my memory failed me – the argument flagged for want of material. But why, I continued, moving on towards Headingley, have we stopped humming under our breath at luncheon parties? Why has Alfred ceased to sing

> She is coming, my dove, my dear.

Why has Christina ceased to respond

> My heart is gladder than all these
> Because my love is come to me?

Shall we lay the blame on the war? When the guns fired in August 1914, did the faces of men and women show so plain in each other's eyes that romance was killed? Certainly it was a shock (to women in particular with their illusions about education, and so on) to see the faces of our rulers in the light of the shellfire. So ugly they looked – German, English, French – so stupid. But lay the blame where one will, on whom one will, the illusion which inspired Tennyson and Christina Rossetti to sing so passionately about the coming of their loves is far rarer now than then. One has only to read, to look, to listen, to remember. But why say 'blame'? Why, if it was an illusion, not praise the catastrophe, whatever it was, that destroyed illusion and put truth in its place? For truth . . . those dots mark the spot where, in search of truth, I missed the turning up to Fernham. Yes indeed, which was truth and which was illusion? I asked myself. What was the truth about these houses, for example, dim and festive now with their red windows in the dusk, but raw and red and squalid, with their sweets and their bootlaces, at nine o'clock in the morning? And the willows and the river and the gardens that run down to the river, vague now with the mist stealing over them, but gold and red in the sunlight – which was the truth, which was the illusion about them? I spare you the twists and turns of my cogitations, for no conclusion was found on the road to Headingley, and I ask you to suppose that I soon found out my mistake about the turning and retraced my steps to Fernham.

As I have said already that it was an October day, I dare not forfeit your respect and imperil the fair name of fiction by changing the season and describing lilacs hanging over garden walls, crocuses, tulips and other flowers of spring. Fiction must stick to facts, and the truer the facts the better the fiction – so we are told. Therefore it was still autumn and the leaves were still yellow and falling, if anything, a little faster than before, because it was now evening (seven twenty-three to be precise) and a breeze (from the south-west to be exact) had risen. But for all that there was something odd at work:

> My heart is like a singing bird
> Whose nest is in a water'd shoot;
> My heart is like an apple tree
> Whose boughs are bent with thick-set fruit –

perhaps the words of Christina Rossetti were partly responsible for the folly of the fancy – it was nothing of course but a fancy – that the lilac was shaking its flowers over the garden walls, and the brimstone butterflies were scudding hither and thither, and the dust of the pollen was in the air. A wind blew, from what quarter I know not, but it lifted the half-grown leaves so that there was a flash of silver grey in the air. It was the time between the lights when colours undergo their intensification and purples and golds burn in window-panes like the beat of an excitable heart; when for some reason the beauty of the world revealed and yet soon to perish (here I pushed into the garden, for, unwisely, the door was left open and no beadles seemed about), the beauty of the world which is so soon to perish, has two edges, one of laughter, one of anguish, cutting the heart asunder. The gardens of Fernham lay before me in the spring twilight, wild and open, and in the long grass, sprinkled and carelessly flung, were daffodils and bluebells, not orderly perhaps at the best of times, and now wind-blown and waving as they tugged at their roots. The windows of the building, curved like ships' windows among generous waves of red brick, changed from lemon to silver under the flight of the quick spring clouds. Somebody was in a hammock, somebody, but in this light they were phantoms only, half guessed, half seen, raced across the grass – would no one stop her? – and then on the terrace, as if popping out to breathe the air, to glance at the garden, came a bent figure, formidable yet humble, with her great forehead and her shabby dress – could it be the famous scholar, could it be J— H—[16] herself? All was dim, yet intense too, as if the scarf which the dusk had flung over the garden were torn asunder by star or sword – the gash of some terrible reality leaping, as its way is, out of the heart of the spring. For youth –

Here was my soup. Dinner was being served in the great dining-hall. Far from being spring it was in fact an evening in October. Everybody was assembled in the big dining-room. Dinner was ready. Here was the soup. It was a plain gravy soup. There was nothing to stir the fancy in that. One could have seen through the transparent liquid any pattern that there might have been on the plate itself. But there was no pattern. The plate was plain. Next came beef with its attendant greens and potatoes – a homely trinity, suggesting the rumps of cattle in a muddy market, and sprouts curled and yellowed at the edge, and bargaining and cheapening and women with string bags on Monday morning. There was no reason to complain of human nature's daily food, seeing that the supply was sufficient and coal-miners doubtless were sitting down to less. Prunes and custard followed. And if anyone complains that prunes, even when mitigated by custard, are an uncharitable vegetable (fruit they are not), stringy as a miser's heart and exuding a fluid such as might run in misers' veins who have denied themselves wine and warmth for eighty years and yet not given to the poor, he should reflect that there are people whose charity embraces even the prune. Biscuits and cheese came next, and here the water-jug was liberally passed round, for it is the nature of biscuits to be dry, and these were biscuits to the core. That was all. The meal was over. Everybody scraped their chairs back; the swing-doors swung violently to and fro; soon the hall was emptied of every sign of food and made ready no doubt for breakfast next morning. Down corridors and up staircases the youth of England went banging and singing. And was it for a guest, a stranger (for I had no more right here in Fernham than in Trinity or Somerville or Girton or Newnham or Christchurch[17]), to say, 'The dinner was not good,' or to say (we were now, Mary Seton and I, in her sitting-room), 'Could we not have dined up here alone?' for if I had said anything of the kind I should have been prying and searching into the secret economies of a house which to the stranger wears so fine a front of gaiety and courage. No, one could say nothing of the sort. Indeed, conversation for a moment flagged. The human frame being what it is, heart, body and brain all mixed together, and not contained in separate compartments as they will be no doubt in another million years, a good dinner is of great importance to good talk. One cannot think well, love well, sleep well, if one has not dined well. The lamp in the spine does not light on beef and prunes. We are all *probably* going to heaven, and Van Dyck is, we *hope*, to meet us round the next corner – that is the dubious and qualifying state of mind that beef and prunes at the end of the day's work breed between them. Happily my friend, who taught science, had a cupboard where there was a squat bottle and little glasses – (but there should have been sole and partridge to begin with) – so that we were able to draw up to the fire and repair some of the damages of the day's living. In a minute or so we were slipping freely in and out among all those objects of curiosity and interest which form in the mind in the absence of a particular person, and are naturally to be discussed on coming together again – how somebody has married, another has not; one thinks this, another that; one has improved out of all knowledge, the other most amazingly gone to the bad – with all those speculations upon human nature and the character of the amazing world we live in which spring naturally from such beginnings. While these things were being said, however, I became shamefacedly aware of a current setting in of its own accord and carrying everything forward to an end of its own. One might be talking of Spain or Portugal, of book or racehorse, but the real interest of whatever was said was none of those things, but a scene of masons on a high roof some five centuries ago. Kings and nobles brought treasure in huge sacks and poured it under the earth. This scene was forever coming alive in my mind and placing itself by another of lean cows and a muddy market and withered greens and the stringy hearts of old men – these two pictures, disjointed and disconnected and nonsensical as they were, were forever coming together and combating each other and had me entirely at their mercy. The best course, unless the whole talk was to be distorted, was to expose what was in my mind to the air, when with good luck it would fade and crumble like the head of the dead king when they opened the coffin at Windsor. Briefly, then, I told Miss Seton about the masons who had been all those years on the roof of the chapel, and about the kings and queens and nobles bearing sacks of gold and silver on their shoulders, which they shovelled into the earth; and then how the great financial magnates of our own time came and laid cheques and bonds, I suppose, where the others had laid ingots and rough lumps of gold. All that lies beneath the colleges down there, I said; but this college, where we are now sitting, what lies beneath its gallant red brick and the wild unkempt grasses of the garden? What force is behind that plain china off which we dined, and (here it popped out of my mouth before I could stop it) the beef, the custard and the prunes?

Well, said Mary Seton, about the year 1860 – Oh, but you know the story, she said, bored, I suppose, by the recital. And she told me – rooms were hired. Committees met. Envelopes were addressed. Circulars were drawn up. Meetings were held; letters were read out; so-and-so has promised so much; on the contrary, Mr— won't give a penny. The *Saturday Review* has been very rude. How can we raise a fund to pay for offices? Shall we hold a bazaar? Can't we find a pretty girl to sit in the front row? Let us look up what John Stuart Mill[18] said on the subject. Can anyone persuade the editor of the — to print a letter? Can we get Lady — to sign it? Lady — is out of town. That was the way it was done, presumably, sixty years ago, and it was a prodigious effort, and a great deal of time was spent on it. And it was only after a long struggle and with the utmost difficulty that they got thirty thousand pounds together.* So obviously we cannot have wine and partridges and servants carrying tin dishes on their heads, she said. We cannot have sofas and separate rooms. 'The amenities,' she said, quoting from some book or other, 'will have to wait.'†

At the thought of all those women working year after year and finding it hard to get two thousand pounds together, and as much as they could do to get thirty thousand pounds, we burst out in scorn at the reprehensible poverty of our sex. What had our mothers been doing then that they had no wealth to leave us? Powdering their noses? Looking in at shop windows? Flaunting in the sun at Monte Carlo? There were some photographs on the mantelpiece. Mary's mother – if that was her picture – may have been a wastrel in her spare time (she had thirteen children by a minister of the church), but if so her gay and dissipated life had left too few traces of its pleasures on her face. She was a homely body; an old lady in a plaid shawl which was fastened by a

---

* 'We are told that we ought to ask for £30,000 at least . . . It is not a large sum, considering that there is to be but one college of this sort for Great Britain, Ireland and the Colonies, and considering how easy it is to raise immense sums for boys' schools. But considering how few people really wish women to be educated, it is a good deal.' – LADY STEPHEN, *Emily Davies and Girton College*
† Every penny which could be scraped together was set aside for building, and the amenities had to be postponed. – R. STRACHEY, *The Cause*

large cameo; and she sat in a basket-chair, encouraging a spaniel to look at the camera, with the amused, yet strained expression of one who is sure that the dog will move directly the bulb is pressed. Now if she had gone into business; had become a manufacturer of artificial silk or a magnate on the Stock Exchange; if she had left two or three hundred thousand pounds to Fernham, we could have been sitting at our ease tonight and the subject of our talk might have been archaeology, botany, anthropology, physics, the nature of the atom, mathematics, astronomy, relativity, geography. If only Mrs Seton and her mother and her mother before her had learnt the great art of making money and had left their money, like their fathers and their grandfathers before them, to found fellowships and lectureships and prizes and scholarships appropriated to the use of their own sex, we might have dined very tolerably up here alone off a bird and a bottle of wine; we might have looked forward without undue confidence to a pleasant and honourable lifetime spent in the shelter of one of the liberally endowed professions. We might have been exploring or writing; mooning about the venerable places of the earth; sitting contemplative on the steps of the Parthenon, or going at ten to an office and coming home comfortably at half-past four to write a little poetry. Only, if Mrs Seton and her like had gone into business at the age of fifteen, there would have been – that was the snag in the argument – no Mary. What, I asked, did Mary think of that? There between the curtains was the October night, calm and lovely, with a star or two caught in the yellowing trees. Was she ready to resign her share of it and her memories (for they had been a happy family, though a large one) of games and quarrels up in Scotland, which she is never tired of praising for the fineness of its air and the quality of its cakes, in order that Fernham might have been endowed with fifty thousand pounds or so by a stroke of the pen? For, to endow a college would necessitate the suppression of families altogether. Making a fortune and bearing thirteen children – no human being could stand it. Consider the facts, we said. First there are nine months before the baby is born. Then the baby is born. Then there are three or four months spent in feeding the baby. After the baby is fed there are certainly five years spent in playing with the baby. You cannot, it seems, let children run about the streets. People who have seen them running wild in Russia say that the sight is not a pleasant one. People say, too, that human nature takes its shape in the years between one and five. If Mrs Seton, I said, had been making money, what sort of memories would you have had of games and quarrels? What would you have known of Scotland, and its fine air and cakes and all the rest of it? But it is useless to ask these questions, because you would never have come into existence at all. Moreover, it is equally useless to ask what might have happened if Mrs Seton and her mother and her mother before her had amassed great wealth and laid it under the foundations of college and library, because, in the first place, to earn money was impossible for them, and in the second, had it been possible, the law denied them the right to possess what money they earned. It is only for the last forty-eight years that Mrs Seton has had a penny of her own. For all the centuries before that it would have been her husband's property – a thought which, perhaps, may have had its share in keeping Mrs Seton and her mothers off the Stock Exchange. Every penny I earn, they may have said, will be taken from me and disposed of according to my husband's wisdom – perhaps to found a scholarship or to endow a fellowship in Balliol or Kings,[19] so that to earn money, even if I could earn money, is not a matter that interests me very greatly. I had better leave it to my husband.

At any rate, whether or not the blame rested on the old lady who was looking at the spaniel, there could be no doubt that for some reason or other our mothers had mismanaged their affairs very gravely. Not a penny could be spared for 'amenities'; for partridges and wine, beadles and turf, books and cigars, libraries and leisure. To raise bare walls out of bare earth was the utmost they could do.

So we talked standing at the window and looking, as so many thousands look every night, down on the domes and towers of the famous city beneath us. It was very beautiful, very mysterious in the autumn moonlight. The old stone looked very white and venerable. One thought of all the books that were assembled down there; of the pictures of old prelates and worthies hanging in the panelled rooms; of the painted windows that would be throwing strange globes and crescents on the pavement; of the tablets and memorials and inscriptions; of the fountains and the grass; of the quiet rooms looking across the quiet quadrangles. And (pardon me the thought) I thought, too, of the admirable smoke and drink and the deep armchairs and the pleasant carpets; of the urbanity, the geniality, the dignity which are the offspring of luxury and privacy and space. Certainly our mothers had not provided us with anything comparable to all this – our mothers who found it difficult to scrape together thirty thousand pounds, our mothers who bore thirteen children to ministers of religion at St Andrews.

So I went back to my inn, and as I walked through the dark streets I pondered this and that, as one does at the end of the day's work. I pondered why it was that Mrs Seton had no money to leave us; and what effect poverty has on the mind; and what effect wealth has on the mind; and I thought of the queer old gentlemen I had seen that morning with tufts of fur upon their shoulders; and I remembered how if one whistled one of them ran; and I thought of the organ booming in the chapel and of the shut doors of the library; and I thought how unpleasant it is to be locked out; and I thought how it is worse perhaps to be locked in; and, thinking of the safety and prosperity of the one sex and of the poverty and insecurity of the other and of the effect of tradition and of the lack of tradition upon the mind of a writer, I thought at last that it was time to roll up the crumpled skin of the day, with its arguments and its impressions and its anger and its laughter, and cast it into the hedge. A thousand stars were flashing across the blue wastes of the sky. One seemed alone with an inscrutable society. All human beings were laid asleep – prone, horizontal, dumb. Nobody seemed stirring in the streets of Oxbridge. Even the door of the hotel sprang open at the touch of an invisible hand – not a boots was sitting up to light me to bed, it was so late.

Chapter 2

The scene, if I may ask you to follow me, was now changed. The leaves were still falling, but in London now, not Oxbridge; and I must ask you to imagine a room, like many thousands, with a window looking across people's hats and vans and motor cars to other windows, and on the table inside the room a blank sheet of paper on which was written in large letters *Women and Fiction*, but no more. The inevitable sequel to luncheon and dining at Oxbridge seemed, unfortunately, to be a visit to the British Museum. One must strain off what was personal and accidental in all these impressions and so reach the pure fluid, the essential oil of truth. For that visit to Oxbridge and the luncheon and the dinner had started a swarm of questions. Why did men drink wine and women water? Why was one sex so prosperous and the other so poor? What effect has poverty on fiction? What conditions are necessary for the creation of works of art? – a thousand questions at once suggested themselves. But one needed answers, not questions; and an answer was only to be had by consulting the learned and the unprejudiced, who have removed themselves above the strife of tongue and the confusion of body and issued the result of their reasoning and research in books which are to be found in the British Museum. If truth is not to be found on the shelves of the British Museum, where, I asked myself, picking up a notebook and a pencil, is truth?

Thus provided, thus confident and enquiring, I set out in the pursuit of truth. The day, though not actually wet, was dismal, and the streets in the neighbourhood of the museum were full of open coal-holes, down which sacks were showering; four-wheeled cabs were drawing up and depositing on the pavement corded boxes containing, presumably, the entire wardrobe of some Swiss or Italian family seeking fortune or refuge or some other desirable commodity which is to be found in the boarding-houses of Bloomsbury in the winter. The usual hoarse-voiced men paraded the streets with plants on barrows. Some shouted; others sang. London was like a workshop. London was like a machine. We were all being shot backwards and forwards on this plain foundation to make some pattern. The British Museum was another department of the factory. The swing-doors swung open; and there one stood under the vast dome, as if one were a thought in the huge bald forehead which is so splendidly encircled by a band of famous names. One went to the counter; one took a slip of paper; one opened a volume of the catalogue, and . . . . . – the five dots here indicate five separate minutes of stupefaction, wonder and bewilderment. Have you any notion how many books are written about women in the course of one year? Have you any notion how many are written by men? Are you aware that you are, perhaps, the most discussed animal in the universe? Here had I come with a notebook and a pencil proposing to spend a morning reading, supposing that at the end of the morning I should have transferred the truth to my notebook. But I should need to be a herd of elephants, I thought, and a wilderness of spiders, desperately referring to the animals that are reputed longest lived and most multitudinously eyed, to cope with all this. I should need claws of steel and beak of brass even to penetrate the husk. How shall I ever find the grains of truth embedded in all this mass of paper? I asked myself, and in despair began running my eye up and down the long list of titles. Even the names of the books gave me food for thought. Sex and its nature might well attract doctors and biologists; but what was surprising and difficult of explanation was the fact that sex – woman, that is to say – also attracts agreeable essayists, light-fingered novelists, young men who have taken the M.A. degree; men who have taken no degree; men who have no apparent qualification save that they are not women. Some of these books were, on the face of it, frivolous and facetious; but many, on the other hand, were serious and prophetic, moral and hortatory. Merely to read the titles suggested innumerable schoolmasters, innumerable clergymen mounting their platforms and pulpits and holding forth with loquacity which far exceeded the hour usually allotted to such discourse on this one subject. It was a most strange phenomenon; and apparently – here I consulted the letter M – one confined to the male sex. Women do not write books about men – a fact that I could not help welcoming with relief, for if I had first to read all that men have written about women, then all that women have written about men, the aloe that flowers once in a hundred years would flower twice before I could set pen to paper. So, making a perfectly arbitrary choice of a dozen volumes or so, I sent my slips of paper to lie in the wire tray, and waited in my stall, among the other seekers for the essential oil of truth.

What could be the reason, then, of this curious disparity, I wondered, drawing cartwheels on the slips of paper provided by the British taxpayer for other purposes. Why are women, judging from this catalogue, so much more interesting to men than men are to women? A very curious fact it seemed, and my mind wandered to picture the lives of men who spend their time in writing books about women: whether they were old or young, married or unmarried, red-nosed or hump-backed – anyhow, it was flattering, vaguely, to feel oneself the object of such attention provided that it was not entirely bestowed by the crippled and the infirm – so I pondered until all such frivolous thoughts were ended by an avalanche of books sliding down on to the desk in front of me. Now the trouble began. The student who has been trained in research at Oxbridge has no doubt some method of shepherding his question past all distractions till it runs into his answer as a sheep runs into its pen. The student by my side, for instance, who was copying assiduously from a scientific manual, was, I felt sure, extracting pure nuggets of the essential ore every ten minutes or so. His little grunts of satisfaction indicated so much. But if, unfortunately, one has had no training in a university, the question far from being shepherded to its pen flies like a frightened flock hither and thither, helter-skelter, pursued by a whole pack of hounds. Professors, schoolmasters, sociologists, clergymen, novelists, essayists, journalists, men who had no qualification save that they were not women, chased my simple and single question – Why are some women poor? – until it became fifty questions; until the fifty questions leapt frantically into midstream and were carried away. Every page in my notebook was scribbled over with notes. To show the state of mind I was in, I will read you a few of them, explaining that the page was headed quite simply WOMEN AND POVERTY, in block letters; but what followed was something like this:

> Condition in Middle Ages of,
> Habits in the Fiji Islands of,
> Worshipped as goddesses by,
> Weaker in moral sense than, Idealism of,
> Greater conscientiousness of,
> South Sea Islanders, age of puberty among,
> Attractiveness of,
> Offered as sacrifice to,
> Small size of brain of,
> Profounder subconsciousness of,
> Less hair on the body of,
> Mental, moral and physical inferiority of,
> Love of children of,
> Greater length of life of,
> Weaker muscles of,
> Strength of affections of,
> Vanity of,

> Higher education of,
> Shakespeare's opinion of,
> Lord Birkenhead's[20] opinion of,
> Dean Inge's[21] opinion of,
> La Bruyère's opinion of,
> Dr Johnson's opinion of,
> Mr Oscar Browning's[22] opinion of, . . .

Here I drew breath and added, indeed, in the margin, Why does Samuel Butler[23] say, 'Wise men never say what they think of women'? Wise men never say anything else apparently. But, I continued, leaning back in my chair and looking at the vast dome in which I was a single but by now somewhat harassed thought, what is so unfortunate is that wise men never think the same thing about women. Here is Pope:[24]

> Most women have no character at all.

And here is La Bruyère:[25]

> Les femmes sont extrêmes; elles sont meilleures ou pires
> > que les hommes – [26]

a direct contradiction by keen observers who were contemporary. Are they capable of education or incapable? Napoleon thought them incapable. Dr Johnson[27] thought the opposite.* Have they souls or have they not souls? Some savages say they have none. Others, on the contrary, maintain that women are half divine and worship them on that account.† Some sages hold that they are shallower in the brain; others that they are deeper in the consciousness. Goethe honoured them; Mussolini despises them. Wherever one looked men thought about women and thought differently. It was impossible to make head or tail of it all, I decided, glancing with envy at the reader next door who was making the neatest abstracts, headed often with an A or a B or a C, while my own notebook rioted with the wildest scribble of contradictory jottings. It was distressing, it was bewildering, it was

---

* 'Men know that women are an overmatch for them, and therefore they choose the weakest or the most ignorant. If they did not think so, they never could be afraid of women knowing as much as themselves' . . . In justice to the sex, I think it but candid to acknowledge that, in a subsequent conversation, he told me that he was serious in what he said. – BOSWELL, *The Journal of a Tour to the Hebrides*

† The ancient Germans believed that there was something holy in women, and accordingly consulted them as oracles. – FRAZER, *The Golden Bough*

humiliating. Truth had run through my fingers. Every drop had escaped.

I could not possibly go home, I reflected, and add as a serious contribution to the study of women and fiction that women have less hair on their bodies than men, or that the age of puberty among the South Sea Islanders is nine – or is it ninety? – even the handwriting had become in its distraction indecipherable. It was disgraceful to have nothing more weighty or respectable to show after a whole morning's work. And if I could not grasp the truth about W (as for brevity's sake I had come to call her) in the past, why bother about W in the future? It seemed pure waste of time to consult all those gentlemen who specialise in woman and her effect on whatever it may be – politics, children, wages, morality – numerous and learned as they are. One might as well leave their books unopened.

But while I pondered I had unconsciously, in my listlessness, in my desperation, been drawing a picture where I should, like my neighbour, have been writing a conclusion. I had been drawing a face, a figure. It was the face and the figure of Professor von X, engaged in writing his monumental work entitled *The Mental, Moral and Physical Inferiority of the Female Sex*. He was not in my picture a man attractive to women. He was heavily built; he had a great jowl; to balance that he had very small eyes; he was very red in the face. His expression suggested that he was labouring under some emotion that made him jab his pen on the paper as if he were killing some noxious insect as he wrote, but even when he had killed it that did not satisfy him; he must go on killing it; and even so, some cause for anger and irritation remained. Could it be his wife, I asked, looking at my picture? Was she in love with a cavalry officer? Was the cavalry officer slim and elegant and dressed in astrakhan? Had he been laughed at, to adopt the Freudian theory, in his cradle by a pretty girl? For even in his cradle the professor, I thought, could not have been an attractive child. Whatever the reason, the professor was made to look very angry and very ugly in my sketch, as he wrote his great book upon the mental, moral and physical inferiority of women. Drawing pictures was an idle way of finishing an unprofitable morning's work. Yet it is in our idleness, in our dreams, that the submerged truth sometimes comes to the top. A very elementary exercise in psychology, not to be dignified by the name of psychoanalysis, showed me, on looking at my notebook, that the sketch of the angry professor had been made in anger. Anger had snatched my pencil while I dreamt. But what was anger doing there? Interest, confusion, amusement, boredom – all these emotions I could trace and name as they succeeded each other throughout the morning. Had anger, the black snake, been lurking among them? Yes, said the sketch, anger had. It referred me unmistakably to the one book, to the one phrase, which had roused the demon; it was the professor's statement about the mental, moral and physical inferiority of women. My heart had leapt. My cheeks had burnt. I had flushed with anger. There was nothing specially remarkable, however foolish, in that. One does not like to be told that one is naturally the inferior of a little man – I looked at the student next me – who breathes hard, wears a ready-made tie, and has not shaved this fortnight. One has certain foolish vanities. It is only human nature, I reflected, and began drawing cartwheels and circles over the angry professor's face till he looked like a burning bush or a flaming comet – anyhow, an apparition without human semblance or significance. The professor was nothing now but a faggot burning on the top of Hampstead Heath. Soon my own anger was explained and done with; but curiosity remained. How explain the anger of the professors? Why were they angry? For when it came to analysing the impression left by these books there was always an element of heat. This heat took many forms: it showed itself in satire, in sentiment, in curiosity, in reprobation. But there was another element which was often present and could not immediately be identified. Anger, I called it. But it was anger that had gone underground and mixed itself with all kinds of other emotions. To judge from its odd effects, it was anger disguised and complex, not anger simple and open.

Whatever the reason, all these books, I thought, surveying the pile on the desk, are worthless for my purposes. They were worthless scientifically, that is to say, though humanly they were full of instruction, interest, boredom, and very queer facts about the habits of the Fiji Islanders. They had been written in the red light of emotion and not in the white light of truth. Therefore they must be returned to the central desk and restored each to his own cell in the enormous honeycomb. All that I had retrieved from that morning's work had been the one fact of anger. The professors – I lumped them together thus – were angry. But why, I asked myself, having returned the books, why, I repeated, standing under the colonnade among the pigeons and the prehistoric canoes, why are they angry? And, asking myself this question, I strolled off to find a place for luncheon. What is the real nature of what I call for the moment their anger? I asked. Here was a puzzle that would last all the time that it takes to be served with food in a small restaurant somewhere near the British Museum. Some previous luncher had left the lunch edition of the evening paper on a chair, and, waiting to be served, I began idly reading the headlines. A ribbon of very large letters ran across the page. Somebody had made a big score in South Africa. Lesser ribbons announced that Sir Austen Chamberlain[28] was at Geneva. A meat axe with human hair on it had been found in a cellar. Mr Justice — commented in the divorce courts upon the Shamelessness of Women. Sprinkled about the paper were other pieces of news. A film actress had been lowered from a peak in California and hung suspended in midair. The weather was going to be foggy. The most transient visitor to this planet, I thought, who picked up this paper could not fail to be aware, even from this scattered testimony, that England is under the rule of a patriarchy. Nobody in their senses could fail to detect the dominance of the professor. His was the power and the money and the influence. He was the proprietor of the paper and its editor and sub-editor. He was the Foreign Secretary and the judge. He was the cricketer; he owned the racehorses and the yachts. He was the director of the company that pays two hundred per cent to its shareholders. He left millions to charities and colleges that were ruled by himself. He suspended the film actress in midair. He will decide if the hair on the meat axe is human; he it is who will acquit or convict the murderer, and hang him, or let him go free. With the exception of the fog he seemed to control everything. Yet he was angry. I knew that he was angry by this token. When I read what he wrote about women, I thought not of what he was saying but of himself. When an arguer argues dispassionately he thinks only of the argument; and the reader cannot help thinking of the argument too. If he had written dispassionately about women, had used indisputable proofs to establish his argument and had shown no trace of wishing that the result should be one thing rather than another, one would not have been angry either. One would have accepted the fact, as one accepts the fact that a pea is green or a canary yellow. So be it, I should have said. But I had been angry because he was angry. Yet it seemed absurd, I thought, turning over the evening paper, that a man with all this power should be angry. Or is anger, I wondered, somehow the familiar, the attendant sprite on power? Rich people, for example, are often angry because they suspect that the poor want to seize their wealth. The professors, or patriarchs, as it might be more accurate to call them, might be angry for that reason partly, but partly for one that lies a little less obviously on the surface. Possibly they were not 'angry' at all; often, indeed, they were admiring, devoted, exemplary in the relations of private life. Possibly when the professor insisted a little too emphatically upon the inferiority of women, he was concerned not with their inferiority, but with his own superiority. That was what he was protecting rather hot-headedly and with too much emphasis, because it was a jewel to him of the rarest price. Life for both sexes – and I looked at them, shouldering their way along the pavement – is arduous, difficult, a perpetual struggle. It calls for gigantic courage and strength. More than anything, perhaps, creatures of illusion as we are, it calls for confidence in oneself. Without self-confidence we are as babes in the cradle. And how can we generate this imponderable quality, which is yet so invaluable, most quickly? By thinking that other people are inferior to oneself. By feeling that one has some innate superiority – it may be wealth, or rank, a straight nose, or the portrait of a grandfather by Romney,[29] for there is no end to the pathetic devices of the human imagination – over other people. Hence the enormous importance to a patriarch who has to conquer, who has to rule, of feeling that great numbers of people, half the human race indeed, are by nature inferior to himself. It must indeed be one of the chief sources of his power. But let me turn the light of this observation on to real life, I thought. Does it help to explain some of those psychological puzzles that one notes in the margin of daily life? Does it explain my astonishment of the other day when Z, most humane, most modest of men, taking up some book by Rebecca West[30] and reading a passage in it, exclaimed, 'The arrant feminist! She says that men are snobs!' The exclamation, to me so surprising – for why was Miss West an arrant feminist for making a possibly true if uncomplimentary statement about the other sex? – was not merely the cry of wounded vanity; it was a protest against some infringement of his power to believe in himself. Women have served all these centuries as looking-glasses possessing the magic and delicious power of reflecting the figure of man at twice its natural size. Without that power probably the earth would still be swamp and jungle. The glories of all our wars would be unknown. We should still be scratching the outlines of deer on the remains of mutton bones and bartering flints for sheepskins or whatever simple ornament took our unsophisticated taste. Supermen and Fingers of Destiny would never have existed. The Czar and the Kaiser would never have worn crowns or lost them. Whatever may be their use in civilised societies, mirrors are essential to all violent and heroic action. That is why Napoleon and Mussolini both insist so emphatically upon the inferiority of women, for if they were not inferior, they would cease to enlarge. That serves to explain in part the necessity that women so often are to men. And it serves to explain how restless they are under her criticism; how impossible it is for her to say to them this book is bad, this picture is feeble, or whatever it may be, without giving far more pain and rousing far more anger than a man would do who gave the same criticism. For if she begins to tell the truth, the figure in the looking-glass shrinks; his fitness for life is diminished. How is he to go on giving judgment, civilising natives, making laws, writing books, dressing up and speechifying at banquets, unless he can see himself at breakfast and at dinner at least twice the size he really is? So I reflected, crumbling my bread and stirring my coffee and now and again looking at the people in the street. The looking-glass vision is of supreme importance because it charges the vitality; it stimulates the nervous system. Take it away and man may die, like the drug fiend deprived of his cocaine. Under the spell of that illusion, I thought, looking out of the window, half the people on the pavement are striding to work. They put on their hats and coats in the morning under its agreeable rays. They start the day confident, braced, believing themselves desired at Miss Smith's tea party; they say to themselves as they go into the room, I am the superior of half the people here, and it is thus that they speak with that self-confidence, that self-assurance, which have had such profound consequences in public life and lead to such curious notes in the margin of the private mind.

But these contributions to the dangerous and fascinating subject of the psychology of the other sex – it is one, I hope, that you will investigate when you have five hundred a year of your own – were interrupted by the necessity of paying the bill. It came to five shillings and ninepence. I gave the waiter a ten-shilling note and he went to bring me change. There was another ten-shilling note in my purse; I noticed it, because it is a fact that still takes my breath away – the power of my purse to breed ten-shilling notes automatically. I open it and there they are. Society gives me chicken and coffee, bed and lodging, in return for a certain number of pieces of paper which were left me by an aunt, for no other reason than that I share her name.

My aunt, Mary Beton, I must tell you, died by a fall from her horse when she was riding out to take the air in Bombay. The news of my legacy reached me one night about the same time that the act was passed that gave votes to women. A solicitor's letter fell into the postbox and when I opened it I found that she had left me five hundred pounds a year for ever. Of the two – the vote and the money – the money, I own, seemed infinitely the more important. Before that I had made my living by cadging odd jobs from newspapers, by reporting a donkey show here or a wedding there; I had earned a few pounds by addressing envelopes, reading to old ladies, making artificial flowers, teaching the alphabet to small children in a kindergarten. Such were the chief occupations that were open to women before 1918. I need not, I am afraid, describe in any detail the hardness of the work, for you know perhaps women who have done it; nor the difficulty of living on the money when it was earned, for you may have tried. But what still remains with me as a worse infliction than either was the poison of fear and bitterness which those days bred in me. To begin with, always to be doing work that one did not wish to do, and to do it like a slave, flattering and fawning, not always necessarily perhaps, but it seemed necessary and the stakes were too great to run risks; and then the thought of that one gift which it was death to hide – a small one but dear to the possessor – perishing and with it my self, my soul – all this became like a rust eating away the bloom of the spring, destroying the tree at its heart. However, as I say, my aunt died; and whenever I change a ten-shilling note a little of that rust and corrosion is rubbed off, fear and bitterness go. Indeed, I thought, slipping the silver into my purse, it is remarkable, remembering the bitterness of those days, what a change of temper a fixed income will bring about. No force in the world can take from me my five hundred pounds. Food, house and clothing are mine for ever. Therefore not merely do effort and labour cease, but also hatred and bitterness. I need not hate any man; he cannot hurt me. I need not flatter any man; he has nothing to give me. So imperceptibly I found myself adopting a new attitude towards the other half of the human race. It was absurd to blame any class or any sex, as a whole. Great bodies of people are never responsible for what they do. They are driven by instincts which are not within their control. They too, the patriarchs, the professors, had endless difficulties, terrible drawbacks to contend with. Their education had been in some ways as faulty as my own. It had bred in them defects as great. True, they had money and power, but only at the cost of harbouring in their breasts an eagle, a vulture, forever tearing the liver out and plucking at the lungs – the instinct for possession, the rage for acquisition which drives them to desire other people's fields and goods perpetually; to make frontiers and flags; battleships and poison gas; to offer up their own lives and their children's lives. Walk through the Admiralty Arch (I had reached that monument), or any other avenue given up to trophies and cannon, and reflect upon the kind of glory celebrated there. Or watch in the spring sunshine the stockbroker and the great barrister going indoors to make money and more money and more money when it is a fact that five hundred pounds a year will keep one alive in the sunshine. These are unpleasant instincts to harbour, I reflected. They are bred of the conditions of life; of the lack of civilisation, I thought, looking at the statue of the Duke of Cambridge, and in particular at the feathers in his cocked hat, with a fixity that they have scarcely ever received before. And, as I realised these drawbacks, by degrees fear and bitterness modified themselves into pity and toleration; and then in a year or two, pity and toleration went, and the greatest release of all came, which is freedom to think of things in themselves. That building, for example, do I like it or not? Is that picture beautiful or not? Is that in my opinion a good book or a bad? Indeed my aunt's legacy unveiled the sky to me, and substituted for the large and imposing figure of a gentleman, which Milton recommended for my perpetual adoration, a view of the open sky.

So thinking, so speculating I found my way back to my house by the river. Lamps were being lit and an indescribable change had come over London since the morning hour. It was as if the great machine after labouring all day had made with our help a few yards of something very exciting and beautiful – a fiery fabric flashing with red eyes, a tawny monster roaring with hot breath. Even the wind seemed flung like a flag as it lashed the houses and rattled the hoardings.

In my little street, however, domesticity prevailed. The house painter was descending his ladder; the nursemaid was wheeling the perambulator carefully in and out back to nursery tea; the coal-heaver was folding his empty sacks on top of each other; the woman who keeps the green-grocer's shop was adding up the day's takings with her hands in red mittens. But so engrossed was I with the problem you have laid upon my shoulders that I could not see even these usual sights without referring them to one centre. I thought how much harder it is now than it must have been even a century ago to say which of these employments is the higher, the more necessary. Is it better to be a coal-heaver or a nursemaid; is the charwoman who has brought up eight children of less value to the world than the barrister who has made a hundred thousand pounds? It is useless to ask such questions for nobody can answer them. Not only do the comparative values of charwomen and lawyers rise and fall from decade to decade, but we have no rods with which to measure them even as they are at the moment. I had been foolish to ask my professor to furnish me with 'indisputable proofs' of this or that in his argument about women. Even if one could state the value of any one gift at the moment, those values will change; in a century's time very possibly they will have changed completely. Moreover, in a hundred years, I thought, reaching my own doorstep, women will have ceased to be the protected sex. Logically they will take part in all the activities and exertions that were once denied them. The nursemaid will heave coal. The shopwoman will drive an engine. All assumptions founded on the facts observed when women were the protected sex will have disappeared – as, for example (here a squad of soldiers marched down the street), that women and clergymen and gardeners live longer than other people. Remove that protection, expose them to the same exertions and activities, make them soldiers and sailors and engine-drivers and dock labourers, and will not women die off so much younger, so much quicker, than men that one will say, 'I saw a woman today', as one used to say, 'I saw an aeroplane'? Anything may happen when womanhood has ceased to be a protected occupation, I thought, opening the door. But what bearing has all this upon the subject of my paper, Women and Fiction? I asked, going indoors.

Chapter 3

It was disappointing not to have brought back in the evening some important statement, some authentic fact. Women are poorer than men because – this or that. Perhaps now it would be better to give up seeking for the truth, and receiving on one's head an avalanche of opinion hot as lava, discoloured as dishwater. It would be better to draw the curtains; to shut out distractions; to light the lamp; to narrow the enquiry and to ask the historian, who records not opinions but facts, to describe under what conditions women lived, not throughout the ages, but in England, say, in the time of Elizabeth.

For it is a perennial puzzle why no woman wrote a word of that extraordinary literature when every other man, it seemed, was capable of song or sonnet. What were the conditions in which women lived? I asked myself; for fiction, imaginative work that is, is not dropped like a pebble upon the ground, as science may be; fiction is like a spider's web, attached ever so lightly perhaps, but still attached to life at all four corners. Often the attachment is scarcely perceptible; Shakespeare's plays, for instance, seem to hang there complete by themselves. But when the web is pulled askew, hooked up at the edge, torn in the middle, one remembers that these webs are not spun in midair by incorporeal creatures, but are the work of suffering human beings, and are attached to grossly material things, like health and money and the houses we live in.

I went, therefore, to the shelf where the histories stand and took down one of the latest, Professor Trevelyan's[31] *History of England*. Once more I looked up Women, found 'position of' and turned to the pages indicated. 'Wife-beating,' I read, 'was a recognised right of man, and was practised without shame by high as well as low . . . Similarly,' the historian goes on, 'the daughter who refused to marry the gentleman of her parents' choice was liable to be locked up, beaten and flung about the room, without any shock being inflicted on public opinion. Marriage was not an affair of personal affection, but of family avarice, particularly in the "chivalrous" upper classes . . . Betrothal often took place while one or both of the parties was in the cradle, and marriage when they were scarcely out of the nurses' charge.' That was about 1470, soon after Chaucer's time. The next reference to the position of women is some two hundred years later, in the time of the Stuarts. 'It was still the exception for women of the upper and middle class to choose their own husbands, and when the husband had been assigned, he was lord and master, so far at least as law and custom could make him. Yet even so,' Professor Trevelyan concludes, 'neither Shakespeare's women nor those of authentic seventeenth-century memoirs, like the Verneys and the Hutchinsons, seem wanting in personality and character.' Certainly, if we consider it, Cleopatra must have had a way with her; Lady Macbeth, one would suppose, had a will of her own; Rosalind, one might conclude, was an attractive girl. Professor Trevelyan is speaking no more than the truth when he remarks that Shakespeare's women do not seem wanting in personality and character. Not being a historian, one might go even further and say that women have burnt like beacons in all the works of all the poets from the beginning of time – Clytemnestra,[32] Antigone,[33] Cleopatra,[34] Lady Macbeth,[35] Phèdre,[36] Cressida,[37] Rosalind,[38] Desdemona,[39] the Duchess of Malfi,[40] among the dramatists; then among the prose writers: Millamant,[41] Clarissa,[42] Becky Sharp,[43] Anna Karenina,[44] Emma Bovary,[45] Madame de Guermantes[46] – the names flock to mind, nor do they recall women 'lacking in personality and character'. Indeed, if woman had no existence save in the fiction written by men, one would imagine her a person of the utmost importance; very various; heroic and mean; splendid and sordid; infinitely beautiful and hideous in the extreme; as great as a man, some think even greater.* But this is woman in fiction. In fact, as Professor Trevelyan points out, she was locked up, beaten and flung about the room.

A very queer, composite being thus emerges. Imaginatively she is of

* It remains a strange and almost inexplicable fact that in Athena's city, where women were kept in almost Oriental suppression as odalisques or drudges, the stage should yet have produced figures like Clytemnestra and Cassandra, Atossa and Antigone, Phèdre and Medea, and all the other heroines who dominate play after play of the 'misogynist' Euripides. But the paradox of this world, where in real life a respectable woman could hardly show her face alone in the street and yet on the stage woman equals or surpasses man, has never been satisfactorily explained. In modern tragedy the same predominance exists. At all events, a very cursory survey of Shakespeare's work (similarly with Webster, though not with Marlowe or Jonson) suffices to reveal how this dominance, this initiative of women, persists from Rosalind to Lady Macbeth. So too in Racine: six of his tragedies bear their heroines' names; and what male characters of his shall we set against Hermione and Andromaque, Bérénice and Roxane, Phèdre and Athalie? So again with Ibsen: what men shall we match with Solveig and Nora, Hedda and Hilda Wangel and Rebecca West? – F. L. Lucas, *Tragedy*, pp. 114–15

the highest importance; practically she is completely insignificant. She pervades poetry from cover to cover; she is all but absent from history. She dominates the lives of kings and conquerors in fiction; in fact she was the slave of any boy whose parents forced a ring upon her finger. Some of the most inspired words, some of the most profound thoughts in literature fall from her lips; in real life she could hardly read, could scarcely spell, and was the property of her husband.

It was certainly an odd monster that one made up by reading the historians first and the poets afterwards – a worm winged like an eagle; the spirit of life and beauty in a kitchen chopping up suet. But these monsters, however amusing to the imagination, have no existence in fact. What one must do to bring her to life was to think poetically and prosaically at one and the same moment, thus keeping in touch with fact – that she is Mrs Martin, aged thirty-six, dressed in blue, wearing a black hat and brown shoes; but not losing sight of fiction either – that she is a vessel in which all sorts of spirits and forces are coursing and flashing perpetually. The moment, however, that one tries this method with the Elizabethan woman, one branch of illumination fails: one is held up by the scarcity of facts. One knows nothing detailed, nothing perfectly true and substantial about her. History scarcely mentions her. And I turned to Professor Trevelyan again to see what history meant to him. I found by looking at his chapter headings that it meant – 'The Manor Court and the Methods of Open-field Agriculture . . . The Cistercians and Sheep-farming . . . The Crusades . . . The University . . . The House of Commons . . . The Hundred Years' War . . . The Wars of the Roses . . . The Renaissance Scholars . . . The Dissolution of the Monasteries . . . Agrarian and Religious Strife . . . The Origin of English Sea-power . . . The Armada . . . ' and so on. Occasionally an individual woman is mentioned, an Elizabeth, or a Mary; a queen or a great lady. But by no possible means could middle-class women with nothing but brains and character at their command have taken part in any one of the great movements which, brought together, constitute the historian's view of the past. Nor shall we find her in any collection of anecdotes. Aubrey[47] hardly mentions her. She never writes her own life and scarcely keeps a diary; there are only a handful of her letters in existence. She left no plays or poems by which we can judge her. What one wants, I thought – and why does not some brilliant student at Newnham or Girton supply it? – is a mass of information; at what age did she marry; how many children had she as a rule; what was her house like, had she a room to herself; did she do the cooking; would she be likely to have a servant? All these facts lie somewhere, presumably, in parish registers and account books; the life of the average Elizabethan woman must be scattered about somewhere, could one collect it and make a book of it. It would be ambitious beyond my daring, I thought, looking about the shelves for books that were not there, to suggest to the students of those famous colleges that they should rewrite history, though I own that it often seems a little queer as it is, unreal, lop-sided; but why should they not add a supplement to history, calling it, of course, by some in conspicuous name so that women might figure there without impropriety? For one often catches a glimpse of them in the lives of the great, whisking away into the background, concealing, I sometimes think, a wink, a laugh, perhaps a tear. And, after all, we have lives enough of Jane Austen; it scarcely seems necessary to consider again the influence of the tragedies of Joanna Baillie[48] upon the poetry of Edgar Allan Poe;[49] as for myself, I should not mind if the homes and haunts of Mary Russell Mitford were closed to the public for a century at least. But what I find deplorable, I continued, looking about the bookshelves again, is that nothing is known about women before the eighteenth century. I have no model in my mind to turn about this way and that. Here am I asking why women did not write poetry in the Elizabethan age, and I am not sure how they were educated; whether they were taught to write; whether they had sitting-rooms to themselves; how many women had children before they were twenty-one; what, in short, they did from eight in the morning till eight at night. They had no money evidently; according to Professor Trevelyan they were married whether they liked it or not before they were out of the nursery, at fifteen or sixteen very likely. It would have been extremely odd, even upon this showing, had one of them suddenly written the plays of Shakespeare, I concluded, and I thought of that old gentleman, who is dead now, but was a bishop, I think, who declared that it was impossible for any woman, past, present, or to come, to have the genius of Shakespeare. He wrote to the papers about it. He also told a lady who applied to him for information that cats do not as a matter of fact go to heaven, though they have, he added, souls of a sort. How much thinking those old gentlemen used to save one! How the borders of ignorance shrank back at their approach! Cats do not go to heaven. Women cannot write the plays of Shakespeare.

Be that as it may, I could not help thinking, as I looked at the works of Shakespeare on the shelf, that the bishop was right at least in this: it would have been impossible, completely and entirely, for any woman to have written the plays of Shakespeare in the age of Shakespeare. Let me imagine, since facts are so hard to come by, what would have happened had Shakespeare had a wonderfully gifted sister, called Judith, let us say.

Shakespeare himself went, very probably (his mother was an heiress), to the grammar school, where he may have learnt Latin – Ovid, Virgil and Horace – and the elements of grammar and logic. He was, it is well known, a wild boy who poached rabbits, perhaps shot a deer, and had, rather sooner than he should have done, to marry a woman in the neighbourhood, who bore him a child rather quicker than was right. That escapade sent him to seek his fortune in London. He had, it seemed, a taste for the theatre; he began by holding horses at the stage door. Very soon he got work in the theatre, became a successful actor, and lived at the hub of the universe, meeting everybody, knowing everybody, practising his art on the boards, exercising his wits in the streets, and even getting access to the palace of the queen. Meanwhile his extraordinarily gifted sister, let us suppose, remained at home. She was as adventurous, as imaginative, as agog to see the world as he was. But she was not sent to school. She had no chance of learning grammar and logic, let alone of reading Horace and Virgil. She picked up a book now and then, one of her brother's perhaps, and read a few pages. But then her parents came in and told her to mend the stockings or mind the stew and not moon about with books and papers. They would have spoken sharply but kindly, for they were substantial people who knew the conditions of life for a woman and loved their daughter – indeed, more likely than not she was the apple of her father's eye. Perhaps she scribbled some pages up in an apple loft on the sly but was careful to hide them or set fire to them. Soon, however, before she was out of her teens, she was to be betrothed to the son of a neighbouring wool-stapler. She cried out that marriage was hateful to her, and for that she was severely beaten by her father. Then he ceased to scold her. He begged her instead not to hurt him, not to shame him in this matter of her marriage. He would give her a chain of beads or a fine petticoat, he said; and there were tears in his eyes. How could she disobey him? How could she break his heart? The force of her own gift alone drove her to it. She made up a small parcel of her belongings, let herself down by a rope one summer's night and took the road to London. She was not seventeen. The birds that sang in the hedge were not more musical than she was. She had the quickest fancy, a gift like her brother's, for the tune of words. Like him, she had a taste for the theatre. She stood at the stage door; she wanted to act, she said. Men laughed in her face. The manager – a fat, loose-lipped man – guffawed. He bellowed something about poodles dancing and women acting – no woman, he said, could possibly be an actress. He hinted – you can imagine what. She could get no training in her craft. Could she even seek her dinner in a tavern or roam the streets at midnight? Yet her genius was for fiction and lusted to feed abundantly upon the lives of men and women and the study of their ways. At last – for she was very young, oddly like Shakespeare the poet in her face, with the same grey eyes and rounded brows – at last Nick Greene the actor-manager took pity on her; she found herself with child by that gentleman and so – who shall measure the heat and violence of the poet's heart when caught and tangled in a woman's body? – killed herself one winter's night and lies buried at some crossroads where the omnibuses now stop outside the Elephant and Castle.

That, more or less, is how the story would run, I think, if a woman in Shakespeare's day had had Shakespeare's genius. But for my part, I agree with the deceased bishop, if such he was – it is unthinkable that any woman in Shakespeare's day should have had Shakespeare's genius. For genius like Shakespeare's is not born among labouring, uneducated, servile people. It was not born in England among the Saxons and the Britons. It is not born today among the working classes. How, then, could it have been born among women whose work began, according to Professor Trevelyan, almost before they were out of the nursery, who were forced to it by their parents and held to it by all the power of law and custom? Yet genius of a sort must have existed among women as it must have existed among the working classes. Now and again an Emily Brontë or a Robert Burns blazes out and proves its presence. But certainly it never got itself on to paper. When, however, one reads of a witch being ducked, of a woman possessed by devils, of a wise woman selling herbs, or even of a very remarkable man who had a mother, then I think we are on the track of a lost novelist, a suppressed poet, of some mute and inglorious Jane Austen, some Emily Brontë who dashed her brains out on the moor or mopped and mowed about the highways crazed with the torture that her gift had put her to. Indeed, I would venture to guess that Anon, who wrote so many poems without signing them, was often a woman. It was a woman Edward Fitzgerald,[50] I think, suggested who made the ballads and the folk-songs, crooning them to her children, beguiling her spinning with them, or the length of the winter's night.

This may be true or it may be false – who can say? – but what is true in it, so it seemed to me, reviewing the story of Shakespeare's sister as I had made it, is that any woman born with a great gift in the sixteenth century would certainly have gone crazed, shot herself, or ended her days in some lonely cottage outside the village, half-witch, half-wizard, feared and mocked at. For it needs little skill in psychology to be sure that a highly gifted girl who had tried to use her gift for poetry would have been so thwarted and hindered by other people, so tortured and pulled asunder by her own contrary instincts, that she must have lost her health and sanity to a certainty. No girl could have walked to London and stood at a stage door and forced her way into the presence of actor-managers without doing herself a violence and suffering an anguish which may have been irrational – for chastity may be a fetish invented by certain societies for unknown reasons – but were none the less inevitable. Chastity had then, it has even now, a religious importance in a woman's life, and has so wrapped itself round with nerves and instincts that to cut it free and bring it to the light of day demands courage of the rarest. To have lived a free life in London in the sixteenth century would have meant for a woman who was poet and playwright a nervous stress and dilemma which might well have killed her. Had she survived, whatever she had written would have been twisted and deformed, issuing from a strained and morbid imagination. And undoubtedly, I thought, looking at the shelf where there are no plays by women, her work would have gone unsigned. That refuge she would have sought certainly. It was the relic of the sense of chastity that dictated anonymity to women even so late as the nineteenth century. Currer Bell, George Eliot, George Sand,[51] all the victims of inner strife as their writings prove, sought ineffectively to veil themselves by using the name of a man. Thus they did homage to the convention, which if not implanted by the other sex was liberally encouraged by them (the chief glory of a woman is not to be talked of, said Pericles, himself a much-talked-of man), that publicity in women is detestable. Anonymity runs in their blood. The desire to be veiled still possesses them. They are not even now as concerned about the health of their fame as men are, and, speaking generally, will pass a tombstone or a signpost without feeling an irresistible desire to cut their names on it, as Alf, Bert or Chas must do in obedience to their instinct, which murmurs if it sees a fine woman go by, or even a dog, Ce chien est à moi. And, of course, it may not be a dog, I thought, remembering Parliament Square, the Sièges Allée and other avenues; it may be a piece of land or a man with curly black hair. It is one of the great advantages of being a woman that one can pass even a very fine negress without wishing to make an English-woman of her.

That woman, then, who was born with a gift of poetry in the sixteenth century, was an unhappy woman, a woman at strife against herself. All the conditions of her life, all her own instincts, were hostile to the state of mind which is needed to set free whatever is in the brain. But what is the state of mind that is most propitious to the act of creation? I asked.

Can one come by any notion of the state that furthers and makes possible that strange activity? Here I opened the volume containing the tragedies of Shakespeare. What was Shakespeare's state of mind, for instance, when he wrote *Lear* and *Antony and Cleopatra*? It was certainly the state of mind most favourable to poetry that there has ever existed. But Shakespeare himself said nothing about it. We only know casually and by chance that he 'never blotted a line'. Nothing indeed was ever said by the artist himself about his state of mind until the eighteenth century perhaps. Rousseau[52] perhaps began it. At any rate, by the nineteenth century self-consciousness had developed so far that it was the habit for men of letters to describe their minds in confessions and autobiographies. Their lives also were written, and their letters were printed after their deaths. Thus, though we do not know what Shakespeare went through when he wrote *Lear*, we do know what Carlyle[53] went through when he wrote the *French Revolution*; what Flaubert went through when he wrote *Madame Bovary*; what Keats was going through when he tried to write poetry against the coming of death and the indifference of the world.

And one gathers from this enormous modern literature of confession and self-analysis that to write a work of genius is almost always a feat of prodigious difficulty. Everything is against the likelihood that it will come from the writer's mind whole and entire. Generally material circumstances are against it. Dogs will bark; people will interrupt; money must be made; health will break down. Further, accentuating all these difficulties and making them harder to bear is the world's notorious indifference. It does not ask people to write poems and novels and histories; it does not need them. It does not care whether Flaubert finds the right word or whether Carlyle scrupulously verifies this or that fact. Naturally, it will not pay for what it does not want. And so the writer – Keats, Flaubert,[54] Carlyle – suffers, especially in the creative years of youth, every form of distraction and discouragement. A curse, a cry of agony, rises from those books of analysis and confession. 'Mighty poets in their misery dead' – that is the burden of their song. If anything comes through in spite of all this, it is a miracle, and probably no book is born entire and uncrippled as it was conceived.

But for women, I thought, looking at the empty shelves, these difficulties were infinitely more formidable. In the first place, to have a room of her own, let alone a quiet room or a soundproof room, was out of the question, unless her parents were exceptionally rich or very noble, even up to the beginning of the nineteenth century. Since her pin money, which depended on the goodwill of her father, was only enough to keep her clothed, she was debarred from such alleviations as came even to Keats or Tennyson or Carlyle, all poor men, from a walking tour, a little journey to France, from the separate lodging which, even if it were miserable enough, sheltered them from the claims and tyrannies of their families. Such material difficulties were formidable; but much worse were the immaterial. The indifference of the world which Keats and Flaubert and other men of genius have found so hard to bear was in her case not indifference but hostility. The world did not say to her as it said to them, Write if you choose; it makes no difference to me. The world said with a guffaw, Write? What's the good of your writing? Here the psychologists of Newnham and Girton might come to our help, I thought, looking again at the blank spaces on the shelves. For surely it is time that the effect of discouragement upon the mind of the artist should be measured, as I have seen a dairy company measure the effect of ordinary milk and Grade A milk upon the body of the rat. They set two rats in cages side by side, and of the two one was furtive, timid and small, and the other was glossy, bold and big. Now what food do we feed women as artists upon? I asked, remembering, I suppose, that dinner of prunes and custard. To answer that question I had only to open the evening paper and to read that Lord Birkenhead is of opinion – but really I am not going to trouble to copy out Lord Birkenhead's opinion upon the writing of women. What Dean Inge says I will leave in peace. The Harley Street specialist may be allowed to rouse the echoes of Harley Street with his vociferations without raising a hair on my head. I will quote, however, Mr Oscar Browning, because Mr Oscar Browning was a great figure in Cambridge at one time, and used to examine the students at Girton and Newnham. Mr Oscar Browning was wont to declare 'that the impression left on his mind, after looking over any set of examination papers, was that, irrespective of the marks he might give, the best woman was intellectually the inferior of the worst man'. After saying that Mr Browning went back to his rooms – and it is this sequel that endears him and makes him a human figure of some bulk and majesty – he went back to his rooms and found a stable-boy lying on the sofa – 'a mere skeleton, his cheeks were cavernous and sallow, his teeth were black, and he did not appear to have the full use of his limbs. "That's Arthur" [said Mr Browning]. "He's a dear boy really and most high-minded." ' The two pictures always seem to me to complete each other. And happily in this age of biography the two pictures often do complete each other, so that we are able to interpret the opinions of great men not only by what they say, but by what they do.

But though this is possible now, such opinions coming from the lips of important people must have been formidable enough even fifty years ago. Let us suppose that a father from the highest motives did not wish his daughter to leave home and become writer, painter or scholar. 'See what Mr Oscar Browning says,' he would say; and there was not only Mr Oscar Browning; there was the *Saturday Review*; there was Mr Greg – the 'essentials of a woman's being,' said Mr Greg emphatically, 'are that *they are supported by, and they minister to, men*' – there was an enormous body of masculine opinion to the effect that nothing could be expected of women intellectually. Even if her father did not read out loud these opinions, any girl could read them for herself; and the reading, even in the nineteenth century, must have lowered her vitality, and told profoundly upon her work. There would always have been that assertion – you cannot do this, you are incapable of doing that – to protest against, to overcome. Probably for a novelist this germ is no longer of much effect; for there have been women novelists of merit. But for painters it must still have some sting in it; and for musicians, I imagine, is even now active and poisonous in the extreme. The woman composer stands where the actress stood in the time of Shakespeare. Nick Greene,[55] I thought, remembering the story I had made about Shakespeare's sister, said that a woman acting put him in mind of a dog dancing. Johnson repeated the phrase two hundred years later of women preaching. And here, I said, opening a book about music, we have the very words used again in this year of grace, 1928, of women who try to write music. 'Of Mlle Germaine Tailleferre one can only repeat Dr Johnson's dictum[56] concerning a woman preacher, transposed into terms of music. "Sir, a woman's composing is like a dog's walking on his hind legs. It is not done well, but you are surprised to find it done at all." '* So accurately does history repeat itself.

Thus, I concluded, shutting Mr Oscar Browning's life and pushing away the rest, it is fairly evident that even in the nineteenth century a woman was not encouraged to be an artist. On the contrary, she was snubbed, slapped, lectured and exhorted. Her mind must have been strained and her vitality lowered by the need of opposing this, of disproving that. For here again we come within range of that very interesting and obscure masculine complex which has had so much influence upon the woman's movement: that deep-seated desire, not so much that *she* shall be inferior as that *he* shall be superior, which plants

---

* *A Survey of Contemporary Music*, Cecil Gray, p. 246

him wherever one looks, not only in front of the arts but barring the way to politics too, even when the risk to himself seems infinitesimal and the suppliant humble and devoted. Even Lady Bessborough, I remembered, with all her passion for politics, must humbly bow herself and write to Lady Granville Leveson-Gower: ' . . . notwithstanding all my violence in politicks and talking so much on that subject, I perfectly agree with you that no woman has any business to meddle with that or any other serious business, further than giving her opinion (if she is ask'd)'. And so she goes on to spend her enthusiasm where it meets with no obstacle whatsoever, upon that immensely important subject, Lord Granville's maiden speech in the House of Commons. The spectacle is certainly a strange one, I thought. The history of men's opposition to women's emancipation is more interesting perhaps than the story of that emancipation itself. An amusing book might be made of it if some young student at Girton or Newnham would collect examples and deduce a theory – but she would need thick gloves on her hands and bars to protect her of solid gold.

But what is amusing now, I recollected, shutting Lady Bessborough, had to be taken in desperate earnest once. Opinions that one now pastes in a book labelled cock-a-doodle-dum and keeps for reading to select audiences on summer nights once drew tears, I can assure you. Among your grandmothers and great-grandmothers there were many that wept their eyes out. Florence Nightingale shrieked aloud in her agony.* Moreover, it is all very well for you, who have got yourselves to college and enjoy sitting-rooms – or is it only bed-sitting-rooms? – of your own to say that genius should disregard such opinions; that genius should be above caring what is said of it. Unfortunately, it is precisely the men or women of genius who mind most what is said of them. Remember Keats.[57] Remember the words he had cut on his tombstone. Think of Tennyson; think – but I need hardly multiply instances of the undeniable, if very unfortunate, fact that it is the nature of the artist to mind excessively what is said about him. Literature is strewn with the wreckage of men who have minded beyond reason the opinions of others.

And this susceptibility of theirs is doubly unfortunate, I thought, returning again to my original enquiry into what state of mind is most propitious for creative work, because the mind of an artist, in order to achieve the prodigious effort of freeing whole and entire the work that is in him, must be incandescent, like Shakespeare's mind, I conjectured,

* See *Cassandra* by Florence Nightingale, printed in *The Cause* by R. Strachey.

looking at the book which lay open at *Antony and Cleopatra*. There must be no obstacle in it, no foreign matter unconsumed.

For though we say that we know nothing about Shakespeare's state of mind, even as we say that, we are saying something about Shakespeare's state of mind. The reason perhaps why we know so little of Shakespeare – compared with Donne or Ben Jonson or Milton – is that his grudges and spites and antipathies are hidden from us. We are not held up by some 'revelation' which reminds us of the writer. All desire to protest, to preach, to proclaim an injury, to pay off a score, to make the world the witness of some hardship or grievance was fired out of him and consumed. Therefore his poetry flows from him free and unimpeded. If ever a human being got his work expressed completely, it was Shakespeare. If ever a mind was incandescent, unimpeded, I thought, turning again to the bookcase, it was Shakespeare's mind.

Chapter 4

That one would find any woman in that state of mind in the sixteenth century was obviously impossible. One has only to think of the Elizabethan tombstones with all those children kneeling with clasped hands; and their early deaths; and to see their houses with their dark, cramped rooms, to realise that no woman could have written poetry then. What one would expect to find would be that rather later perhaps some great lady would take advantage of her comparative freedom and comfort to publish something with her name to it and risk being thought a monster. Men, of course, are not snobs, I continued, carefully eschewing 'the arrant feminism' of Miss Rebecca West; but they appreciate with sympathy for the most part the efforts of a countess to write verse. One would expect to find a lady of title meeting with far greater encouragement than an unknown Miss Austen or a Miss Brontë at that time would have met with. But one would also expect to find that her mind was disturbed by alien emotions like fear and hatred and that her poems showed traces of that disturbance. Here is Lady Winchilsea,[58] for example, I thought, taking down her poems. She was born in the year 1661; she was noble both by birth and by marriage; she was childless; she wrote poetry, and one has only to open her poetry to find her bursting out in indignation against the position of women:

> How we are fallen! fallen by mistaken rules,
> And Education's more than Nature's fools;
> Debarred from all improvements of the mind,
> And to be dull, expected and designed;
> And if someone would soar above the rest,
> With warmer fancy, and ambition pressed,
> So strong the opposing faction still appears,
> The hopes to thrive can ne'er outweigh the fears.

Clearly her mind has by no means 'consumed all impediments and become incandescent'. On the contrary, it is harassed and distracted with hates and grievances. The human race is split up for her into two parties. Men are the 'opposing faction'; men are hated and feared, because they have the power to bar her way to what she wants to do – which is to write.

> Alas! a woman that attempts the pen,
> Such a presumptuous creature is esteemed,
> The fault can by no virtue be redeemed.
> They tell us we mistake our sex and way;
> Good breeding, fashion, dancing, dressing, play,
> Are the accomplishments we should desire;
> To write, or read, or think, or to enquire,
> Would cloud our beauty, and exhaust our time,
> And interrupt the conquests of our prime.
> Whilst the dull manage of a servile house
> Is held by some our utmost art and use.

Indeed she has to encourage herself to write by supposing that what she writes will never be published; to soothe herself with the sad chant:

> To some few friends, and to thy sorrows sing,
> For groves of laurel thou wert never meant;
> Be dark enough thy shades, and be thou there content.

Yet it is clear that could she have freed her mind from hate and fear and not heaped it with bitterness and resentment, the fire was hot within her. Now and again words issue of pure poetry:

> Nor will in fading silks compose,
> Faintly the inimitable rose.

– they are rightly praised by Mr Murry,[59] and Pope, it is thought, remembered and appropriated those others:

> Now the jonquille o'ercomes the feeble brain;
> We faint beneath the aromatic pain.

It was a thousand pities that the woman who could write like that, whose mind was tuned to nature and reflection, should have been forced to anger and bitterness. But how could she have helped herself? I asked, imagining the sneers and the laughter, the adulation of the toadies, the scepticism of the professional poet. She must have shut herself up in a room in the country to write, and been torn asunder by bitterness and scruples perhaps, though her husband was of the kindest, and their married life perfection. She 'must have', I say, because when one comes to seek out the facts about Lady Winchilsea, one finds, as usual, that almost nothing is known about her. She suffered terribly from melancholy, which we can explain at least to some extent when we find her telling us how in the grip of it she would imagine:

> My lines decried, and my employment thought
> An useless folly or presumptuous fault.

The employment which was thus censured was, as far as one can see, the harmless one of rambling about the fields and dreaming:

> My hand delights to trace unusual things,
> And deviates from the known and common way,
> Nor will in fading silks compose,
> Faintly the inimitable rose.

Naturally, if that was her habit and that was her delight, she could only expect to be laughed at; and, accordingly, Pope or Gay[60] is said to have satirised her 'as a blue-stocking with an itch for scribbling'. Also it is thought that she offended Gay by laughing at him. She said that his *Trivia* showed that 'he was more proper to walk before a chair than to ride in one'. But this is all 'dubious gossip' and, says Mr Murry, 'uninteresting'. But there I do not agree with him, for I should have liked to have had more even of dubious gossip so that I might have found out or made up some image of this melancholy lady, who loved wandering in the fields and thinking about unusual things and scorned, so rashly, so unwisely, 'the dull manage of a servile house'. But she became diffuse, Mr Murry says. Her gift is all grown about with weeds and bound with briars. It had no chance of showing itself for the fine distinguished gift it was.

And so, putting her back on the shelf, I turned to the other great lady, the duchess whom Lamb loved, hare-brained, fantastical Margaret of Newcastle, her elder, but her contemporary. They were very different, but alike in this – that both were noble and both childless and both were married to the best of husbands. In both burnt the same passion for poetry and both are disfigured and deformed by the same causes. Open the duchess and one finds the same outburst of rage: 'Women live like Bats or Owls, labour like Beasts, and die like Worms . . . ' Margaret too might have been a poet; in our day all that activity would have turned a wheel of some sort. As it was, what could bind, tame or civilise for human use that wild, generous, untutored intelligence? It poured itself out, higgledy-piggledy, in torrents of rhyme and prose, poetry and philosophy which stand congealed in quartos and folios that nobody ever reads. She should have had a microscope put in her hand. She should have been taught to look at the stars and reason scientifically. Her wits were turned with solitude and freedom. No one checked her. No one taught her. The professors fawned on her. At Court they jeered at her. Sir Egerton Brydges[61] complained of her coarseness – 'as flowing from a female of high rank brought up in the Courts'. She shut herself up at Welbeck alone.

What a vision of loneliness and riot the thought of Margaret Cavendish[62] brings to mind! as if some giant cucumber had spread itself over all the roses and carnations in the garden and choked them to death. What a waste that the woman who wrote 'the best bred women are those whose minds are civilest' should have frittered her time away scribbling nonsense and plunging ever deeper into obscurity and folly till the people crowded round her coach when she issued out. Evidently the crazy duchess became a bogey to frighten clever girls with. Here, I remembered, putting away the duchess and opening Dorothy Osborne's[63] letters, is Dorothy writing to Temple about the duchess's new book. 'Sure the poore woman is a little distracted, shee could never bee soe rediculous else as to venture at writeing book's and in verse too, if I should not sleep this fortnight I should not come to that.'

And so, since no woman of sense and modesty could write books, Dorothy, who was sensitive and melancholy, the very opposite of the duchess in temper, wrote nothing. Letters did not count. A woman might write letters while she was sitting by her father's sick-bed. She could write them by the fire whilst the men talked without disturbing them. The strange thing is, I thought, turning over the pages of Dorothy's letters, what a gift that untaught and solitary girl had for the framing of a sentence, for the fashioning of a scene. Listen to her running on:

After dinner wee sitt and talk till Mr B. com's in question and then I am gon. the heat of the day is spent in reading or working and about sixe or seven a Clock, I walke out into a Common that lyes hard by the house where a great many young wenches keep Sheep and Cow's and sitt in the shades singing of Ballads; I goe to them and compare their voyces and Beauty's to some Ancient Shepherdesses that I have read of and finde a vaste difference there, but trust mee I think these are as innocent as those could bee. I talke to them, and finde they want nothing to make them the happiest People in the world, but the knoledge that they are soe. most commonly when we are in the middest of our discourse one looks aboute her and spyes her Cow's goeing into the Corne and then away they all run, as if they had wing's at theire heels. I that am not soe nimble stay behinde, and when I see them driveing home theire Cattle I think tis time for mee to retyre too. when I have supped I goe into the Garden and soe to the syde of a small River that runs by it where I sitt downe and wish you with mee . . .

One could have sworn that she had the makings of a writer in her. But 'if I should not sleep this fortnight I should not come to that' – one can measure the opposition that was in the air to a woman writing when one finds that even a woman with a great turn for writing has brought herself to believe that to write a book was to be ridiculous, even to show oneself distracted. And so we come, I continued, replacing the single short volume of Dorothy Osborne's letters upon the shelf, to Mrs Behn.[64]

And with Mrs Behn we turn a very important corner on the road. We leave behind, shut up in their parks among their folios, those solitary great ladies who wrote without audience or criticism, for their own delight alone. We come to town and rub shoulders with ordinary people in the streets. Mrs Behn was a middle-class woman with all the plebeian virtues of humour, vitality and courage; a woman forced by the death of her husband and some unfortunate adventures of her own to make her living by her wits. She had to work on equal terms with men. She made, by working very hard, enough to live on. The importance of that fact outweighs anything that she actually wrote, even the splendid 'A Thousand Martyrs I have made', or 'Love in Fantastic Triumph sat', for here begins the freedom of the mind, or rather the possibility that in the course of time the mind will be free to write what it likes. For now that Aphra Behn had done it, girls could go to their parents and say, You need not give me an allowance; I can make money by my pen. Of course the answer for many years to come was, Yes, by living the life of Aphra Behn! Death would be better! and the door was slammed faster than ever. That profoundly interesting subject, the value that men set upon women's chastity and its effect upon their education, here suggests itself for discussion, and might provide an interesting book if any student at Girton or Newnham cared to go into the matter. Lady Dudley, sitting in diamonds among the midges of a Scottish moor, might serve for frontispiece. Lord Dudley, *The Times* said when Lady Dudley died the other day, 'a man of cultivated taste and many accomplishments, was benevolent and bountiful, but whimsically despotic. He insisted upon his wife's wearing full dress, even at the remotest shooting-lodge in the Highlands; he loaded her with gorgeous jewels', and so on, 'he gave her everything – always excepting any measure of responsibility'. Then Lord Dudley had a stroke and she nursed him and ruled his estates with supreme competence for ever after. That whimsical despotism was in the nineteenth century too.

But to return. Aphra Behn proved that money could be made by writing at the sacrifice, perhaps, of certain agreeable qualities; and so by degrees writing became not merely a sign of folly and a distracted mind, but was of practical importance. A husband might die, or some disaster overtake the family. Hundreds of women began as the eighteenth century drew on to add to their pin money, or to come to the rescue of their families by making translations or writing the innumerable bad novels which have ceased to be recorded even in textbooks, but are to be picked up in the fourpenny boxes in the Charing Cross Road. The extreme activity of mind which showed itself in the later eighteenth century among women – the talking, and the meeting, the writing of essays on Shakespeare, the translating of the classics – was founded on the solid fact that women could make money by writing. Money dignifies what is frivolous if unpaid for. It might still be well to sneer at 'blue stockings with an itch for scribbling', but it could not be denied that they could put money in their purses. Thus, towards the end of the eighteenth century a change came about which, if I were rewriting history, I should describe more fully and think of greater importance than the Crusades or the Wars of the Roses.

The middle-class woman began to write. For if *Pride and Prejudice*[65] matters, and *Middlemarch*[66] and *Villette*[67] and *Wuthering Heights*[68] matter, then it matters far more than I can prove in an hour's discourse that women generally, and not merely the lonely aristocrat shut up in her country house among her folios and her flatterers, took to writing. Without those forerunners, Jane Austen and the Brontës and George Eliot could no more have written than Shakespeare could have written without Marlowe,[69] or Marlowe without Chaucer, or Chaucer without those forgotten poets who paved the ways and tamed the natural savagery of the tongue. For masterpieces are not single and solitary births; they are the outcome of many years of thinking in common, of thinking by the body of the people, so that the experience of the mass is behind the single voice. Jane Austen should have laid a wreath upon the grave of Fanny Burney, and George Eliot done homage to the robust shade of Eliza Carter – the valiant old woman who tied a bell to her bedstead in order that she might wake early and learn Greek. All women together ought to let flowers fall upon the tomb of Aphra Behn, which is, most scandalously but rather appropriately, in Westminster Abbey, for it was she who earned them the right to speak their minds. It is she – shady and amorous as she was – who makes it not quite fantastic for me to say to you tonight: Earn five hundred a year by your wits.

Here, then, one had reached the early nineteenth century. And here, for the first time, I found several shelves given up entirely to the works of women. But why, I could not help asking, as I ran my eyes over them, were they, with very few exceptions, all novels? The original impulse was to poetry. The 'supreme head of song' was a poetess. Both in France and in England the women poets precede the women novelists. Moreover, I thought, looking at the four famous names, what had George Eliot in common with Emily Brontë? Did not Charlotte Brontë fail entirely to understand Jane Austen? Save for the possibly relevant fact that not one of them had a child, four more incongruous characters could not have met together in a room – so much so that it is tempting to invent a meeting and a dialogue between them. Yet by some strange force they were all compelled, when they wrote, to write novels. Had it something to do with being born of the middle class, I asked; and with the fact, which Miss Emily Davies a little later was so strikingly to demonstrate, that the middle-class family in the early nineteenth century was possessed only of a single sitting-room between them? If a woman wrote, she would have to write in the common sitting-room. And, as Miss Nightingale[70] was so vehemently to complain – 'women never have an half-hour . . . that they can call their own' – she was always interrupted. Still it would be easier to write prose and fiction there than to write poetry or a play. Less concentration is required. Jane Austen wrote like that to the end of her days. 'How she was able to effect all this,' her nephew writes in his memoir, 'is surprising, for she had no separate study to repair to, and most of the work must have been done in the general sitting-room, subject to all kinds of casual interruptions. She was careful that her occupation should not be suspected by servants or visitors or any persons beyond her own family party.'* Jane Austen hid her manuscripts or covered them with a piece of blotting-paper. Then, again, all the literary training that a woman had in the early nineteenth century was training in the observation of character, in the analysis of emotion. Her sensibility had been educated for centuries by the influences of the common sitting-room. People's feelings were impressed on her; personal relations were always before her eyes. Therefore, when the middle-class woman took to writing, she naturally wrote novels, even though, as seems evident enough, two of the four famous women here named were not by nature novelists. Emily Brontë should have written poetic plays; the overflow of George Eliot's capacious mind should have spread itself when the creative impulse was spent upon history or biography. They wrote novels, however; one may even go further, I said, taking *Pride and Prejudice* from the shelf, and say that they wrote good novels. Without boasting

* *Memoir of Jane Austen* by her nephew, James Edward Austen-Leigh

or giving pain to the opposite sex, one may say that *Pride and Prejudice* is a good book. At any rate, one would not have been ashamed to have been caught in the act of writing *Pride and Prejudice*. Yet Jane Austen was glad that a hinge creaked, so that she might hide her manuscript before anyone came in. To Jane Austen there was something discreditable in writing *Pride and Prejudice*. And, I wondered, would *Pride and Prejudice* have been a better novel if Jane Austen had not thought it necessary to hide her manuscript from visitors? I read a page or two to see, but I could not find any signs that her circumstances had harmed her work in the slightest. That, perhaps, was the chief miracle about it. Here was a woman about the year 1800 writing without hate, without bitterness, without fear, without protest, without preaching. That was how Shakespeare wrote, I thought, looking at *Antony and Cleopatra*; and when people compare Shakespeare and Jane Austen, they may mean that the minds of both had consumed all impediments; and for that reason we do not know Jane Austen and we do not know Shakespeare, and for that reason Jane Austen pervades every word that she wrote, and so does Shakespeare. If Jane Austen suffered in any way from her circumstances it was in the narrowness of life that was imposed upon her. It was impossible for a woman to go about alone. She never travelled; she never drove through London in an omnibus or had luncheon in a shop by herself. But perhaps it was the nature of Jane Austen not to want what she had not. Her gift and her circumstances matched each other completely. But I doubt whether that was true of Charlotte Brontë, I said, opening *Jane Eyre* and laying it beside *Pride and Prejudice*.

I opened it at Chapter Twelve and my eye was caught by the phrase, 'Anybody may blame me who likes.' What were they blaming Charlotte Brontë for? I wondered. And I read how Jane Eyre used to go up on to the roof when Mrs Fairfax was making jellies and looked over the fields at the distant view. And then she longed – and it was for this that they blamed her –

I longed for a power of vision which might overpass that limit; which might reach the busy world, towns, regions full of life I had heard of but never seen: that then I desired more of practical experience than I possessed; more of intercourse with my kind, of acquaintance with variety of character than was here within my reach. I valued what was good in Mrs Fairfax, and what was good in Adèle; but I believed in the existence of other and more vivid kinds of goodness, and what I believed in I wished to behold.

Who blames me? Many, no doubt, and I shall be called discontented. I could not help it: the restlessness was in my nature; it agitated me to pain sometimes . . .

It is vain to say human beings ought to be satisfied with tranquillity: they must have action; and they will make it if they cannot find it. Millions are condemned to a stiller doom than mine, and millions are in silent revolt against their lot. Nobody knows how many rebellions ferment in the masses of life which people earth. Women are supposed to be very calm generally: but women feel just as men feel; they need exercise for their faculties and a field for their efforts as much as their brothers do; they suffer from too rigid a restraint, too absolute a stagnation, precisely as men would suffer; and it is narrow-minded in their more privileged fellow-creatures to say that they ought to confine themselves to making puddings and knitting stockings, to playing on the piano and embroidering bags. It is thoughtless to condemn them, or laugh at them, if they seek to do more or learn more than custom has pronounced necessary for their sex.

When thus alone I not unfrequently heard Grace Poole's laugh . . .

That is an awkward break, I thought. It is upsetting to come upon Grace Poole all of a sudden. The continuity is disturbed. One might say, I continued, laying the book down beside *Pride and Prejudice*, that the woman who wrote those pages had more genius in her than Jane Austen; but if one reads them over and marks that jerk in them, that indignation, one sees that she will never get her genius expressed whole and entire. Her books will be deformed and twisted. She will write in a rage where she should write calmly. She will write foolishly where she should write wisely. She will write of herself where she should write of her characters. She is at war with her lot. How could she help but die young, cramped and thwarted?

One could not but play for a moment with the thought of what might have happened if Charlotte Brontë had possessed say three hundred a year – but the foolish woman sold the copyright of her novels outright for fifteen hundred pounds; had somehow possessed more knowledge of the busy world, and towns and regions full of life; more practical experience, and intercourse with her kind and acquaintance with a variety of character. In those words she puts her finger exactly not only upon her own defects as a novelist but upon those of her sex, at that time. She knew, no one better, how enormously her genius would have profited if it had not spent itself in solitary visions over distant fields; if experience and intercourse and travel had been granted her. But they were not granted; they were withheld; and we must accept the fact that all those good novels, *Villette*, *Emma*, *Wuthering Heights*, *Middlemarch*, were written by women without more experience of life than could enter the house of a respectable clergyman; written too in the common sitting-room of that respectable house and by women so poor that they could not afford to buy more than a few quires of paper at a time upon which to write *Wuthering Heights* or *Jane Eyre*. One of them, it is true, George Eliot, escaped after much tribulation, but only to a secluded villa in St John's Wood. And there she settled down in the shadow of the world's disapproval. 'I wish it to be understood,' she wrote, 'that I should never invite anyone to come and see me who did not ask for the invitation'; for was she not living in sin with a married man and might not the sight of her damage the chastity of Mrs Smith or whoever it might be that chanced to call? One must submit to the social convention, and be 'cut off from what is called the world'. At the same time, on the other side of Europe, there was a young man living freely with this gypsy or with that great lady; going to the wars; picking up unhindered and uncensored all that varied experience of human life which served him so splendidly later when he came to write his books. Had Tolstoy lived at the Priory in seclusion with a married lady, 'cut off from what is called the world', however edifying the moral lesson, he could scarcely, I thought, have written *War and Peace*.

But one could perhaps go a little deeper into the question of novel-writing and the effect of sex upon the novelist. If one shuts one's eyes and thinks of the novel as a whole, it would seem to be a creation owning a certain looking-glass likeness to life, though of course with simplifications and distortions innumerable. At any rate, it is a structure leaving a shape on the mind's eye, built now in squares, now pagoda shaped, now throwing out wings and arcades, now solidly compact and domed like the Cathedral of St Sofia at Constantinople. This shape, I thought, thinking back over certain famous novels, starts in one the kind of emotion that is appropriate to it. But that emotion at once blends itself with others, for the 'shape' is not made by the relation of stone to stone, but by the relation of human being to human being. Thus a novel starts in us all sorts of antagonistic and opposed emotions. Life conflicts with something that is not life. Hence the difficulty of coming to any agreement about novels, and the immense sway that our private prejudices have upon us. On the one hand we feel You – John the hero – must live, or I shall be in the depths of despair. On the other, we feel, Alas, John, you must die, because the shape of the book requires it. Life conflicts with something that is not life. Then since life it is in part, we judge it as life. James is the sort of man I most detest, one says. Or, This is a farrago of absurdity. I could never feel anything of the sort myself. The whole structure, it is obvious, thinking back on any famous novel, is one of infinite complexity, because it is thus made up of so many different judgements, of so many different kinds of emotion. The wonder is that any book so composed holds together for more than a year or two, or can possibly mean to the English reader what it means for the Russian or the Chinese. But they do hold together occasionally very remarkably. And what holds them together in these rare instances of survival (I was thinking of *War and Peace*) is something that one calls integrity, though it has nothing to do with paying one's bills or behaving honourably in an emergency. What one means by integrity, in the case of the novelist, is the conviction that he gives one that this is the truth. Yes, one feels, I should never have thought that this could be so; I have never known people behaving like that. But you have convinced me that so it is, so it happens. One holds every phrase, every scene to the light as one reads – for Nature seems, very oddly, to have provided us with an inner light by which to judge of the novelist's integrity or disintegrity. Or perhaps it is rather that Nature, in her most irrational mood, has traced in invisible ink on the walls of the mind a premonition which these great artists confirm; a sketch which only needs to be held to the fire of genius to become visible. When one so exposes it and sees it come to life one exclaims in rapture, But this is what I have always felt and known and desired! And one boils over with excitement, and, shutting the book even with a kind of reverence as if it were something very precious, a stand-by to return to as long as one lives, one puts it back on the shelf, I said, taking *War and Peace* and putting it back in its place. If, on the other hand, these poor sentences that one takes and tests rouse first a quick and eager response with their bright colouring and their dashing gestures but there they stop: something seems to check them in their development; or if they bring to light only a faint scribble in that corner and a blot over there, and nothing appears whole and entire, then one heaves a sigh of disappointment and says, Another failure. This novel has come to grief somewhere.

And for the most part, of course, novels do come to grief somewhere. The imagination falters under the enormous strain. The insight is confused; it can no longer distinguish between the true and the false, it has no longer the strength to go on with the vast labour that calls at every moment for the use of so many different faculties. But how would all this be affected by the sex of the novelist, I wondered, looking at *Jane*

Eyre and the others. Would the fact of her sex in any way interfere with the integrity of a woman novelist – that integrity which I take to be the backbone of the writer? Now, in the passages I have quoted from *Jane Eyre*, it is clear that anger was tampering with the integrity of Charlotte Brontë the novelist. She left her story, to which her entire devotion was due, to attend to some personal grievance. She remembered that she had been starved of her proper due of experience – she had been made to stagnate in a parsonage mending stockings when she wanted to wander free over the world. Her imagination swerved from indignation and we feel it swerve. But there were many more influences than anger tugging at her imagination and deflecting it from its path. Ignorance, for instance. The portrait of Rochester is drawn in the dark. We feel the influence of fear in it; just as we constantly feel an acidity which is the result of oppression, a buried suffering smouldering beneath her passion, a rancour which contracts those books, splendid as they are, with a spasm of pain.

And since a novel has this correspondence to real life, its values are to some extent those of real life. But it is obvious that the values of women differ very often from the values which have been made by the other sex; naturally, this is so. Yet it is the masculine values that prevail. Speaking crudely, football and sport are 'important'; the worship of fashion, the buying of clothes 'trivial'. And these values are inevitably transferred from life to fiction. This is an important book, the critic assumes, because it deals with war. This is an insignificant book because it deals with the feelings of women in a drawing-room. A scene in a battlefield is more important than a scene in a shop – everywhere and much more subtly the difference of value persists. The whole structure, therefore, of the early nineteenth-century novel was raised, if one was a woman, by a mind which was slightly pulled from the straight, and made to alter its clear vision in deference to external authority. One has only to skim those old forgotten novels and listen to the tone of voice in which they are written to divine that the writer was meeting criticism; she was saying this by way of aggression, or that by way of conciliation. She was admitting that she was 'only a woman', or protesting that she was 'as good as a man'. She met that criticism as her temperament dictated, with docility and diffidence, or with anger and emphasis. It does not matter which it was; she was thinking of something other than the thing itself. Down comes her book upon our heads. There was a flaw in the centre of it. And I thought of all the women's novels that lie scattered, like small pock-marked apples in an orchard, about the second-hand bookshops of London. It was the flaw in the centre that had rotted them. She had altered her values in deference to the opinion of others.

But how impossible it must have been for them not to budge either to the right or to the left. What genius, what integrity it must have required in face of all that criticism, in the midst of that purely patriarchal society, to hold fast to the thing as they saw it without shrinking. Only Jane Austen did it and Emily Brontë. It is another feather, perhaps the finest, in their caps. They wrote as women write, not as men write. Of all the thousand women who wrote novels then, they alone entirely ignored the perpetual admonitions of the eternal pedagogue – write this, think that. They alone were deaf to that persistent voice, now grumbling, now patronising, now domineering, now grieved, now shocked, now angry, now avuncular, that voice which cannot let women alone, but must be at them, like some too-conscientious governess, adjuring them, like Sir Egerton Brydges, to be refined; dragging even into the criticism of poetry criticism of sex;* admonishing them, if they would be good and win, as I suppose, some shiny prize, to keep within certain limits which the gentleman in question thinks suitable – ' . . . female novelists should only aspire to excellence by courageously acknowledging the limitations of their sex'.† That puts the matter in a nutshell, and when I tell you, rather to your surprise, that this sentence was written not in August 1828 but in August 1928, you will agree, I think, that however delightful it is to us now, it represents a vast body of opinion – I am not going to stir those old pools; I take only what chance has floated to my feet – that was far more vigorous and far more vocal a century ago. It would have needed a very stalwart young woman in 1828 to disregard all those snubs and chidings and promises of prizes. One must have been something of a firebrand to say to oneself, Oh, but they can't buy literature too. Literature is open to everybody. I refuse to allow you, beadle though you are, to turn me off the grass. Lock up your libraries if you like; but there is no gate, no lock, no bolt, that you can set upon the freedom of my mind.

* '[She] has a metaphysical purpose, and that is a dangerous obsession, especially with a woman, for women rarely possess men's healthy love of rhetoric. It is a strange lack in the sex which is in other things more primitive and more materialistic.' *New Criterion*, June 1928

† 'If, like the reporter, you believe that female novelists should only aspire to excellence by courageously acknowledging the limitations of their sex, Jane Austen [has] demonstrated how gracefully this gesture can be accomplished . . . ' *Life and Letters*, August 1928

But whatever effect discouragement and criticism had upon their writing – and I believe that they had a very great effect – that was unimportant compared with the other difficulty which faced them (I was still considering those early nineteenth-century novelists) when they came to set their thoughts on paper – that is that they had no tradition behind them, or one so short and partial that it was of little help. For we think back through our mothers if we are women. It is useless to go to the great men writers for help, however much one may go to them for pleasure. Lamb, Browne,[71] Thackeray, Newman,[72] Sterne,[73] Dickens, De Quincey[74] – whoever it may be – never helped a woman yet, though she may have learnt a few tricks of them and adapted them to her use. The weight, the pace, the stride of a man's mind are too unlike her own for her to lift anything substantial from him successfully. The ape is too distant to be sedulous. Perhaps the first thing she would find, setting pen to paper, was that there was no common sentence ready for her use. All the great novelists like Thackeray and Dickens and Balzac[75] have written a natural prose, swift but not slovenly, expressive but not precious, taking their own tint without ceasing to be common property. They have based it on the sentence that was current at the time. The sentence that was current at the beginning of the nineteenth century ran something like this perhaps: 'The grandeur of their works was an argument with them, not to stop short, but to proceed. They could have no higher excitement or satisfaction than in the exercise of their art and endless generations of truth and beauty. Success prompts to exertion; and habit facilitates success.' That is a man's sentence; behind it one can see Johnson, Gibbon[76] and the rest. It was a sentence that was unsuited for a woman's use. Charlotte Brontë, with all her splendid gift for prose, stumbled and fell with that clumsy weapon in her hands. George Eliot committed atrocities with it that beggar description. Jane Austen looked at it and laughed at it and devised a perfectly natural, shapely sentence proper for her own use and never departed from it. Thus, with less genius for writing than Charlotte Brontë, she got infinitely more said. Indeed, since freedom and fullness of expression are of the essence of the art, such a lack of tradition, such a scarcity and inadequacy of tools, must have told enormously upon the writing of women. Moreover, a book is not made of sentences laid end to end, but of sentences built, if an image helps, into arcades or domes. And this shape too has been made by men out of their own needs for their own uses. There is no reason to think that the form of the epic or of the poetic play suit a woman any more than the sentence suits her. But all the older forms of literature were hardened and set by the time she became a writer. The novel alone was young enough to be soft in her hands – another reason, perhaps, why she wrote novels. Yet who shall say that even now 'the novel' (I give it inverted commas to mark my sense of the words' inadequacy), who shall say that even this most pliable of all forms is rightly shaped for her use? No doubt we shall find her knocking that into shape for herself when she has the free use of her limbs; and providing some new vehicle, not necessarily in verse, for the poetry in her. For it is the poetry that is still denied outlet. And I went on to ponder how a woman nowadays would write a poetic tragedy in five acts. Would she use verse? – would she not use prose rather?

But these are difficult questions which lie in the twilight of the future. I must leave them, if only because they stimulate me to wander from my subject into trackless forests where I shall be lost and, very likely, devoured by wild beasts. I do not want, and I am sure that you do not want me, to broach that very dismal subject, the future of fiction, so that I will only pause here one moment to draw your attention to the great part which must be played in that future so far as women are concerned by physical conditions. The book has somehow to be adapted to the body, and at a venture one would say that women's books should be shorter, more concentrated, than those of men, and framed so that they do not need long hours of steady and uninterrupted work. For interruptions there will always be. Again, the nerves that feed the brain would seem to differ in men and women, and if you are going to make them work their best and hardest, you must find out what treatment suits them – whether these hours of lectures, for instance, which the monks devised, presumably, hundreds of years ago, suit them – what alternations of work and rest they need, interpreting rest not as doing nothing but as doing something but something that is different; and what should that difference be? All this should be discussed and discovered; all this is part of the question of women and fiction. And yet, I continued, approaching the bookcase again, where shall I find that elaborate study of the psychology of women by a woman? If through their incapacity to play football women are not going to be allowed to practise medicine –

Happily my thoughts were now given another turn.

Chapter 5

I had come at last, in the course of this rambling, to the shelves which hold books by the living; by women and by men; for there are almost as many books written by women now as by men. Or if that is not yet quite true, if the male is still the voluble sex, it is certainly true that women no longer write novels solely. There are Jane Harrison's books on Greek archaeology; Vernon Lee's[77] books on aesthetics; Gertrude Bell's[78] books on Persia. There are books on all sorts of subjects which a generation ago no woman could have touched. There are poems and plays and criticism; there are histories and biographies, books of travel and books of scholarship and research; there are even a few philosophies and books about science and economics. And though novels predominate, novels themselves may very well have changed from association with books of a different feather. The natural simplicity, the epic age of women's writing, may have gone. Reading and criticism may have given her a wider range, a greater subtlety. The impulse towards autobiography may be spent. She may be beginning to use writing as an art, not as a method of self-expression. Among these new novels one might find an answer to several such questions.

I took down one of them at random. It stood at the very end of the shelf, was called *Life's Adventure*, or some such title, by Mary Carmichael,[79] and was published in this very month of October. It seems to be her first book, I said to myself, but one must read it as if it were the last volume in a fairly long series, continuing all those other books that I have been glancing at – Lady Winchilsea's poems and Aphra Behn's plays and the novels of the four great novelists. For books continue each other, in spite of our habit of judging them separately. And I must also consider her – this unknown woman – as the descendant of all those other women whose circumstances I have been glancing at and see what she inherits of their characteristics and restrictions. So, with a sigh, because novels so often provide an anodyne and not an antidote, glide one into torpid slumbers instead of rousing one with a burning brand, I settled down with a notebook and a pencil to make what I could of Mary Carmichael's first novel, *Life's Adventure*.

To begin with, I ran my eye up and down the page. I am going to get the hang of her sentences first, I said, before I load my memory with blue eyes and brown and the relationship that there may be between

Chloe and Roger. There will be time for that when I have decided whether she has a pen in her hand or a pickaxe. So I tried a sentence or two on my tongue. Soon it was obvious that something was not quite in order. The smooth gliding of sentence after sentence was interrupted. Something tore, something scratched; a single word here and there flashed its torch in my eyes. She was 'unhanding' herself as they say in the old plays. She is like a person striking a match that will not light, I thought. But why, I asked her as if she were present, are Jane Austen's sentences not of the right shape for you? Must they all be scrapped because Emma and Mr Woodhouse are dead? Alas, I sighed, that it should be so. For while Jane Austen breaks from melody to melody as Mozart from song to song, to read this writing was like being out at sea in an open boat. Up one went, down one sank. This terseness, this short-windedness, might mean that she was afraid of something; afraid of being called 'sentimental' perhaps; or she remembers that women's writing has been called flowery and so provides a superfluity of thorns; but until I have read a scene with some care, I cannot be sure whether she is being herself or someone else. At any rate, she does not lower one's vitality, I thought, reading more carefully. But she is heaping up too many facts. She will not be able to use half of them in a book of this size (it was about half the length of *Jane Eyre*). However, by some means or other she succeeded in getting us all – Roger, Chloe, Olivia, Tony and Mr Bigham – in a canoe up the river. Wait a moment, I said, leaning back in my chair, I must consider the whole thing more carefully before I go any further.

I am almost sure, I said to myself, that Mary Carmichael is playing a trick on us. For I feel as one feels on a switchback railway when the car, instead of sinking, as one has been led to expect, swerves up again. Mary is tampering with the expected sequence. First she broke the sentence; now she has broken the sequence. Very well, she has every right to do both these things if she does them not for the sake of breaking, but for the sake of creating. Which of the two it is I cannot be sure until she has faced herself with a situation. I will give her every liberty, I said, to choose what that situation shall be; she shall make it of tin cans and old kettles if she likes; but she must convince me that she believes it to be a situation; and then when she has made it she must face it. She must jump. And, determined to do my duty by her as reader if she would do her duty by me as writer, I turned the page and read . . . I am sorry to break off so abruptly. Are there no men present? Do you promise me that behind that red curtain over there the figure of Sir Charles Biron[80] is not concealed? We are all women you assure me? Then I may tell you that the very next words I read were these – 'Chloe liked Olivia . . . ' Do not start. Do not blush. Let us admit in the privacy of our own society that these things sometimes happen. Sometimes women do like women.

'Chloe liked Olivia,' I read. And then it struck me how immense a change was there. Chloe liked Olivia perhaps for the first time in literature. Cleopatra did not like Octavia. And how completely *Antony and Cleopatra* would have been altered had she done so! As it is, I thought, letting my mind, I am afraid, wander a little from *Life's Adventure*, the whole thing is simplified, conventionalised, if one dared say it, absurdly. Cleopatra's only feeling about Octavia is one of jealousy. Is she taller than I am? How does she do her hair? The play, perhaps, required no more. But how interesting it would have been if the relationship between the two women had been more complicated. All these relationships between women, I thought, rapidly recalling the splendid gallery of fictitious women, are too simple. So much has been left out, unattempted. And I tried to remember any case in the course of my reading where two women are represented as friends. There is an attempt at it in *Diana of the Crossways*.[81] They are confidantes, of course, in Racine[82] and the Greek tragedies. They are now and then mothers and daughters. But almost without exception they are shown in their relation to men. It was strange to think that all the great women of fiction were, until Jane Austen's day, not only seen by the other sex, but seen only in relation to the other sex. And how small a part of a woman's life is that; and how little can a man know even of that when he observes it through the black or rosy spectacles which sex puts upon his nose. Hence, perhaps, the peculiar nature of woman in fiction; the astonishing extremes of her beauty and horror; her alternations between heavenly goodness and hellish depravity – for so a lover would see her as his love rose or sank, was prosperous or unhappy. This is not so true of the nineteenth-century novelists, of course. Woman becomes much more various and complicated there. Indeed it was the desire to write about women perhaps that led men by degrees to abandon the poetic drama which, with its violence, could make so little use of them, and to devise the novel as a more fitting receptacle. Even so it remains obvious, even in the writing of Proust, that a man is terribly hampered and partial in his knowledge of women, as a woman in her knowledge of men.

Also, I continued, looking down at the page again, it is becoming evident that women, like men, have other interests besides the perennial interests of domesticity. 'Chloe liked Olivia. They shared a laboratory together . . . ' I read on and discovered that these two young women were engaged in mincing liver, which is, it seems, a cure for pernicious anaemia; although one of them was married and had – I think I am right in stating – two small children. Now all that, of course, has had to be left out, and thus the splendid portrait of the fictitious woman is much too simple and much too monotonous. Suppose, for instance, that men were only represented in literature as the lovers of women, and were never the friends of men, soldiers, thinkers, dreamers; how few parts in the plays of Shakespeare could be allotted to them; how literature would suffer! We might perhaps have most of Othello; and a good deal of Antony; but no Caesar,[83] no Brutus,[84] no Hamlet,[85] no Lear,[86] no Jaques[87] – literature would be incredibly impoverished, as indeed literature is impoverished beyond our counting by the doors that have been shut upon women. Married against their will, kept in one room, and to one occupation, how could a dramatist give a full or interesting or truthful account of them? Love was the only possible interpreter. The poet was forced to be passionate or bitter, unless indeed he chose to 'hate women', which meant more often than not that he was unattractive to them.

Now if Chloe likes Olivia and they share a laboratory, which of itself will make their friendship more varied and lasting because it will be less personal; if Mary Carmichael knows how to write, and I was beginning to enjoy some quality in her style; if she has a room to herself, of which I am not quite sure; if she has five hundred a year of her own – but that remains to be proved – then I think that something of great importance has happened.

For if Chloe likes Olivia and Mary Carmichael knows how to express it she will light a torch in that vast chamber where nobody has yet been. It is all half lights and profound shadows like those serpentine caves where one goes with a candle peering up and down, not knowing where one is stepping. And I began to read the book again, and read how Chloe watched Olivia put a jar on a shelf and say how it was time to go home to her children. That is a sight that has never been seen since the world began, I exclaimed. And I watched too, very curiously. For I wanted to see how Mary Carmichael set to work to catch those unrecorded gestures, those unsaid or half-said words, which form themselves, no more palpably than the shadows of moths on the ceiling, when women are alone, unlit by the capricious and coloured light of the other sex. She will need to hold her breath, I said, reading on, if she is to do it; for women are so suspicious of any interest that has not some obvious motive behind it, so terribly accustomed to concealment and suppression, that they are off at the flicker of an eye turned observingly in their direction. The only way for you to do it, I thought, addressing Mary Carmichael as if she were there, would be to talk of something else, looking steadily out of the window, and thus note, not with a pencil in a notebook, but in the shortest of shorthand, in words that are hardly syllabled yet, what happens when Olivia – this organism that has been under the shadow of the rock these million years – feels the light fall on it, and sees coming her way a piece of strange food – knowledge, adventure, art. And she reaches out for it, I thought, again raising my eyes from the page, and has to devise some entirely new combination of her resources, so highly developed for other purposes, so as to absorb the new into the old without disturbing the infinitely intricate and elaborate balance of the whole.

But, alas, I had done what I had determined not to do; I had slipped unthinkingly into praise of my own sex. 'Highly developed' – 'infinitely intricate' – such are undeniably terms of praise, and to praise one's own sex is always suspect, often silly; moreover, in this case, how could one justify it? One could not go to the map and say Columbus discovered America and Columbus was a woman; or take an apple and remark, Newton discovered the laws of gravitation and Newton was a woman; or look into the sky and say aeroplanes are flying overhead and aeroplanes were invented by women. There is no mark on the wall to measure the precise height of women. There are no yard measures, neatly divided into the fractions of an inch, that one can lay against the qualities of a good mother, or the devotion of a daughter, or the fidelity of a sister, or the capacity of a housekeeper. Few women even now have been graded at the universities; the great trials of the professions, army and navy, trade, politics and diplomacy have hardly tested them. They remain even at this moment almost unclassified. But if I want to know all that a human being can tell me about Sir Hawley Butts, for instance, I have only to open Burke or Debrett[88] and I shall find that he took such and such a degree; owns a hall; has an heir; was Secretary to a Board; represented Great Britain in Canada; and has received a certain number of degrees, offices, medals and other distinctions by which his merits are stamped upon him indelibly. Only Providence can know more about Sir Hawley Butts than that.

When, therefore, I say 'highly developed', 'infinitely intricate' of women, I am unable to verify my words either in Whitaker,[89] Debrett or the University Calendar. In this predicament what can I do? And I looked at the bookcase again. There were the biographies: Johnson and Goethe[90] and Carlyle and Sterne and Cowper[91] and Shelley and Voltaire[92] and Browning[93] and many others. And I began thinking of all those great men who have for one reason or another admired, sought out, lived with, confided in, made love to, written of, trusted in, and shown what can only be described as some need of and dependence upon certain persons of the opposite sex. That all these relationships were absolutely Platonic I would not affirm, and Sir William Joynson Hicks[94] would probably deny. But we should wrong these illustrious men very greatly if we insisted that they got nothing from these alliances but comfort, flattery and the pleasures of the body. What they got, it is obvious, was something that their own sex was unable to supply; and it would not be rash, perhaps, to define it further, without quoting the doubtless rhapsodical words of the poets, as some stimulus; some renewal of creative power which is in the gift only of the opposite sex to bestow. He would open the door of drawing-room or nursery, I thought, and find her among her children perhaps, or with a piece of embroidery on her knee – at any rate, the centre of some different order and system of life, and the contrast between this world and his own, which might be the law courts or the House of Commons, would at once refresh and invigorate; and there would follow, even in the simplest talk, such a natural difference of opinion that the dried ideas in him would be fertilised anew; and the sight of her creating in a different medium from his own would so quicken his creative power that insensibly his sterile mind would begin to plot again, and he would find the phrase or the scene which was lacking when he put on his hat to visit her. Every Johnson has his Thrale,[95] and holds fast to her for some such reasons as these, and when the Thrale marries her Italian music master Johnson goes half mad with rage and disgust, not merely that he will miss his pleasant evenings at Streatham, but that the light of his life will be 'as if gone out'.

And without being Dr Johnson or Goethe or Carlyle or Voltaire, one may feel, though very differently from these great men, the nature of this intricacy and the power of this highly developed creative faculty among women. One goes into the room – but the resources of the English language would be much put to the stretch, and whole flights of words would need to wing their way illegitimately into existence before a woman could say what happens when she goes into a room. The rooms differ so completely: they are calm or thunderous; open on to the sea, or, on the contrary, give on to a prison yard; are hung with washing; or alive with opals and silks; are hard as horsehair or soft as feathers – one has only to go into any room in any street for the whole of that extremely complex force of femininity to fly in one's face. How should it be otherwise? For women have sat indoors all these millions of years, so that by this time the very walls are permeated by their creative force, which has, indeed, so overcharged the capacity of bricks and mortar that it must needs harness itself to pens and brushes and business and politics. But this creative power differs greatly from the creative power of men. And one must conclude that it would be a thousand pities if it were hindered or wasted, for it was won by centuries of the most drastic discipline, and there is nothing to take its place. It would be a thousand pities if women wrote like men, or lived like men, or looked like men, for if two sexes are quite inadequate, considering the vastness and variety of the world, how should we manage with one only? Ought not education to bring out and fortify the differences rather than the similarities? For we have too much likeness as it is, and if an explorer should come back and bring word of other sexes looking through the branches of other trees at other skies, nothing would be of greater service to humanity; and we should have the immense pleasure into the bargain of watching Professor X rush for his measuring-rods to prove himself 'superior'.

Mary Carmichael, I thought, still hovering at a little distance above the page, will have her work cut out for her merely as an observer. I am afraid indeed that she will be tempted to become, what I think the less interesting branch of the species – the naturalist-novelist, and not the contemplative. There are so many new facts for her to observe. She will not need to limit herself any longer to the respectable houses of the upper middle classes. She will go without kindness or condescension, but in the spirit of fellowship, into those small, scented rooms where sit the courtesan, the harlot and the lady with the pug dog. There they still sit in the rough and ready-made clothes that the male writer has had perforce to clap upon their shoulders. But Mary Carmichael will have out her scissors and fit them close to every hollow and angle. It will be a curious sight, when it comes, to see these women as they are, but we must wait a little, for Mary Carmichael will still be encumbered with that self-consciousness in the presence of 'sin' which is the legacy of our sexual barbarity. She will still wear the shoddy old fetters of class on her feet.

However, the majority of women are neither harlots nor courtesans; nor do they sit clasping pug dogs to dusty velvet all through the summer afternoon. But what do they do then? and there came to my mind's eye one of those long streets somewhere south of the river whose infinite rows are innumerably populated. With the eye of the imagination I saw a very ancient lady crossing the street on the arm of a middle-aged woman, her daughter, perhaps, both so respectably booted and furred that their dressing in the afternoon must be a ritual, and the clothes themselves put away in cupboards with camphor, year after year, throughout the summer months. They cross the road when the lamps are being lit (for the dusk is their favourite hour), as they must have done year after year. The elder is close on eighty; but if one asked her what her life has meant to her, she would say that she remembered the streets lit for the Battle of Balaclava,[96] or had heard the guns fire in Hyde Park for the birth of King Edward VII. And if one asked her, longing to pin down the moment with date and season, but what were you doing on the fifth of April 1868, or the second of November 1875, she would look vague and say that she could remember nothing. For all the dinners are cooked; the plates and cups washed; the children sent to school and gone out into the world. Nothing remains of it all. All has vanished. No biography or history has a word to say about it. And the novels, without meaning to, inevitably lie.

All these infinitely obscure lives remain to be recorded, I said, addressing Mary Carmichael as if she were present; and went on in thought through the streets of London feeling in imagination the pressure of dumbness, the accumulation of unrecorded life, whether from the women at the street corners with their arms akimbo, and the rings embedded in their fat swollen fingers, talking with a gesticulation like the swing of Shakespeare's words; or from the violet-sellers and match-sellers and old crones stationed under doorways; or from drifting girls whose faces, like waves in sun and cloud, signal the coming of men and women and the flickering lights of shop windows. All that you will have to explore, I said to Mary Carmichael, holding your torch firm in your hand. Above all, you must illumine your own soul with its profundities and its shallows, and its vanities and its generosities, and say what your beauty means to you or your plainness, and what is your relation to the ever-changing and turning world of gloves and shoes and stuffs swaying up and down among the faint scents that come through chemists' bottles down arcades of dress material over a floor of pseudo-marble. For in imagination I had gone into a shop; it was laid with black and white paving; it was hung, astonishingly beautifully, with coloured ribbons. Mary Carmichael might well have a look at that in passing, I thought, for it is a sight that would lend itself to the pen as fittingly as any snowy peak or rocky gorge in the Andes. And there is the girl behind the counter too – I would as soon have her true history as the hundred and fiftieth life of Napoleon or seventieth study of Keats and his use of Miltonic inversion[97] which old Professor Z and his like are now inditing. And then I went on very warily, on the very tips of my toes (so cowardly am I, so afraid of the lash that was once almost laid on my own shoulders), to murmur that she should also learn to laugh, without bitterness, at the vanities – say rather at the peculiarities, for it is a less offensive word – of the other sex. For there is a spot the size of a shilling at the back of the head which one can never see for oneself. It is one of the good offices that sex can discharge for sex – to describe that spot the size of a shilling at the back of the head. Think how much women have profited by the comments of Juvenal;[98] by the criticism of Strindberg.[99] Think with what humanity and brilliancy men, from the earliest ages, have pointed out to women that dark place at the back of the head! And if Mary were very brave and very honest, she would go behind the other sex and tell us what she found there. A true picture of man as a whole can never be painted until a woman has described that spot the size of a shilling. Mr Woodhouse[100] and Mr Casuabon[101] are spots of that size and nature. Not of course that anyone in their senses would counsel her to hold up to scorn and ridicule of set purpose – literature shows the futility of what is written in that spirit. Be truthful, one would say, and the result is bound to be amazingly interesting. Comedy is bound to be enriched. New facts are bound to be discovered.

However, it was high time to lower my eyes to the page again. It would be better, instead of speculating what Mary Carmichael might write and should write, to see what in fact Mary Carmichael did write. So I began to read again. I remembered that I had certain grievances against her. She had broken up Jane Austen's sentence, and thus given me no chance of pluming myself upon my impeccable taste, my fastidious ear. For it was useless to say, 'Yes, yes, this is very nice; but Jane Austen wrote much better than you do', when I had to admit that there was no point of likeness between them. Then she had gone further and broken the sequence – the expected order. Perhaps she had done this unconsciously, merely giving things their natural order, as a woman would, if she wrote like a woman. But the effect was somehow baffling; one could not see a wave heaping itself, a crisis coming round the next corner. Therefore I could not plume myself either upon the depths of my feelings and my profound knowledge of the human heart. For whenever I was about to feel the usual things in the usual places, about love, about death, the annoying creature twitched me away, as if the important point were just a little further on. And thus she made it impossible for me to roll out my sonorous phrases about 'elemental feelings', the 'common stuff of humanity', 'the depths of the human heart', and all those other phrases which support us in our belief that, however clever we may be on top, we are very serious, very profound and very humane underneath. She made me feel, on the contrary, that instead of being serious and profound and humane, one might be – and the thought was far less seductive – merely lazy minded and conventional into the bargain.

But I read on, and noted certain other facts. She was no 'genius' that was evident. She had nothing like the love of nature, the fiery imagination, the wild poetry, the brilliant wit, the brooding wisdom of her great predecessors, Lady Winchilsea, Charlotte Brontë, Emily Brontë, Jane Austen and George Eliot; she could not write with the melody and the dignity of Dorothy Osborne – indeed she was no more than a clever girl whose books will no doubt be pulped by the publishers in ten years' time. But, nevertheless, she had certain advantages which women of far greater gift lacked even half a century ago. Men were no longer to her 'the opposing faction'; she need not waste her time railing against them; she need not climb on to the roof and ruin her peace of mind longing for travel, experience and a knowledge of the world and character that were denied her. Fear and hatred were almost gone, or traces of them showed only in a slight exaggeration of the joy of freedom, a tendency to the caustic and satirical, rather than to the romantic, in her treatment of the other sex. Then there could be no doubt that as a novelist she enjoyed some natural advantages of a high order. She had a sensibility that was very wide, eager and free. It responded to an almost imperceptible touch on it. It feasted like a plant newly stood in the air on every sight and sound that came its way. It ranged, too, very subtly and curiously, among almost unknown or unrecorded things; it lighted on small things and showed that perhaps they were not small after all. It brought buried things to light and made one wonder what need there had been to bury them. Awkward though she was and without the unconscious bearing of long descent which makes the least turn of the pen of a Thackeray or a Lamb delightful to the ear, she had – I began to think – mastered the first great lesson: she wrote as a woman, but as a woman who has forgotten that she is a woman, so that her pages were full of that curious sexual quality which comes only when sex is unconscious of itself.

All this was to the good. But no abundance of sensation or fineness of perception would avail unless she could build up out of the fleeting and the personal the lasting edifice which remains unthrown. I had said that I would wait until she faced herself with 'a situation'. And I meant by that until she proved by summoning, beckoning and getting together that she was not a skimmer of surfaces merely, but had looked beneath into the depths. Now is the time, she would say to herself at a certain moment, when without doing anything violent I can show the meaning of all this. And she would begin – how unmistakable that quickening is! – beckoning and summoning, and there would rise up in memory, half forgotten, perhaps quite trivial things in other chapters dropped by the way. And she would make their presence felt while someone sewed or smoked a pipe as naturally as possible, and one would feel, as she went on writing, as if one had gone to the top of the world and seen it laid out, very majestically, beneath.

At any rate, she was making the attempt. And as I watched her lengthening out for the test, I saw, but hoped that she did not see, the bishops and the deans, the doctors and the professors, the patriarchs and the pedagogues all at her shouting warning and advice. You can't do this and you shan't do that! Fellows and scholars only allowed on the grass! Ladies not admitted without a letter of introduction! Aspiring and graceful female novelists this way! So they kept at her like the crowd at a fence on the racecourse, and it was her trial to take her fence without looking to right or to left. If you stop to curse you are lost, I said to her; equally, if you stop to laugh. Hesitate or fumble and you are done for. Think only of the jump, I implored her, as if I had put the whole of my money on her back; and she went over it like a bird. But there was a fence beyond that and a fence beyond that. Whether she had the staying power I was doubtful, for the clapping and the crying were fraying to the nerves. But she did her best. Considering that Mary Carmichael was no genius, but an unknown girl writing her first novel in a bed-sitting-room, without enough of those desirable things, time, money and idleness, she did not do so badly, I thought.

Give her another hundred years, I concluded, reading the last chapter – people's noses and bare shoulders showed naked against a starry sky, for someone had twitched the curtain in the drawing-room – give her a room of her own and five hundred a year, let her speak her mind and leave out half that she now puts in, and she will write a better book one of these days. She will be a poet, I said, putting *Life's Adventure* by Mary Carmichael at the end of the shelf, in another hundred years' time.

Chapter 6

Next day the light of the October morning was falling in dusty shafts through the uncurtained windows, and the hum of traffic rose from the street. London then was winding itself up again; the factory was astir; the machines were beginning. It was tempting, after all this reading, to look out of the window and see what London was doing on the morning of the 26th of October 1928. And what was London doing? Nobody, it seemed, was reading *Antony and Cleopatra*. London was wholly indifferent, it appeared, to Shakespeare's plays. Nobody cared a straw – and I do not blame them – for the future of fiction, the death of poetry or the development by the average woman of a prose style completely expressive of her mind. If opinions upon any of these matters had been chalked on the pavement, nobody would have stooped to read them. The nonchalance of the hurrying feet would have rubbed them out in half an hour. Here came an errand-boy; here a woman with a dog on a lead. The fascination of the London street is that no two people are ever alike; each seems bound on some private affair of his own. There were the businesslike, with their little bags; there were the drifters rattling sticks upon area railings; there were affable characters to whom the streets serve for clubroom, hailing men in carts and giving information without being asked for it. Also there were funerals to which men, thus suddenly reminded of the passing of their own bodies, lifted their hats. And then a very distinguished gentleman came slowly down a doorstep and paused to avoid collision with a bustling lady who had, by some means or other, acquired a splendid fur coat and a bunch of Parma violets. They all seemed separate, self-absorbed, on business of their own.

At this moment, as so often happens in London, there was a complete lull and suspension of traffic. Nothing came down the street; nobody passed. A single leaf detached itself from the plane tree at the end of the street, and in that pause and suspension fell. Somehow it was like a signal falling, a signal pointing to a force in things which one had overlooked. It seemed to point to a river, which flowed past, invisibly, round the corner, down the street, and took people and eddied them along, as the stream at Oxbridge had taken the undergraduate in his boat and the dead leaves. Now it was bringing from one side of the street to the other diagonally a girl in patent-leather boots, and then a young man in a maroon overcoat; it was also bringing a taxicab; and it brought all three together at a point directly beneath my window; where the taxi stopped; and the girl and the young man stopped; and they got into the taxi; and then the cab glided off as if it were swept on by the current elsewhere.

The sight was ordinary enough; what was strange was the rhythmical order with which my imagination had invested it; and the fact that the ordinary sight of two people getting into a cab had the power to communicate something of their own seeming satisfaction. The sight of two people coming down the street and meeting at the corner seems to ease the mind of some strain, I thought, watching the taxi turn and make off. Perhaps to think, as I had been thinking these two days, of one sex as distinct from the other is an effort. It interferes with the unity of the mind. Now that effort had ceased and that unity had been restored by seeing two people come together and get into a taxicab. The mind is certainly a very mysterious organ, I reflected, drawing my head in from the window, about which nothing whatever is known, though we depend upon it so completely. Why do I feel that there are severances and oppositions in the mind, as there are strains from obvious causes on the body? What does one mean by 'the unity of the mind'? I pondered, for clearly the mind has so great a power of concentrating at any point at any moment that it seems to have no single state of being. It can separate itself from the people in the street, for example, and think of itself as apart from them, at an upper window looking down on them. Or it can think with other people spontaneously, as, for instance, in a crowd waiting to hear some piece of news read out. It can think back through its fathers or through its mothers, as I have said that a woman writing thinks back through her mothers. Again if one is a woman one is often surprised by a sudden splitting off of consciousness, say in walking down Whitehall, when from being the natural inheritor of that civilisation, she becomes, on the contrary, outside of it, alien and critical. Clearly the mind is always altering its focus, and bringing the world into different perspectives. But some of these states of mind seem, even if adopted spontaneously, to be less comfortable than others. In order to keep oneself continuing in them one is unconsciously holding something back, and gradually the repression becomes an effort. But there may be some state of mind in which one could continue without effort because nothing is required to be held back. And this perhaps, I thought, coming in from the window, is one of them. For certainly when I saw the couple get into the taxicab the mind felt as if, after being divided, it had come together again in a natural fusion. The obvious reason would be that it is natural for the sexes to co-operate. One has a profound, if irrational, instinct in favour of the theory that the union of man and woman makes for the greatest satisfaction, the most complete happiness. But the sight of the two people getting into the taxi and the satisfaction it gave me made me also ask whether there are two sexes in the mind corresponding to the two sexes in the body, and whether they also require to be united in order to get complete satisfaction and happiness? And I went on amateurishly to sketch a plan of the soul so that in each of us two powers preside, one male, one female; and in the man's brain the man predominates over the woman, and in the woman's brain the woman predominates over the man. The normal and comfortable state of being is that when the two live in harmony together, spiritually co-operating. If one is a man, still the woman part of his brain must have effect; and a woman also must have intercourse with the man in her. Coleridge[102] perhaps meant this when he said that a great mind is androgynous. It is when this fusion takes place that the mind is fully fertilised and uses all its faculties. Perhaps a mind that is purely masculine cannot create, any more than a mind that is purely feminine, I thought. But it would be well to test what one meant by man-womanly, and conversely by woman-manly, by pausing and looking at a book or two.

Coleridge certainly did not mean, when he said that a great mind is androgynous, that it is a mind that has any special sympathy with women; a mind that takes up their cause or devotes itself to their interpretation. Perhaps the androgynous mind is less apt to make these distinctions than the single-sexed mind. He meant, perhaps, that the androgynous mind is resonant and porous; that it transmits emotion without impediment; that it is naturally creative, incandescent and undivided. In fact one goes back to Shakespeare's mind as the type of the androgynous, of the man-womanly mind, though it would be impossible to say what Shakespeare thought of women. And if it be true that it is one of the tokens of the fully developed mind that it does not think specially or separately of sex, how much harder it is to attain that condition now than ever before. Here I came to the books by living writers, and there paused and wondered if this fact were not at the root of something that had long puzzled me. No age can ever have been as stridently sex-conscious as our own; those innumerable books by men about women in the British Museum are a proof of it. The Suffrage campaign[103] was no doubt to blame. It must have roused in men an extraordinary desire for self-assertion; it must have made them lay an emphasis upon their own sex and its characteristics which they would not have troubled to think about had they not been challenged. And when one is challenged, even by a few women in black bonnets, one retaliates, if one has never been challenged before, rather excessively. That perhaps accounts for some of the characteristics that I remember to have found here, I thought, taking down a new novel by Mr A, who is in the prime of life and very well thought of, apparently, by the reviewers. I opened it. Indeed, it was delightful to read a man's writing again. It was so direct, so straightforward after the writing of women. It indicated such freedom of mind, such liberty of person, such confidence in himself. One had a sense of physical well-being in the presence of this well-nourished, well-educated, free mind, which had never been thwarted or opposed, but had had full liberty from birth to stretch itself in whatever way it liked. All this was admirable. But after reading a chapter or two a shadow seemed to lie across the page. It was a straight dark bar, a shadow shaped something like the letter 'I'. One began dodging this way and that to catch a glimpse of the landscape behind it. Whether that was indeed a tree or a woman walking I was not quite sure. Back one was always hailed to the letter 'I'. One began to be tired of 'I'. Not but what this 'I' was a most respectable 'I'; honest and logical; as hard as a nut, and polished for centuries by good teaching and good feeding. I respect and admire that 'I' from the bottom of my heart. But – here I turned a page or two, looking for something or other – the worst of it is that in the shadow of the letter 'I' all is shapeless as mist. Is that a tree? No, it is a woman. But . . . she has not a bone in her body, I thought, watching Phoebe, for that was her name, coming across the beach. Then Alan got up and the shadow of Alan at once obliterated Phoebe. For Alan had views and Phoebe was quenched in the flood of his views. And then Alan, I thought, has passions; and here I turned page after page very fast, feeling that the crisis was approaching, and so it was. It took place on the beach under the sun. It was done very openly. It was done very vigorously. Nothing could have been more indecent. But . . . I had said 'but' too often. One cannot go on saying 'but'. One must finish the sentence somehow, I rebuked myself. Shall I finish it, 'But – I am bored!' But why was I bored? Partly because of the dominance of the letter 'I' and the aridity, which, like the giant beech tree, it casts within its shade. Nothing will grow there. And partly for some more obscure reason. There seemed to be some obstacle, some impediment in Mr A's mind which blocked the fountain of creative energy and shored it within narrow limits. And remembering the lunch party at Oxbridge, and the cigarette ash and the Manx cat and Tennyson and Christina Rossetti all in a bunch, it seemed possible that the impediment lay there. As he no longer hums under his breath, 'There has fallen a splendid tear from the passion-flower at the gate', when Phoebe crosses the beach, and she no longer replies, 'My heart is like a singing bird whose nest is in a water'd shoot', when Alan approaches what can he do? Being honest as the day and logical as the sun, there is only one thing he can do. And that he does, to do him justice, over and over (I said turning the pages) and over again. And that, I added, aware of the awful nature of the confession, seems somehow dull. Shakespeare's indecency uproots a thousand other things in one's mind, and is far from being dull. But Shakespeare does it for pleasure; Mr A, as the nurses say, does it on purpose. He does it in protest. He is protesting against the equality of the other sex by asserting his own superiority. He is therefore impeded and inhibited and self-conscious as Shakespeare might have been if he too had known Miss Clough and Miss Davies. Doubtless Elizabethan literature would have been very different from what it is if the women's movement had begun in the sixteenth century and not in the nineteenth.

What, then, it amounts to, if this theory of the two sides of the mind holds good, is that virility has now become self-conscious – men, that is to say, are now writing only with the male side of their brains. It is a mistake for a woman to read them, for she will inevitably look for something that she will not find. It is the power of suggestion that one most misses, I thought, taking Mr B the critic in my hand and reading, very carefully and very dutifully, his remarks upon the art of poetry. Very able they were, acute and full of learning; but the trouble was that his feelings no longer communicated; his mind seemed separated into different chambers; not a sound carried from one to the other. Thus, when one takes a sentence of Mr B into the mind it falls plump to the ground – dead; but when one takes a sentence of Coleridge into the mind, it explodes and gives birth to all kinds of other ideas, and that is the only sort of writing of which one can say that it has the secret of perpetual life.

But whatever the reason may be, it is a fact that one must deplore. For it means – here I had come to rows of books by Mr Galsworthy[104] and Mr Kipling[105] – that some of the finest works of our greatest living writers fall upon deaf ears. Do what she will a woman cannot find in them that fountain of perpetual life which the critics assure her is there. It is not only that they celebrate male virtues, enforce male values and describe the world of men; it is that the emotion with which these books are permeated is to a woman incomprehensible. It is coming, it is gathering, it is about to burst on one's head, one begins saying long before the end. That picture will fall on old Jolyon's head; he will die of the shock; the old clerk will speak over him two or three obituary words; and all the swans on the Thames will simultaneously burst out singing. But one will rush away before that happens and hide in the gooseberry bushes, for the emotion which is so deep, so subtle, so symbolical to a man moves a woman to wonder. So with Mr Kipling's officers who turn their backs; and his Sowers who sow the Seed; and his Men who are alone with their Work; and the Flag – one blushes at all these capital letters as if one had been caught eavesdropping at some purely masculine orgy. The fact is that neither Mr Galsworthy nor Mr Kipling has a spark of the woman in him. Thus all their qualities seem to a woman, if one may generalise, crude and immature. They lack suggestive power. And when a book lacks suggestive power, however hard it hits the surface of the mind it cannot penetrate within.

And in that restless mood in which one takes books out and puts them back again without looking at them I began to envisage an age to come of pure, of self-assertive virility, such as the letters of professors (take Sir Walter Raleigh's letters, for instance) seem to forebode, and the rulers of Italy have already brought into being. For one can hardly fail to be impressed in Rome by the sense of unmitigated masculinity; and whatever the value of unmitigated masculinity upon the state, one may question the effect of it upon the art of poetry. At any rate, according to the newspapers, there is a certain anxiety about fiction in Italy. There has been a meeting of academicians whose object it is 'to develop the Italian novel'. 'Men famous by birth, or in finance, industry or the Fascist corporations' came together the other day and discussed the matter, and a telegram was sent to the Duce expressing the hope 'that the Fascist era would soon give birth to a poet worthy of it'. We may all join in that pious hope, but it is doubtful whether poetry can come out of an incubator. Poetry ought to have a mother as well as a father. The Fascist poem, one may fear, will be a horrid little abortion such as one sees in a glass jar in the museum of some county town. Such monsters never live long, it is said; one has never seen a prodigy of that sort cropping grass in a field. Two heads on one body do not make for length of life.

However, the blame for all this, if one is anxious to lay blame, rests no more upon one sex than upon the other. All seducers and reformers are responsible: Lady Bessborough when she lied to Lord Granville; Miss Davies when she told the truth to Mr Greg. All who have brought about a state of sex-consciousness are to blame, and it is they who drive me, when I want to stretch my faculties on a book, to seek it in that happy age, before Miss Davies and Miss Clough were born, when the writer used both sides of his mind equally. One must turn back to Shakespeare then, for Shakespeare was androgynous; and so were Keats and Sterne and Cowper and Lamb and Coleridge. Shelley perhaps was sexless. Milton and Ben Jonson had a dash too much of the male in them. So had Wordsworth and Tolstoy. In our time Proust was wholly androgynous, if not perhaps a little too much of a woman. But that failing is too rare for one to complain of it, since without some mixture of the kind the intellect seems to predominate and the other faculties of the mind harden and become barren. However, I consoled myself with the reflection that this is perhaps a passing phase; much of what I have said in obedience to my promise to give you the course of my thoughts will seem out of date; much of what flames in my eyes will seem dubious to you who have not yet come of age.

Even so, the very first sentence that I would write here, I said, crossing over to the writing-table and taking up the page headed Women and Fiction, is that it is fatal for anyone who writes to think of their sex. It is fatal to be a man or woman pure and simple; one must be woman-manly or man-womanly. It is fatal for a woman to lay the least stress on any grievance; to plead even with justice any cause; in any way to speak consciously as a woman. And fatal is no figure of speech, for anything written with that conscious bias is doomed to death. It ceases to be fertilised. Brilliant and effective, powerful and masterly, as it may appear for a day or two, it must wither at nightfall; it cannot grow in the minds of others. Some collaboration has to take place in the mind between the woman and the man before the art of creation can be accomplished. Some marriage of opposites has to be consummated. The whole of the mind must lie wide open if we are to get the sense that the writer is communicating his experience with perfect fullness. There must be freedom and there must be peace. Not a wheel must grate, not a light glimmer. The curtains must be close drawn. The writer, I thought, once his experience is over, must lie back and let his mind celebrate its nuptials in darkness. He must not look or question what is being done. Rather, he must pluck the petals from a rose or watch the swans float calmly down the river. And I saw again the current which took the boat and the undergraduate and the dead leaves; and the taxi took the man and the woman, I thought, seeing them come together across the street, and the current swept them away, I thought, hearing far off the roar of London's traffic, into that tremendous stream.

Here, then, Mary Beton ceases to speak. She has told you how she reached the conclusion – the prosaic conclusion – that it is necessary to have five hundred a year and a room with a lock on the door if you are to write fiction or poetry. She has tried to lay bare the thoughts and impressions that led her to think this. She has asked you to follow her flying into the arms of a beadle, lunching here, dining there, drawing pictures in the British Museum, taking books from the shelf, looking out of the window. While she has been doing all these things, you no doubt have been observing her failings and foibles and deciding what effect they have had on her opinions. You have been contradicting her and making whatever additions and deductions seem good to you. That is all as it should be, for in a question like this truth is only to be had by laying together many varieties of error. And I will end now in my own person by anticipating two criticisms, so obvious that you can hardly fail to make them.

No opinion has been expressed, you may say, upon the comparative merits of the sexes even as writers. That was done purposely, because, even if the time had come for such a valuation – and it is far more important at the moment to know how much money women have and how many rooms than to theorise about their capacities – even if the time had come I do not believe that gifts, whether of mind or character, can be weighed like sugar and butter, not even in Cambridge, where they are so adept at putting people into classes and fixing caps on their heads and letters after their names. I do not believe that even the Table of Precedency which you will find in Whitaker's *Almanack* represents a final order of values, or that there is any sound reason to suppose that a Commander of the Bath will ultimately walk in to dinner behind a Master in Lunacy. All this pitting of sex against sex, of quality against quality; all this claiming of superiority and imputing of inferiority, belong to the private-school stage of human existence where there are 'sides', and it is necessary for one side to beat another side, and of the utmost importance to walk up to a platform and receive from the hands of the headmaster himself a highly ornamental pot. As people mature they cease to believe in sides or in headmasters or in highly ornamental pots. At any rate, where books are concerned, it is notoriously difficult to fix labels of merit in such a way that they do not come off. Are not reviews of current literature a perpetual illustration of the difficulty of judgement? 'This great book', 'this worthless book', the same book is called by both names. Praise and blame alike mean nothing. No, delightful as the pastime of measuring may be, it is the most futile of all occupations, and to submit to the decrees of the measurers the most servile of attitudes. So long as you write what you wish to write, that is all that matters; and whether it matters for ages or only for hours, nobody can say. But to sacrifice a hair of the head of your vision, a shade of its colour, in deference to some headmaster with a silver pot in his hand or to some professor with a measuring-rod up his sleeve, is the most abject treachery, and the sacrifice of wealth and chastity which used to be said to be the greatest of human disasters, a mere flea bite in comparison.

Next I think that you may object that in all this I have made too much of the importance of material things. Even allowing a generous margin for symbolism, that five hundred a year stands for the power to contemplate, that a lock on the door means the power to think for oneself, still you may say that the mind should rise above such things; and that great poets have often been poor men. Let me then quote to you the words of your own Professor of Literature, who knows better than I do what goes to the making of a poet. Sir Arthur Quiller-Couch[106] writes:

What are the great poetical names of the last hundred years or so? Coleridge, Wordsworth, Byron, Shelley, Landor,[107] Keats, Tennyson, Browning, Arnold,[108] Morris,[109] Rossetti,[110] Swinburne[111] – we may stop there. Of these, all but Keats, Browning, Rossetti were University men, and of these three, Keats, who died young, cut off in his prime, was the only one not fairly well to do. It may seem a brutal thing to say, and it is a sad thing to say: but, as a matter of hard fact, the theory that poetical genius bloweth where it listeth, and equally in poor and rich, holds little truth. As a matter of hard fact, nine out of those twelve were University men: which means that somehow or other they procured the means to get the best education England can give. As a matter of hard fact, of the remaining three you know that Browning was well to do, and I challenge you that, if he had not been well to do, he would no more have attained to write *Saul* or *The Ring and the Book* than Ruskin[112] would have attained to writing *Modern Painters* if his father had not dealt prosperously in business. Rossetti had a small private income; and, moreover, he painted. There remains but Keats; whom Atropos[113] slew young, as she slew John Clare[114] in a madhouse, and James Thomson[115] by the laudanum he took to drug disappointment. These are dreadful facts, but let us face them. It is – however dishonouring to us as a nation – certain that, by some fault in our commonwealth, the poor poet has not in these days, nor has had for two hundred years, a dog's chance. Believe me – and I have spent a great part of ten years in watching some three hundred and twenty elementary schools – we may prate of democracy, but actually, a poor child in England has little more hope than had the son of an Athenian slave to be emancipated into that intellectual freedom of which great writings are born.*

Nobody could put the point more plainly. 'The poor poet has not in these days, nor has had for two hundred years, a dog's chance . . . a poor child in England has little more hope than had the son of an Athenian slave to be emancipated into that intellectual freedom of which great writings are born.' That is it. Intellectual freedom depends upon material things. Poetry depends upon intellectual freedom. And women have always been poor, not for two hundred years merely, but from the beginning of time. Women have had less intellectual freedom than the sons of Athenian slaves. Women, then, have not had a dog's chance of writing poetry. That is why I have laid so much stress on money and a room of one's own. However, thanks to the toils of those obscure women in the past, of whom I wish we knew more, thanks, curiously enough to two wars, the Crimean which let Florence Nightingale out of her drawing-room, and the European War which opened the doors to the average woman some sixty years later, these evils are in the way to be bettered. Otherwise you would not be here tonight, and your chance of earning five hundred pounds a year, precarious as I am afraid that it still is, would be minute in the extreme.

Still, you may object, why do you attach so much importance to this writing of books by women when, according to you, it requires so much effort, leads perhaps to the murder of one's aunts, will make one almost certainly late for luncheon, and may bring one into very grave disputes with certain very good fellows? My motives, let me admit, are partly selfish. Like most uneducated Englishwomen, I like reading – I like reading books in the bulk. Lately my diet has become a trifle monotonous: history is too much about wars; biography too much about great men; poetry has shown, I think, a tendency to sterility; and fiction – but I have sufficiently exposed my disabilities as a critic of modern fiction and will say no more about it. Therefore I would ask you to write all kinds of books, hesitating at no subject however trivial or however vast. By hook or by crook, I hope that you will possess yourselves of money enough to travel and to idle, to contemplate the future or the past of the world, to dream over books and loiter at street corners and let the line of thought dip deep into the stream. For I am by no means confining you to fiction. If you would please me – and there are thousands like me – you would write books of travel and adventure, and research and

* *The Art of Writing* by Sir Arthur Quiller-Couch

scholarship, and history and biography, and criticism and philosophy and science. By so doing you will certainly profit the art of fiction. For books have a way of influencing each other. Fiction will be much the better for standing cheek by jowl with poetry and philosophy. Moreover, if you consider any great figure of the past, like Sappho,[116] like the Lady Murasaki,[117] like Emily Brontë, you will find that she is an inheritor as well as an originator, and has come into existence because women have come to have the habit of writing naturally; so that even as a prelude to poetry such activity on your part would be invaluable.

But when I look back through these notes and criticise my own train of thought as I made them, I find that my motives were not altogether selfish. There runs through these comments and discursions the conviction – or is it the instinct? – that good books are desirable and that good writers, even if they show every variety of human depravity, are still good human beings. Thus when I ask you to write more books I am urging you to do what will be for your good and for the good of the world at large. How to justify this instinct or belief I do not know, for philosophic words, if one has not been educated at a university, are apt to play one false. What is meant by 'reality'? It would seem to be something very erratic, very undependable – now to be found in a dusty road, now in a scrap of newspaper in the street, now a daffodil in the sun. It lights up a group in a room and stamps some casual saying. It overwhelms one walking home beneath the stars and makes the silent world more real than the world of speech – and then there it is again in an omnibus in the uproar of Piccadilly. Sometimes, too, it seems to dwell in shapes too far away for us to discern what their nature is. But whatever it touches, it fixes and makes permanent. That is what remains over when the skin of the day has been cast into the hedge; that is what is left of past time and of our loves and hates. Now the writer, as I think, has the chance to live more than other people in the presence of this reality. It is his business to find it and collect it and communicate it to the rest of us. So at least I infer from reading *Lear* or *Emma* or *La Recherché du Temps Perdu*. For the reading of these books seems to perform a curious couching operation on the senses; one sees more intensely afterwards; the world seems bared of its covering and given an intenser life. Those are the enviable people who live at enmity with unreality; and those are the pitiable who are knocked on the head by the thing done without knowing or caring. So that when I ask you to earn money and have a room of your own, I am asking you to live in the presence of reality, an invigorating life, it would appear, whether one can impart it or not.

Here I would stop, but the pressure of convention decrees that every speech must end with a peroration. And a peroration addressed to women should have something, you will agree, particularly exalting and ennobling about it. I should implore you to remember your responsibilities, to be higher, more spiritual; I should remind you how much depends upon you, and what an influence you can exert upon the future. But those exhortations can safely, I think, be left to the other sex, who will put them, and indeed have put them, with far greater eloquence than I can compass. When I rummage in my own mind I find no noble sentiments about being companions and equals and influencing the world to higher ends. I find myself saying briefly and prosaically that it is much more important to be oneself than anything else. Do not dream of influencing other people, I would say, if I knew how to make it sound exalted. Think of things in themselves.

And again I am reminded by dipping into newspapers and novels and biographies that when a woman speaks to women she should have something very unpleasant up her sleeve. Women are hard on women. Women dislike women. Women – but are you not sick to death of the word? I can assure you that I am. Let us agree, then, that a paper read by a woman to women should end with something particularly disagreeable.

But how does it go? What can I think of? The truth is, I often like women. I like their unconventionality. I like their completeness. I like their anonymity. I like – but I must not run on in this way. That cupboard there – you say it holds clean table-napkins only; but what if Sir Archibald Bodkin were concealed among them? Let me then adopt a sterner tone. Have I, in the preceding words, conveyed to you sufficiently the warnings and reprobation of mankind? I have told you the very low opinion in which you were held by Mr Oscar Browning. I have indicated what Napoleon once thought of you and what Mussolini[118] thinks now. Then, in case any of you aspire to fiction, I have copied out for your benefit the advice of the critic about courageously acknowledging the limitations of your sex. I have referred to Professor X and given prominence to his statement that women are intellectually, morally and physically inferior to men. I have handed on all that has come my way without going in search of it, and here is a final warning – from Mr John Langdon Davies.* Mr John Langdon Davies warns women 'that when children cease to be altogether desirable, women cease to be altogether necessary'. I hope you will make a note of it.

* *A Short History of Women* by John Langdon Davies

How can I further encourage you to go about the business of life? Young women, I would say, and please attend, for the peroration is beginning, you are, in my opinion, disgracefully ignorant. You have never made a discovery of any sort of importance. You have never shaken an empire or led an army into battle. The plays of Shakespeare are not by you, and you have never introduced a barbarous race to the blessings of civilisation. What is your excuse? It is all very well for you to say, pointing to the streets and squares and forests of the globe swarming with black and white and coffee-coloured inhabitants, all busily engaged in traffic and enterprise and love making, we have had other work on our hands. Without our doing, those seas would be unsailed and those fertile lands a desert. We have borne and bred and washed and taught, perhaps to the age of six or seven years, the one thousand six hundred and twenty-three million human beings who are, according to statistics, at present in existence, and that, allowing that some had help, takes time.

There is truth in what you say – I will not deny it. But at the same time may I remind you that there have been at least two colleges for women in existence in England since the year 1866; that after the year 1880 a married woman was allowed by law to possess her own property;[119] and that in 1919 – which is a whole nine years ago she was given a vote? May I also remind you that most of the professions have been open to you for close on ten years now? When you reflect upon these immense privileges and the length of time during which they have been enjoyed, and the fact that there must be at this moment some two thousand women capable of earning over five hundred a year in one way or another, you will agree that the excuse of lack of opportunity, training, encouragement, leisure and money no longer holds good. Moreover, the economists are telling us that Mrs Seton has had too many children. You must, of course, go on bearing children, but, so they say, in twos and threes, not in tens and twelves.

Thus, with some time on your hands and with some book learning in your brains – you have had enough of the other kind, and are sent to college partly, I suspect, to be uneducated – surely you should embark upon another stage of your very long, very laborious and highly obscure career. A thousand pens are ready to suggest what you should do and what effect you will have. My own suggestion is a little fantastic, I admit; I prefer, therefore, to put it in the form of fiction.

I told you in the course of this paper that Shakespeare had a sister; but do not look for her in Sir Sidney Lee's life of the poet. She died young – alas, she never wrote a word. She lies buried where the omnibuses now stop, opposite the Elephant and Castle. Now my belief is that this poet who never wrote a word and was buried at the cross-roads still lives. She lives in you and in me, and in many other women who are not here tonight, for they are washing up the dishes and putting the children to bed. But she lives; for great poets do not die; they are continuing presences; they need only the opportunity to walk among us in the flesh. This opportunity, as I think, it is now coming within your power to give her. For my belief is that if we live another century or so – I am talking of the common life which is the real life and not of the little separate lives which we live as individuals – and have five hundred a year each of us and rooms of our own; if we have the habit of freedom and the courage to write exactly what we think; if we escape a little from the common sitting-room and see human beings not always in their relation to each other but in relation to reality; and the sky, too, and the trees or whatever it may be in themselves; if we look past Milton's bogey, for no human being should shut out the view; if we face the fact, for it is a fact, that there is no arm to cling to, but that we go alone and that our relation is to the world of reality and not only to the world of men and women, then the opportunity will come and the dead poet who was Shakespeare's sister will put on the body which she has so often laid down. Drawing her life from the lives of the unknown who were her forerunners, as her brother did before her, she will be born. As for her coming without that preparation, without that effort on our part, without that determination that when she is born again she shall find it possible to live and write her poetry, that we cannot expect, for that would be impossible. But I maintain that she would come if we worked for her, and that so to work, even in poverty and obscurity, is worth while.

NOTES TO
A Room of One's Own

Chapter 1

1 (p. 29) *Fanny Burney* (1752–1840), novelist and diarist

2 (p. 29) *Haworth Parsonage* home of the Brontë sisters

3 (p. 29) *Miss Mitford* Mary Russell Mitford (1786–1865), dramatist and novelist

4 (p. 30) *Mary Beton, Mary Seton, Mary Carmichael* these notional names Woolf proposes for herself to distance herself from being autobiographical. The names are drawn from 'The Ballad of the Four Marys' (sometimes known as 'Mary Hamilton'); the fourth Mary is the ballad-singer, Mary Hamilton. The ballad is thought to refer to Mary Queen of Scots.

5 (p. 30) *collar* Woolf is using the term metaphorically, to suggest that her subject of women and fiction is a tight restraint on her.

6 (p. 31) *beadle* official of the university

7 (p. 31) *Oxbridge* Woolf combines the two universities to avoid being specific about one or the other, but also to suggest their being classed together as a particular sort of place and culture.

8 (p. 31) *Charles Lamb* (1775–1834), essayist who used the pen name Elia

9 (p. 31) *Max Beerbohm* (1872–1956), caricaturist and writer

10 (p. 31) *Lycidas* Milton's elegy (1637) on the death of Edward King

11 (p. 32) *Thackeray* William Makepeace Thackeray (1811–63), novelist

12 (p. 34) *Van Dyck* Sir Anthony Van Dyck (1599–1641), Flemish painter who lived and worked in England in the latter part of his life. Woolf is perhaps referring to the presence of Van Dyck through his portraits hanging on the walls of the college.

13 (p. 35) *There has fallen . . .* Alfred, Lord Tennyson, *Maud* (1855), section XXII, stanza X

14 (p. 36) *My heart is like a singing bird . . .*   Christina Rossetti, 'A Birthday' (1861)

15 (p. 36) *Fernham*   one of several disguised names Woolf uses in combining her experience of Oxford and Cambridge

16 (p. 39) *J— H—*   Jane Harrison (1850–1928), classical scholar and anthropologist

17 (p. 39) *Trinity . . . Somerville . . . Girton . . . Newnham . . . Christchurch*   actual Oxford and Cambridge colleges. Somerville, Girton and Newnham were then women's colleges, Trinity and Christchurch men's; Woolf is perhaps making the point that she is an outsider to both.

18 (p. 41) *John Stuart Mill*   (1806–73), philosopher and very early exponent of women's suffrage

19 (p. 43) *Balliol or Kings*   Oxford and Cambridge colleges respectively, at that time solely for men.

Chapter 2

20 (p. 48) *Lord Birkenhead*   Frederick Edward Smith, 1st Earl of Birkenhead (1872–1930), Secretary of State for India 1924–28

21 (p. 48) *Dean Inge*   William Ralph Inge (1860–1954), Dean of St Paul's Cathedral 1911–34

22 (p. 48) *Oscar Browning*   (1837–1923), Fellow of King's College, Cambridge

23 (p. 48) *Samuel Butler*   (1612–80), author of the satirical poem *Hudibras*

24 (p. 48) *Pope*   Alexander Pope (1688–1744), poet. The line comes from *Moral Essays*: Epistle II – To a Lady, Of the Characters of Women, l. 2.

25 (p. 48) *La Bruyère*   Jean de La Bruyère (1645–96), French essayist

26 (p. 48) *Les femmes . . .*   'Women are at one extreme or the other; they are either better or worse than men.' The quotation is from La Bruyère, *Les Caractères*.

27 (p. 48) *Dr Johnson*   Samuel Johnson (1709–84), man of letters

28 (p. 51) *Sir Austen Chamberlain*   (1863–1937), Conservative politician, Foreign Minister at this point

29 (p. 52) *Romney*   George Romney (1734–1802), portrait painter

30 (p. 52) *Rebecca West*   (1892–1983), novelist

Chapter 3

31 (p. 57) *Professor Trevelyan*   G. M. Trevelyan (1876–1962), Regius Professor of History at Cambridge at this point. Woolf refers to his *History of England* (1926).

32 (p. 58) *Clytemnestra*   wife of Agamemnon, mother of Orestes, and central female figure in Aeschylus' *Oresteia* (458 BC)

33 (p. 58) *Antigone*   eponymous tragic heroine of Sophocles' play *Antigone* (c.442 BC)

34 (p. 58) *Cleopatra*   Queen of Egypt 51–30BC, and heroine of Shakespeare's play *Antony and Cleopatra*

35 (p. 58) *Lady Macbeth*   key female character in Shakespeare's *Macbeth*

36 (p. 58) *Phèdre*   eponymous heroine of Jean Racine's *Phèdre*

37 (p. 58) *Cressida*   heroine of Shakespeare's *Troilus and Cressida*

38 (p. 58) *Rosalind*   heroine of Shakespeare's *As You Like It*

39 (p. 58) *Desdemona*   heroine of Shakespeare's *Othello*

40 (p. 58) *Duchess of Malfi*   eponymous heroine of John Webster's play *The Duchess of Malfi*

41 (p. 58) *Millamant*   heroine of William Congreve's comedy, *The Way of the World*

42 (p. 58) *Clarissa*   eponymous heroine of Samuel Richardson's novel *Clarissa*

43 (p. 58) *Becky Sharp*   central female character in Thackeray's novel *Vanity Fair*

44 (p. 58) *Anna Karenina*   eponymous heroine of Leo Tolstoy's novel *Anna Karenina*

45 (p. 58) *Emma Bovary*   heroine of Flaubert's novel *Madame Bovary*

46 (p. 58) *Madame de Guermantes*   key female character in Marcel Proust's novel *À la Recherche du Temps Perdu*

47 (p. 59) *Aubrey*   John Aubrey (1626–97), author of *Brief Lives*

48 (p. 60) *Joanna Baillie*   (1762–1851), Romantic poet and playwright

49 (p. 60) *Edgar Allan Poe*   (1809–49), American writer and poet

50 (p. 62) *Edward Fitzgerald*   (1809–83), poet and translator best known for his version of *The Rubáiyát* of Omar Khayyám

51 (p. 63) *Currer Bell, George Eliot, George Sand*   the pen names respectively of Charlotte Brontë, Marian Evans and Aurore-Lucile Dupin

52 (p. 64) *Rousseau*   Jean-Jacques Rousseau (1712–78), French writer and philosopher

53 (p. 64) *Carlyle*   Thomas Carlyle (1795–1881), Scottish historian and essayist whose best known work is *The History of the French Revolution* (1837)

54 (p. 64) *Flaubert*   Gustave Flaubert (1821–80), French novelist

55 (p. 66) *Nick Greene*   character who appears in Woolf's novel *Orlando*

56 (p. 66) *Dr Johnson's dictum*   Johnson opined that a woman preaching was like a dog walking on its hind legs.

57 (p. 67) *Remember Keats*   The words Keats requested for his tombstone were: 'Here lies one whose name was writ in water.'

Chapter 4

58 (p. 69) *Lady Winchilsea*   Anne Finch, Countess of Winchilsea (1661–1720), poet

59 (p. 70) *Mr Murry*   John Middleton Murry (1889–1957), writer and critic

60 (p. 71) *Gay*   John Gay (1685–1732), poet and dramatist best known for *The Beggar's Opera*. *Trivia* (1716) was a satirical account of London life.

61 (p. 71) *Sir Egerton Brydges*   (1762–1837), literary historian

62 (p. 72) *Margaret Cavendish, Duchess of Newcastle*   (1623–73), poet

63 (p. 72) *Dorothy Osborne*   (1627–95), letter writer whose love letters to William Temple also provided a detailed picture of English life at the time

64 (p. 73) *Mrs Behn*   Aphra Behn (1640–89), generally thought to be the first woman to make a living by writing. See the Introduction for more detail on Aphra Behn.

65 (p. 74) *Pride and Prejudice*   novel (1813) by Jane Austen

66 (p. 74) *Middlemarch*   novel (1872) by George Eliot

67 (p. 74) *Villette*   novel (1853) by Charlotte Brontë

68 (p. 74) *Wuthering Heights*   novel (1847) by Emily Brontë

69 (p. 74) *Marlowe*   Christopher Marlowe (1564–93), playwright contemporary with Shakespeare

70 (p. 75) *Miss Nightingale*   Florence Nightingale (1820–1910), reforming nurse most notable for her work in the Crimean War

71 (p. 82) *Browne*   Sir Thomas Browne (1605–82), thinker, author of *Religio Medici* and *Urn Burial*

72 (p. 82) *Newman*   John Henry Newman (1801–90), theologian and religious writer, a central figure in the Oxford Movement which sought to return Anglicanism to its Catholic roots.

73 (p. 82) *Sterne*   Laurence Sterne (1713–68), novelist, author of *Tristram Shandy*

74 (p. 82) *De Quincey*   Thomas de Quincey (1785–1859), best known for his *Confessions of an English Opium Eater*

75 (p. 82) *Balzac*   Honoré de Balzac (1799–1850), French novelist

76 (p. 82) *Gibbon*   Edward Gibbon (1737–94), famous stylist and author of *The Decline and Fall of the Roman Empire*

Chapter 5

77 (p. 84) *Vernon Lee*   pen name of Violet Paget (1856–1935), novelist and essayist

78 (p. 84) *Gertrude Bell*   (1868–1926), travel writer and authority on Arabia

79 (p. 84) *Mary Carmichael*   This repetition of the name Woolf fancifully suggests earlier might stand for her ('call me . . . Mary Carmichael', p. 30) alerts us to the fact that *Life's Adventure* is Woolf's invention.

80 (p. 85) *Sir Charles (Chartres) Biron*   presiding magistrate at the 1928 trial for obscenity of Radclyffe Hall's *The Well of Loneliness*. Biron adjudged the novel to be obscene. It was not freely available in the United Kingdom until 1949.

81 (p. 86) *Diana of the Crossways*   novel (1885) by George Meredith

82 (p. 86) *Racine*   Jean Racine (1639–99), French classical playwright

83 (p. 87) *Caesar*   eponymous hero of Shakespeare's *Julius Caesar*

84 (p. 87) *Brutus*   one time friend to Caesar

85 (p. 87) *Hamlet*   eponymous hero of Shakespeare's *Hamlet*

86 (p. 87) *Lear*   eponymous hero of Shakespeare's *King Lear*

87 (p. 87) *Jaques*   key character in Shakespeare's *As You Like It*

88 (p. 88) *Burke or Debrett*   reference books delineating the British titled aristocracy

89 (p. 88) *Whitaker*   Whitaker's *Almanack* which had a section on the peerage

90 (p. 88) *Goethe*   German poet and playwright (1749–1832)

91 (p. 88) *Cowper*   William Cowper (1731–1800), poet

92 (p. 88) *Voltaire*   French writer (1694–1778)

93 (p. 88) *Browning*   Robert Browning (1812–89), poet

94 (p. 89) *Sir William Joynson Hicks*   (1865–1932), Home Secretary 1924–9

95 (p. 89) *Every Johnson has his Thrale*   Dr Johnson had a long and close friendship with Mrs. Hester Thrale, a writer and intellectual. When her first husband died, she married Gabriel Piozzi, an Italian musician, causing Johnson to break with her completely.

96 (p. 91) *Battle of Balaclava*   battle of the Crimean War (October 1854) during which the Charge of the Light Brigade took place

97 (p. 91) *Miltonic inversion*   inverting the natural English word order in a Latinate way, as Milton did

98 (p. 92) *Juvenal*   (c.60–c.130), Roman satirical poet

99 (p. 92) *Strindberg*   August Strindberg (1849–1912), Swedish dramatist

100 (p. 92) *Mr Woodhouse*   Emma's father in Jane Austen's novel *Emma*

101 (p. 92) *Mr Casaubon*   ageing scholar in George Eliot's *Middlemarch*, whom the young heroine Dorothea chooses to marry

Chapter 6

102 (p. 97) *Coleridge*   Samuel Taylor Coleridge (1772–1834), Romantic poet and philosopher

103 (p. 97) *the Suffrage campaign*   the campaign for votes for women

104 (p. 99) *Mr Galsworthy*   John Galsworthy (1867–1933), writer

105 (p. 99) *Mr Kipling*   Rudyard Kipling (1865–1936), writer

106 (p. 103) *Sir Arthur Quiller-Couch*   (1863–1944), King Edward Professor of English Literature at Cambridge from 1912 until his death

107 (p. 103) *Landor*   Walter Savage Landor (1775–1864), writer

108 (p. 103) *Arnold*   Matthew Arnold (1822–88), poet and critic

109 (p. 103) *Morris*   William Morris (1834–96), artist and writer

110 (p. 103) *Rossetti*   Dante Gabriel Rossetti (1828–82), artist and poet, now better known for his painting than his poetry; brother of Christina

111 (p. 103) *Swinburne*   Algernon Swinburne (1837–1909), poet

112 (p. 103) *Ruskin*   John Ruskin (1819–1900), writer and thinker

113 (p. 103) *Atropos*   one of the three Fates, who used her scissors to cut off the thread of life

114 (p. 103) *John Clare*   (1793–1864), poet who ended his life in an asylum

115 (p. 103) *James Thomson*   (1834–82), poet, author of *The City of Dreadful Night*, which draws on his own experiences of addiction to opium and alcohol

116 (p. 105) *Sappho*   (b. 612 BC), female lyric poet who gathered a group of female followers around her on the Isle of Lesbos

117 (p. 105) *the Lady Murasaki*   Murasaki Shikibu (dates uncertain but possibly 973–1020), Japanese court lady who wrote a novel, *The Tale of Genji*, and an important diary about court life

118 (p. 106) *Mussolini*   Benito Mussolini (1883–1945), leader of Italy and ally of Hitler

119 (p. 107) *after the year 1880 a married woman was allowed by law to possess her own property*   The Married Women's Property Act was actually passed in 1870.

THE VOYAGE OUT

The Voyage Out

---◆---

VIRGINIA WOOLF

A novel by
VIRGINIA WOOLF
first published in 1915

INTRODUCTION TO
The Voyage Out

The voyage out – but not back: the title of Virginia Woolf's first venture on to the sea of fiction positively invites us to see it as a metaphor for the whole business of writing novels, and for the place of that writing in Woolf's life. She set sail hopefully. Her first mention of this her first novel is in October 1907,[1] but it is from May 1908 onwards that she is fully engaged; and in August of that year she seems to have been writing continuously, mentioning her work regularly in the frequent letters to those nearest to her – her sister Vanessa, Vanessa's husband Clive Bell, and her intimate friend Violet Dickinson. Even when she is, in the initial stages, self-deprecatory,[2] that tone characteristically sits only on the surface, undercut by the vigour of her language: 'I have been slashing at Melymbrosia! [her working title]'[3] (to Clive Bell, May 1908, *Letters*, Vol. I, p. 334); 'I screwed out a page of Melymbrosia . . . this morning, but with such rage' (to Clive Bell, 3 August 1908, p. 340); 'a page of Melymbrosia was strangled in the birth this morning' (to Clive Bell, 9 August 1908, p. 345). The barely suppressed zest of creative pride bursts through as something like triumph as she gradually makes progress with her work: 'Ah, I'm so excited about my novel! I read 2 pages, and thought them good' (to Vanessa Bell, 11 August 1908, p. 350). From there it is but a short step to imagining – well, anything, everything: 'I think a great deal of my future, and settle what book I am to write – how

1 See letter to Violet Dickinson, 15? October 1907, *Letters*, Vol. I, p. 315. For full details of this and all other works cited, please turn to the Bibliography which follows this Introduction.

2 See *Letters*, Vol. I, pp. 315–31 *passim*, October 1907–May 1908.

3 This seems to have been a coinage of Woolf's, since it is not in the standard Greek dictionaries. The combined roots suggest 'honeyed food of the gods', but Jan Montefiore has helpfully pointed out that the original meaning of 'ambrosia' was 'immortal' (from which the secondary meaning 'food of the gods' stems). This accentuates the irony of the title.

I shall re-form the novel and capture multitudes of things at present fugitive, enclose the whole, and shape infinite strange shapes' (to Clive Bell, 19 August 1908, p. 356). Woolf's statement could be both epigraph and epitaph for her *oeuvre*; that she could prefigure it so exactly, at twenty-six, when she had completed only a hundred pages of her first novel, is extraordinary.

Yet *The Voyage Out* did not reach its public until 1915, seven years after that fine statement of high authorial ambition. Those years were arduous; if writing was Woolf's life, at times it also threatened her life. The pattern set in the writing of this first novel is a template for her subsequent ones: a period of extreme creativity followed by a descent into despair and disconnection from reality. While this pattern looks obviously bipolar in twenty-first-century terms,[4] Woolf's psychological and psychiatric history is complicated by other factors, including the now well-documented early, and continued, sexual abuse at the hands of both of her half brothers. I raise these issues here both to recognise their centrality and to set them to one side. Woolf acknowledged throughout her life that her half brother George Duckworth had sexually molested her in the period after her mother's death; but at a late point in her life when writing a retrospective memoir she revealed that her other half brother Gerald had molested her similarly 'when I was very small'.[5] It was Gerald who was to publish *The Voyage Out* under the Duckworth imprint. The reverberations of this irony must surely have affected Woolf, possibly in the process of revision, when she knew the novel would be offered to Duckworth, and certainly at proof correction – her first work of the imagination, which we know to have been invested with all her high ambition to re-form the novel, delivered to the world by the hands of her first abuser. This process of revision (so extensive that it has been argued that the first draft, *Melymbrosia*, is effectively a separate work from the finalised *The Voyage Out*),[6] with its cycles of suicidal depression and recovery, was more

4 Leonard Woolf describes Virginia's illness as 'technically . . . manic-depressive' (*Beginning Again: An Autobiography of the Years 1911–1918*, p. 76); and he notes that 'whenever she finished a book, she was in a state of mental exhaustion and for weeks in danger of a breakdown', p. 81.

5 Virginia Woolf, 'A Sketch of the Past', in *Moments of Being: Unpublished Autobiographical Writings*, ed. Jeanne Schulkind, pp. 79–80

6 Louise De Salvo, *Virginia Woolf's First Voyage*, pp. 31–66, especially pp. 63–4. De Salvo has edited the draft that she identifies as the completed *Melymbrosia* and published it as a separate work; see the Bibliography for full details.

intense and prolonged than with any of her subsequent novels.[7] The strain of reading and correcting the proofs in May to June 1913 brought on such a severe breakdown that the novel's publication was put on hold; and in September of that year Woolf took a drug overdose that was almost fatal. Her struggle to produce this first novel is nothing short of heroic, perhaps because she realised that all her imagined future fiction also depended on her winning that struggle.

But while the fact of Woolf's mental illness, and its possible origins, underlie her life, we limit our understanding of her writing if we look at it only through the lens of that illness. Hermione Lee has it right when she notes that Woolf 'violently resisted simplistic Freudian explanations of a life through childhood traumas, and would have been horrified by interpretations of her work which reduced it to a coded expression of neurotic symptoms'.[8] Her many revisions, right up to proof stage, of *The Voyage Out* may have both precipitated and been precipitated by her breakdowns; but once she is at work on them, and making her artistic judgements, she is the pure creative artist striving for the right form for this her first novel, and thinking also about her larger plans 'to re-form the novel'. If we think back to her statement of artistic intent: 'how I shall capture multitudes of things at present fugitive, enclose the whole, and shape infinite strange shapes' – this she by no means achieves in *The Voyage Out*, but it is a crucial first step on the way. The final long passage dealing with the central character's illness and the outcome of that illness is among the finest of Woolf's writings and prefigures the concerns and ways of representing those concerns which were to characterise her fiction. This passage alone justifies both the writing and the reading of *The Voyage Out*, since in it Woolf breaks through to her own characteristic voice.

The novel begins quietly, and to one side of the main plot (if plot there can be said to be), with the characters of Helen Ambrose and her husband; that is the right ordering, since Helen is to be one of the influential figures in the story. Helen is aunt by marriage to Rachel Vinrace, the central protagonist. Rachel's mother is long dead, and Helen takes up a quasi-mothering role to her on the long journey they undertake to South America. It seems highly improbable that Rachel, 'an unlicked girl' (p. 160), educated at home, who 'had scarcely walked

---

7 Woolf herself saw the struggles of *The Voyage Out* as the index of all subsequent distress connected with her writing: see *Diary*, Vol. V, entries for 16 March 1936 (p. 17) and 11 June 1936 (p. 24).

8 Hermione Lee, *Virginia Woolf*, p. 159

through a poor street, and always under the escort of father, maid or aunts' (p. 195) should be flung so suddenly towards this exotic and distant world, albeit on board her father's ship. The Ambroses have slightly more reason for their journey, since Helen's brother has been living in the outpost of Santa Marina and has given them the use of his villa there. Yet the first pages of the novel are wholly concerned with Helen's distress at leaving her children. So the 'why' of the journey is not a question that can be usefully answered, except in terms of the requirements of the fiction. These characters are there, together, first on board ship (with one significant embarkation and debarkation of passengers, Mr and Mrs Dalloway); then on land on the other side of the world (where a fresh set of characters is already installed, to alter the mix); then undertaking, with some of those new characters, a journey upriver into the unknown. This journey culminates in Rachel finding love, perhaps finding herself, but then succumbing to a fever which is fatal. The voyage out ends with her death.

So Woolf, by the device first of the ship, then the contained social world of Santa Marina, has her characters where she wants them – in flux, but also in deadly stasis, joined together in the endless social round on board ship, then freed into uncertainty when they strike land, only to find others who are stalwartly keeping up a social apparatus determined by English manners and mores. Indeed, the South American part of the novel deals almost exclusively with those English visitors who have washed up there. One of the oddities of the novel is that the transportation of the voyage out is not in fact that; the characters seem hardly affected by their change of scene, they carry with them their outer social beings, on the one hand, and their inner concerns on the other, the two often seeming at odds, when we are made privy to that distinction. This may be what Woolf wants us to see – that there is something essentially inner in character, whose mutability isn't determined by circumstance, and whose nature is sheered off from the social surface. Yet at this point in the novel she is not yet thinking of the inherent otherness and individuality of consciousness. For the moment, her cast of characters is explored through dialogue, the work of discovery being conducted through set pieces of action which allow them to interact in different ways.

The first phase of action is the voyage itself, aboard the *Euphrosyne*. Names are significant for Woolf: we know from the letters recounting her revisions that the names she chose for the eventual Rachel and Helen took long time and thought to settle on. Similarly the ship carries several names over time. The final choice of 'Euphrosyne', the

name of one of the three Graces, signifying joy, is undoubtedly freighted
with irony, since it carries Rachel on a voyage from which she will not
return. But perhaps none the less joy is found on the way, through
freedom; and both the vessel's name and the brief rowing-boat trip
which Helen and Ridley Ambrose take over the dark and turbulent
Thames to embark are reminiscent of Lucy Snowe's boarding of the
aptly named *Vivid* in Charlotte Brontë's *Villette*. For both Lucy and
Rachel, the journeys they make take them to an understanding of the
self; and for the reader, each character will come into relief as the novel
unfurls. From almost-blankness each acquires colour, form, definition.

This parallel is almost certainly intentional, given Woolf's deep
immersion in literature; but it is also her intended task to set aside
traditional fictional norms. No sooner does she set up a parallel than she
undermines it. While Lucy's inner drama is highly lit by certain passages
and events which are almost sensational, Woolf continually refuses any
chance for the reader to over-interpret, withdrawing anything too overtly
symbolic by surrounding it with circumstantial, often trivial, conversation
and action. The laconic way in which she counterposes the mundane and
the dramatic was to produce, in her mature work, a deliberately
modernist bathos which allowed for illumination, epiphany even, whilst
always reminding the reader that these are undercut in such a way that
we can never be sure where meaning settles or whether it inheres in
anything. In *The Voyage Out* we see the beginnings of this technique,
but not yet surely handled, so that in the first chapters we sometimes
feel that we are in the middle of nothing more than social comedy. The
storm which takes the feet from under the pompous Dalloways (Mrs
Dalloway here so different from what she would become in the eponymous novel) helps to prepare us for a disruption of the social order:

> On the following day they met – but as flying leaves meet in the
> air ... Their sensations were the sensations of potatoes in a sack on
> a galloping horse. The world outside was merely a violent grey
> tumult. For two days they had a perfect rest from their old emotions.
>
> [p. 200]

But order is quickly reasserted:

> ... they were no longer atoms flying in the void, but people riding a
> triumphant ship on the back of the sea ... after their view of the
> strange underworld, inhabited by phantoms, people began to live
> among teapots and loaves of bread with greater zest than ever.
>
> [p. 202]

It is only in this re-calmed world, with Helen mentally congratulating Mrs Dalloway for 'her spirit and her desire, even in the throes of sickness, for a tidy bedroom' (p. 201), that Richard and Rachel are, literally, thrown together in her cabin:

> Holding her tight, he kissed her passionately, so that she felt the hardness of his body and the roughness of his cheek printed upon hers. She fell back in her chair, with tremendous beats of the heart, each of which sent black waves across her eyes.
>
> He clasped his forehead in his hands. 'You tempt me,' he said. The tone of his voice was terrifying. He seemed choked in fright. They were both trembling.   [p. 205]

The language alone signals this as a significant moment in Rachel's understanding of her self and the world. But, storm aside, what are we to think of Rachel's response? That night she dreams of 'a little deformed man who squatted on the floor gibbering, with long nails. His face was pitted and like the face of an animal . . . Still and cold as death she lay' (p. 206). It is, after all, only a kiss – a view also taken by Helen when Rachel tells her about it ('Helen could hardly restrain herself from saying out loud what she thought of a man who brought up his daughter so that at the age of twenty-four she scarcely knew that men desired women and was terrified by a kiss' [p. 209]). Somehow, between Helen's response (spoken and unspoken), the speedy re-assertion of the world of 'teapots and loaves of bread', and the equally speedy disembarking of the Dalloways from both ship and novel, we are left with as strong impressions of the brilliantly observed effects of sea-sickness (see p. 207) as we are of the kiss.

This is characteristic of Woolf's approach throughout the novel; she at once endorses significance and removes it, often through the accumulation of inconsequential dialogue and detail which drifts around key moments, sometimes dousing them, sometimes making us as readers doubt the rightness of our response to them. Helen's reaction to the story of the kiss is to undertake Rachel's social and emotional education, to lead her out into the world. That the particular world they are heading towards is one of danger, treacherous rivers, unknown hinterlands and unfamiliar diseases, initially hardly impinges on these characters in their cocoon of imperialism. Only the ridiculous William Pepper recognises it, moving to the safety of a hotel that was once a monastery, and warning: ' "If you all die of typhoid I won't be responsible!" ' ' "If you die of dullness, neither will I" ' (p. 220), is Helen's response, and in the circumstances it seems the right one. What point to travel to South

America but not experience it? What point to live at all, and not experience it?

In this way one of the key questions of the novel is summarily answered. Those who conduct their lives in the dry pursuit of scholar-ship, or in thrall to political power, or oiling the cogs of industry and trade – put bluntly, men – these are shown to be on an empty journey. The norms of society are reversed, and all of Woolf's considerable irony is directed against those who think themselves irreducibly important. Here is Richard Dalloway contemplating Englishness and history – and himself:

> A vision of English history, King following King, Prime Minister Prime Minister and Law Law, had come over him while his wife spoke. He ran his mind along the line of conservative policy, which went steadily from Lord Salisbury to Alfred, and gradually enclosed, as though it were a lasso that opened and caught things, enormous chunks of the habitable globe.   [p. 184]

The world of men is ruthlessly exposed in these early chapters. Clive Bell, to whom Woolf showed early drafts of the novel, chided her for the lack of balance in her depictions of men and women:

> . . . to draw such sharp & marked contrast between the subtle, sensitive, tactful, gracious, delicately perceptive, & perspicacious women, & the obtuse, vulgar, blind, florid, rude, tactless, emphatic, indelicate, vain, tyrannical, stupid men, is not only rather absurd, but rather bad art, I think.[9] [? 5 February 1909]

Hmm. But – the Richard Dalloway contemplating life so orotundly is the very same Dalloway who is to kiss Rachel, in a moment of passion and loss of restraint which is not itself ironised. Woolf is kinder to men's moments of weakness, even where they involve an exploitation of their strength.

Helen Ambrose has a different sort of strength, and that too is subtly criticised by Woolf over the structure of the novel as a whole. Her taking responsibility for Rachel is well meant, as is her promise to 'take great care of her' (p. 213). Perhaps her taking care in this instance consists of freeing her. Even so, when she has won the consent both of Rachel's

---

9 Bell's letters, to the then Virginia Stephen, regarding the drafts of the novel he was shown are included in Quentin Bell, *Virginia Woolf, A Biography*, Vol. 1, 1882–1912, Appendix D. See p. 209 for the remark on male and female characters.

father and Rachel herself for Rachel to alight at Santa Marina rather than continuing in the safety of the *Euphrosyne* up the Amazon, Helen 'was beset by doubts, and more than once regretted the impulse which had entangled her with the fortunes of another human being' (p. 214).

As it turns out, Rachel's education is largely conducted as it might have been at home, among other English people, mostly of her own class. After a stultifying few months at Helen's villa, they uncover one night the life of the hotel. This is introduced to us fictionally through the eyes of Helen and Rachel, who walk to it and peer through the windows, like Cathy and Heathcliff staring in wonder at the Lintons in *Wuthering Heights*. In a clever novelistic stroke, Woolf moves from their eyes looking in, realistically, through a downstairs window, at the end of Chapter 8, to her own omniscient eyes looking into the interior of the hotel at the start of Chapter 9. Thus we meet a whole new cast of characters, who are to restart the narrative. Here again Woolf's satirical eye reasserts itself, ranging over various figures who are to play a lesser or greater part in the coming story.

Several new characters are now introduced: Miss Allan, Susan Warrington, Arthur Venning, Terence Hewet and St John Hirst, exposed to the all-seeing narrator's eye just as they have been to the concealed Rachel and Helen spying through the window. Of course, the narrator sees, and hears, more, including inner thoughts. Susan is cruelly exposed, rather as the men have been in the *Euphrosyne* section; indeed, the Santa Marina passages are generally kinder to the men than to the women, reversing the balance of the earlier chapters. This is partly because Hewet and Hirst are to be central figures, Hewet cleaving to Rachel, and Hirst to Helen. But at this stage, naked as it were in their bedrooms, we see them innocently assuming a sort of mastery they don't have, and planning an expedition up the mountain. This is to be a key event in the novel, prefiguring the later trip upriver into the unknown, but also calling up echoes of Englishness by summoning to mind the Box Hill party in Jane Austen's *Emma*, decisive for its part in Emma's moral education.[10]

Hewet and Hirst meet Rachel and Helen for the first time at the start of this trip up the mountain. In an aside, we see, through the men's eyes, a 'woman . . . kneeling by the stream lapping water out of her

---

10 Clive Bell makes specific reference to the echo: 'And then the pic-nic . . . Honestly, I think it challenges comparison with Box Hill & holds its own, & something more' (Bell, *Virginia Woolf: A Biography*, Vol. 1, Appendix D, p. 210).

palms' (p. 248). This, it turns out, is Rachel, who at the end of the novel dies of what is almost certainly typhoid fever.[11] Here she laps the water as innocently as previously Hewet and Hirst have been exposing their ignorance of the social world. Helen, who has sworn to Rachel's father that she would take great care of his daughter, is idly standing by. The time scales in the novel mean that this careless moment is probably not the cause of Rachel's illness; but it is the height of folly to drink untreated water which could so easily be contaminated. And it demonstrates the thoughtlessness, or perhaps the sense of indomitability, that these English people bring to an unknown environment. Woolf does not judge that in itself, rather perhaps she shows the English as incapable of anything other, reared as they are on a sense of the inevitability of supremacy. Yet the people we see playing there on a foreign shore are not there by right or duty, which might at least excuse them their blinkered view; they are there at leisure, only borrowing their absurd confidence from characters such as Ridley Ambrose, Richard Dalloway and Willoughby Vinrace, whose world of affairs has already been demonstrated to be hollow.

Just before Hewet and Hirst discover Rachel and Helen, they are discussing the unknowability of the springs of human action:

' " . . . do we really love each other, or do we, on the other hand, live in a state of perpetual uncertainty, knowing nothing, leaping from moment to moment as from world to world?" ' [Hewet, p. 247–8]

Though the discussion is artificial, it signals one of the deep concerns of the novel. Random actions can have consequences; they have causality, which in turn invokes the issue of human responsibility, though they may remain, at the point when they are enacted, random.

The expedition up the mountain, by contrast, is planned, and is a moment of climax in the plot too. The social comedy continues as the English visitors attempt a foray into the unknown. But they remain themselves, and the Box Hill picnic party analogy sustains. None the less, the climb gives them a vantage point:

11 I am indebted to Elizabeth Mitchell for drawing my attention to the significance of this passage. A number of commentators regard the fever which Rachel contracts as unspecified; certainly it is left unnamed. But both the circumstantial detail and the pattern of the illness, which follows exactly the stages of typhoid fever, as well as the parallels with the illness and death from typhoid of Woolf's brother Thoby in 1906, seem to me to point overwhelmingly to its being typhoid.

> Before them they beheld an immense space – grey sands running
> into forest, and forest merging in mountains, and mountains washed
> by air, the infinite distances of South America. A river ran across the
> plain, as flat as the land, and appearing quite as stationary. The effect
> of so much space was at first rather chilling. They felt themselves
> very small, and for some time no one said anything.   [p. 251]

This is one of several moments in the novel when we suddenly see a
known reality from an immense distance, and our vision is reordered.
Woolf was to become very good at this trick, and it is interesting to
see these first attempts at it. Here, up the mountain, it is a realistic
distance that is created. Elsewhere, it is a sudden change of perspective,
as when she imagines the *Euphrosyne*'s being seen through a telescope
from other passing ships ('From a distance the *Euphrosyne* looked very
small . . . The insect-like figures of Dalloways, Ambroses and Vinraces
were also derided . . . Mr Pepper with all his learning had been
mistaken for a cormorant' [p. 215]). Then, too, we find her trying out
the sort of magisterial distance that was later perfected in the 'Time
Passes' section of *To the Lighthouse*:

> All over the shadowed half of the world people lay prone, and a few
> flickering lights in empty streets marked the places where their cities
> were built. Red and yellow omnibuses were crowding each other in
> Piccadilly; sumptuous women were rocking at a standstill; but here
> in the darkness an owl flitted from tree to tree, and when the breeze
> lifted the branches the moon flashed as if it were a torch. Until all
> people should awake again the houseless animals were abroad . . .
>   [p. 234]

There is a remarkable confidence in the freedom with which Woolf
changes authorial perspective in this first novel. At times this is to the
detriment of the reader's confidence, since it can be difficult to know
what view we are meant to have of individual characters. But the
distance which the narrative affords us, as we observe the 'human beings'
(p. 254) placed within our vision, is inevitably turned upon ourselves.

There is a moral compass here, just as there is in Jane Austen. A most
interesting element of Woolf's work is the way in which she inserts a
moral position whilst seeming to be morally neutral in her fictional
form and method. Poor Susan Warrington and Arthur Venning, seen
through the eyes of the accidental observers Hewet and Rachel, are
made somewhat ridiculous in their love. Yet later, when Rachel and
Hewet come to an understanding, their love is endorsed by the narrator:

Rachel is allowed the dignity of choosing to love, and Hewet accrues virtue by her loving him. Woolf may be trying to show us both that love is inherently suspect, and ridiculous in its expressions (Susan and Arthur Venning), but still central and necessary to human lives (Rachel and Hewet). But what makes them the superior of the two couples? After all, Susan knows herself, and the prospects of her life, far better than Rachel does. The superiority Woolf implies can only be a matter of class and education; this streak of snobbishness was to remain a weakness in her writing.

The picnic trip up the mountain, which begins with Rachel lapping water from the stream, is the first of several events in the South American section through which we see the central characters and their relationships with each other develop. In this, Woolf's method remains purely traditional; but within it, we see her experiment with different modes of writing to delve into character and consciousness, and into the meanings and non-meanings that life can have. The picnic marks the first coming together of Rachel and Hewet, and of Helen and Hirst, though it is the 'understanding' between Susan and Arthur Venning that is the apparently central event. Hewet and Rachel observe their promissory embrace ('They saw a man and a woman lying on the ground beneath them, rolling slightly this way and that as the embrace tightened and slackened . . . ' [p. 258]) but remain themselves unobserved, in an echo of Helen and Rachel's spying through the hotel window. This in turn brings Hewet and Rachel together in joint discomfort, but it also precipitates a conversation between them about love, and initiates an intimacy between them. In the main, then, in this 'picnic' episode the characters discover themselves to each other through banal conversation, with the Susan/Arthur embrace the hidden undercurrent. And, though the distant prospect of South America lying below them when they reach the top of their climb and the distant fireworks in Santa Marina as they descend at the end of the day hint at a larger vision, this journey is merely a vapid rehearsal for the journey upriver (the very river they observe from their high vantage point), just as the relationship between Susan and Arthur is an empty version of Hewet and Rachel's deep encounter there.

There is a further, similarly and deliberately banal, set piece in the ball at the hotel, again with Austenian echoes, where Helen and Rachel and Hewet and Hirst make an interchangeable foursome. But here, though dialogue is again the central mode, the excitement and sheer animal vigour of the dance frees spirits, even that of Hirst, though he scarcely dances, and treats sitting out with Helen as their own kind of

dance. It is after the ball, when Hirst and Hewet accompany Helen
and Rachel back to their house in the light of the rising sun, that Hirst
has his moment of epiphany: ' "I see through everything – absolutely
everything. Life has no more mysteries for me" ' (p. 281). At this
moment we might see this as we see many of his remarks, not to be
taken at face value. But much later in the novel (after the trip upriver)
it is revealed that this was indeed a true moment of epiphany. Hewet
and Rachel are engaged, and are walking together, with Hirst in
attendance. Hirst conducts an internal conversation with himself,
comparing their happiness (which is flawed by its inferiority) with his
own lack of happiness (which is none the less founded on superiority);
and he comes to a moment of revelation:

> 'D'you remember the morning after the dance?' he demanded. 'It
> was here we sat, and you talked nonsense, and Rachel made little
> heaps of stones. I, on the other hand, had the whole meaning of life
> revealed to me in a flash.' He paused for a second, and drew his lips
> together in a tight little purse. 'Love,' he said. 'It seems to me to
> explain everything. So, on the whole, I'm very glad that you two are
> going to be married.'   [p. 405]

It is characteristic of Woolf's method that it is only here, over a
hundred pages after the event, that the meaning of life according to Hirst
is revealed. That it turns out to be something so obvious and common
makes it, in her eyes, the more true since it is Hirst who has understood
it. Again this is part of Woolf's intellectual snobbery. Susan Warrington
and Arthur Venning also come to an understanding through love:

> 'You've made the difference to me,' he jerked out, 'I don't see why I
> shouldn't tell you. I've felt it ever since I knew you . . . It's because
> I love you.'   [p. 257]

But that is never given the status of Hirst's discovery, perhaps because
he makes it in contradistinction from being in love himself. None the
less, there is a pathos in his final blurting out to Rachel and Hewet his
discovery of the all-importance of love. It can be regarded as an
epiphany only because, it seems, he himself will never partake in love in
that way.

Rachel and Hewet stand somewhere between Hirst, and Susan and
Arthur Venning. Their love is given an extra significance in the novel,
one not bleared and blurred by ordinary convenience as Susan and
Venning's is shown to be. In part this is made evident by their declaration
of love to each other's taking place on the trip upriver. This trip, at the

heart of the novel, inevitably calls up comparisons with Joseph Conrad's *Heart of Darkness*. In certain ways such comparisons are risible. Woolf's journey into the jungle is like a vicarage tea-party with a back-projection of the Amazon. And they are not even going up the Amazon; that is the trip Rachel would have taken if she had stayed aboard her father's ship. They go upriver, but not the big river.

When Helen first hatches her plan to take Rachel with her to Santa Marina, she is engaged on a work of embroidery:

> She chose a thread from the vari-coloured tangle that lay in her lap, and sewed red into the bark of a tree, or yellow into the river torrent. She was working at a great design of a tropical river running through a tropical forest, where spotted deer would eventually browse upon masses of fruit – bananas, oranges and giant pomegranates – while a troop of naked natives whirled darts into the air. [p. 168]

This brilliant, throwaway microcosm of imperialism is Helen's everyday activity; but there is perhaps a connection between her embroidering the Amazon into a few inches of cloth and her attempt to divert Rachel into a smaller adventure, which she none the less sees as larger because it is taking her away from the known strictures of her father's world. Yet when she tells Rachel that she has agreed with her father to take her off the *Euphrosyne* at Santa Marina, 'Rachel ... showed less enthusiasm than Helen could have wished':

> Visions of a great river, now blue, now yellow in the tropical sun and crossed by bright birds, now white in the moon, now deep in shade with moving trees and canoes sliding out from the tangled banks, beset her. Helen promised a river. [p. 214]

Woolf's images of the Amazon and its environs are as limited as Rachel and Helen's, but she neatly turns her own imaginative short-comings aside by showing us the limitations of theirs. 'Helen promised a river': bathos is inherent in the contrast between this and the 'great river, now blue, now yellow' of Rachel's imaginings. Similarly, the parallels between the safe trip up the mountain and the trip upriver emphasise that the voyagers are sealed from any real contact with difference:

> Every year at this season English people made parties which steamed a short way up the river, landed and looked at the native village, bought a certain number of things from the natives, and returned again without damage done to mind or body. [p. 365]

This is not Marlow's journey into the heart of darkness, nor was ever meant to be. But undoubtedly Woolf is calling up its echoes. Like Conrad, she can see relationships between the big exotic river and the Thames (see p. 316). Both writers defamiliarise what is apparently known and change our understanding of it by collapsing the distance of history and bringing the Elizabethan or the Roman or even the prehistoric past into the present. And while the horror that Conrad locates may be of a different order, differently expressed, Woolf is just as much in pursuit of the void that lurks at the heart of things. But it is not her way to place it, rather obviously as she would perhaps think, in the midst of the jungle; she wants to keep it firmly within the human consciousness itself. So, as with other fictional models, she rejects this one. She still uses the trip upriver to make something momentous happen, first the deep encounter between Terence and Rachel, and then the subsequent/consequent illness which strikes Rachel down. But Woolf remains true to her own form and to her fictional intention. She refuses to imbue the journey upriver with any significance accrued from the exotic setting: there is no meeting of glances between native and colonial, nor is there the horror of the truly other. But she does draw a deeper significance from what happens to Rachel and Terence when they are set adrift from their known moorings. Primed already as they are to move towards each other, released into the jungle, albeit on a 'wide pathway' that 'resembled a drive in an English forest' (p. 370), they are able to find a space not in any way suggestive of their known lives:

> As they passed into the depths of the forest the light grew dimmer, and the noises of the ordinary world were replaced by those creaking and sighing sounds which suggest to the traveller in a forest that he is walking at the bottom of the sea.   [p. 370]

The couple's declaration to each other almost exactly mimics that of Susan and Arthur earlier, including the embrace:

> Faster and faster they walked; simultaneously they stopped, clasped each other in their arms, then, releasing themselves, dropped to the earth.   [p. 371]

The difference is that there is no observing commentator, other than the omniscient narrator, to give a moral viewpoint on the couple. Furthermore, the strangeness, the very deepness into a landscape so far removed from what is familiar to them, and the deliberateness of taking an unknown path into that unfamiliarity, lends their encounter importance not by the bringing of otherness to it but by its being stripped of known associations. Woolf might not like this comparison, but there is something Lawrentian about the encounter depicted here. This quality, of the rind's being stripped away from the world to expose the true nature of human relations, is also present when Rachel avers the next day: ' "It [marriage] will be a fight" ' (p. 380) – a fight they actually have later:

> He caught her in his arms as she passed him, and they fought for mastery, imagining a rock and the sea heaving beneath them. At last she was thrown to the floor, where she lay gasping and crying for mercy. [p. 394]

Perhaps the Lawrentian dimension is not accidental. This passage has already had a strange forerunner, when during the trip upriver and after Rachel and Terence's declaration of love, Helen performs a full-on tackle on her niece, thrusting her to the ground in a performative expression of – what? Desire? Envy? Fury?

> A hand dropped abrupt as iron on Rachel's shoulder; it might have been a bolt from heaven. She fell beneath it, and the grass whipped across her eyes and filled her mouth and ears. Through the waving stems she saw a figure, large and shapeless against the sky. Helen was upon her. Rolled this way and that, now seeing only forests of green, and now the high blue heaven, she was speechless and almost without sense. [p. 381]

This scenario is punctuated by Rachel's seeing Helen and Hewet kissing above her. The writing throughout this section is again heated, heavily weighted, passionate and speaking of passion, but expressed through natural symbols. We can better understand this encounter by referring to previous drafts of the scene, which are less oblique and show a clearly eroticised encounter between Helen and Rachel, where attempted kisses alternate with Helen's stuffing grass into Rachel's mouth.[12] But in the author's published version, which we must take as her final intention, Helen is both less overt and less dominant. Rachel regains her voice, and it speaks clearly for Terence and marriage – but still a fight.

As if to counterbalance the Lawrentian sway of the river journey, on the return to dry land that supremely rational being Hirst ('one of the three . . . most distinguished men in England' [p. 262]) admits out loud

12 See Mitchell E. Leaska, 'The Death of Rachel Vinrace', in *Virginia Woolf: Critical Assessments*, Vol. III, ed. Elinor McNees, for a fascinating analysis of various drafts, especially p. 18.

to his epiphany about the supreme importance of love (p. 405). Thus the centrality of natural passion, including perhaps that brief glimpse of Helen's for Rachel, is doubly endorsed. Rachel too briefly lapses into a moment of certitude at this point, drawing on Hirst's epiphany to underscore it. Here she is in Chapter 24:

> For the moment she was as detached and disinterested as if she had no longer any lot in life, and she thought that she could now accept anything that came to her without being perplexed by the form in which it appeared. What was there to frighten or to perplex in the prospect of life? Why should this insight ever again desert her? The world was in truth so large, so hospitable, and after all it was so simple. 'Love,' St John had said, 'that seems to explain it all.'
>
> [p. 408]

Rachel then imagines her married life with Terence Hewet, 'thirty, or forty, or fifty years' (p. 409). Soon after this, as if in a distinctive and retributive answer to the hopeful and optimistic passages of love, the novel turns firmly towards death. Chapter 25 is concerned entirely with Rachel's illness, which begins with a headache and ends in oblivion.

Thus her sudden decline follows almost immediately on her moment of understanding of life, and trust in an imaginable future. Woolf perhaps milks the bitter irony a little too much here. But the point is to remind us that such events can spring on us at any time. The unpredictability of Rachel's fatal illness, coming when it does, simply enacts the suddenness, the unknowability, the finiteness of any sort of death in any sort of life. As Woolf described it later, 'What I wanted to do was to give the feeling of a vast tumult of life, as various and disorderly as possible, which could be cut short for a moment by the death, and go on again' (letter to Lytton Strachey, 28 February 1916, *Letters*, Vol. II, p. 82).

In the twenty-four pages of Chapter 25, a piece of writing of sustained virtuosity, Woolf explores the nature of consciousness when it is wrenched by extreme illness. The writing is such that it makes one feel ill to read it. But this has also to do with the way in which extremities of consciousness are themselves explored. These are areas into which we do not really want to go; Woolf takes us to the edge of a void that, if understood fully in the midst of life, would take us down into it. Moreover, she pushes language to its limits, finding a mode of expressing something that inherently eludes expression.[13] In this way

13 In 'A Sketch of the Past', recalling various 'blows', she notes that: 'It is only

the final chapters of *A Voyage Out* mark Woolf's entry into modernism.

In this crucial section of the novel, Woolf draws heavily on her own experience of the sudden death of her brother Thoby from typhoid, not so much for the details of the sickroom, though these are accurate, but for the understanding of the horror that the unexpected death of a young person full of promise can carry. Thoby's death (perhaps taken with her experience of her mother's death when she was thirteen) gives her access to the existential void which was to be the concern that gave her fiction its great originality. Undoubtedly she also draws on her own experience of altered consciousness during mental breakdown, 'how we go down into the pit of death and feel the waters of annihilation close above our heads'.[14]

The remarkable aspect of the writing of Rachel's death is that we are given access to her own consciousness of her slipping away from life. Her illness begins with a headache (the characteristic start of typhoid), but one which alters her apprehension of the world, making it strange, and making language itself strange. When she tells Hewet of the headache he too has a momentary understanding of all that it might mean:

> . . . his sense of dismay and catastrophe were almost physically painful; all round him he seemed to hear the shiver of broken glass which, as it fell to earth, left him sitting in the open air.

[p. 418]

Woolf smuggles such expressionist images into her writing so successfully that one almost misses them, since they are surrounded by ordinariness and trivia. And though calm reasserts itself, Hewet's immediate understanding is correct. In that moment the world collapses around him, and for the reader too; but like him we want to believe that things will come right, we can't believe that Rachel will die. Woolf expertly reveals the way in which human beings cannot bear too much reality. For the observers of Rachel's struggle, a glimpse of what might happen is all that can be borne amidst the day-to-day business of keeping the terror of non-existence at bay.

But for the patient it is another matter: hers is a day-on-day encounter with death itself. Woolf uses the accurate representation of delirium to double for the apprehension of death. For Rachel the passage of time, familiar figures such as Helen and Hewet, the room around her, are all

---

by putting it into words that I make it whole; this wholeness means that it has lost the power to hurt me.' *Moments of Being*, p. 72.

14 'On Being Ill' (1926), *The Essays of Virginia Woolf*, Vol. IV, p. 317

distorted, sometimes giantised into fearful caricatures of themselves. At the same time the process shrinks finally into her own body, her self.

Woolf more than any other writer is able to evoke death for the reader, and we see her discovering that ability in this latter part of *The Voyage Out*. Writing to Vanessa in 1909, in the midst of her first draft of the novel, she tries to think about the act of writing:

> Writing [here, letters] seems to me a queer thing. It does make a difference. I should never talk to you like this . . . The truth is, I am always trying to get behind words; and they flop down on me suddenly.   [16 August 1909, *Letters*, Vol. I, p. 408]

Woolf constantly tries to represent a reality which language, by its nature secondary to experience, will fail to capture. In trying to represent death, her problem is exacerbated since it is something we do not, cannot experience, except, again, at second hand, as the person experiencing someone else's death. Yet it is not just that loss she wants to express, it is the inanition of death itself (' "the one experience I shall never describe" ', *Diary*, 23 November 1926).[15] Hence her wanting to 'get behind words'. Of course she cannot do that. So we see in her fiction, and here notably in her first attempts at it in *The Voyage Out*, a compromise between expression and the inexpressible.

Rachel's consciousness is depicted in constant struggle, with the world around her which has suddenly been made other, and with, eventually, the possibility of losing that consciousness. It is a long struggle too, and the reader is forced to undergo it with her, facing the distortions of reality which belong to delirium but are here brought into the lived world through language:

> . . . the wall of her room was painfully white, and curved slightly, instead of being straight and flat. Turning her eyes to the window, she was not reassured by what she saw there. The movement of the blind as it filled with air and blew slowly out, drawing the cord with a little trailing sound along the floor, seemed to her terrifying, as if it were the movement of an animal in the room.   [pp. 418–19]

Here we see forming Woolf's (as it was to be) characteristic third person interiority, combining authorial distance and supreme knowledge with the subjectivity of an individual apprehension of the world. The experience used here to encapsulate Rachel's terror is almost identical to

15 She records having said this to Vita Sackville-West the day before (*Diary*, Vol. III, p. 117).

that which Woolf uses in her autobiographical 'A Sketch of the Past' to capture her own childhood ecstasy in St Ives, and which she describes as 'the most important of all my memories': 'It is of hearing the blind draw its little acorn across the floor as the wind blew the blind out . . . of feeling the purest ecstasy I can conceive.'[16] While this inversion of something joyful in her own life into something terrifying in fiction might at first seem wilful, it reminds us of Woolf's understanding that objects in the world can be altered completely by the perception of the beholder. Here we see the room through Rachel's eyes, distorted, terrifying. But we also have the omniscient commentary observing her:

> . . . every object in the room, and the bed itself, and her own body with its various limbs and their different sensations were more and more important each day. She was completely cut off, and unable to communicate with the rest of the world, isolated alone with her body. [p. 420]

Although Woolf has used this narrative technique earlier in the novel, it has always been in the service of a 'normal' consciousness, as in Chapter 9, when the omniscient narrator looks into the various hotel bedrooms, and where standard human preoccupations are revealed. There, dialogue and internal thought process are not much distinguished, the one playing into the other. But Rachel's consciousness is now wholly transformed, and with it the world she perceives, so that at points the third person seems to have been absorbed into the first:

> Rachel woke to find herself in the midst of one of those interminable nights which do not end at twelve, but go on into the double figures – thirteen, fourteen, and so on, until they reach the twenties, and then the thirties, and then the forties. She realised that there is nothing to prevent nights from doing this if they choose. [p. 420]

She feels that she is at the will of the world, but at the same time the world she sees is not that seen by others, and not the world she would see were she her 'normal' self. The intolerable lengthening of time is replaced by even more intolerable hallucinatory nightmare visions:

> Rachel . . . found herself walking through a tunnel under the Thames, where there were little deformed women sitting in archways playing cards, while the bricks of which the wall was made oozed with damp, which collected into drops and slid down the wall. [p. 421]

16 *Moments of Being*, p. 75. I am grateful to Andrew Palmer for pointing out this echo and its curious inversion.

This replicates, almost word for word, Rachel's dream following Dalloway's kiss, the only difference being that in her dream it is 'a little deformed man' rather than 'little deformed women' (see p. 206). Woolf no doubt notices something true here, that significant mental events repeat themselves when the mind is under duress. But the repetition seems to suggest the undue importance for Rachel of the experience of Dalloway's kiss, returning here as a form of horror on a par with the disintegration of her own grip on life.[17]

Eventually Rachel's struggle reduces to its essentials:

> Rachel's face was changed. She looked as though she were entirely concentrated upon the effort of keeping alive . . . it needed all her attention to follow the hot, red, quick sights which passed incessantly before her eyes. She knew that it was of enormous importance that she should attend to these sights and grasp their meaning, but she was always being just too late to hear or see something which would explain it all.   [p. 427–9]

Many years after Thoby's death, in her Diary entry for 11 October 1929, Virginia Woolf addresses as fully as she ever does outside her fiction the sense, even in the midst of life's busy apparatus, of death:

> – I was walking up Bedford Place is it – the straight street with all the boarding houses this afternoon, and I said to myself spontaneously, something like this. How I suffer, and no one knows how I suffer, walking up this street, engaged with my anguish, as I was after Thoby died – alone; fighting something alone. But then I had the devil to fight, and now nothing. And when I come indoors it is all so silent – I am not carrying a great rush of wheels in my head – Yet I am writing – oh and we are very successful . . . And it is autumn; and the lights are going up; and Nessa is in Fitzroy Street . . . – and I am richer than I have ever been – and bought a pair of earrings today – and for all this, there is vacancy and silence somewhere in the machine . . . If I could catch the feeling, I would.
>
>   [Diary, Vol. III, pp. 259–60]

17 Here we may see Woolf's own early experience of bodily powerlessness at the hands of George Duckworth powering her understanding of the sense of bodily dissolution in extreme illness. This perhaps explains her intense imaginative apprehension of the presence of death in life, accentuated by Gerald Duckworth's abuse so soon after her mother's death.

The writing of Rachel's death is an early, and bold, attempt to 'catch the feeling'. The final stages of Rachel's falling away into the abyss below the 'little strip of pavement' of life (*Diary*, Vol. II, 25 October 1920, p. 72) coincide ironically with her appearing to those around her to be a little better. The reader is not deceived:

> It was true that she saw Helen and saw her room, but everything had become very pale and semi-transparent. Sometimes she could see through the wall in front of her ... The room also had an odd power of expanding, and though she pushed her voice out as far as possible until sometimes it became a bird and flew away, she thought it doubtful whether it ever reached the person she was talking to.
>
> [p. 434]

The efforts to keep alive have ceased and 'for long spaces of time she would merely lie conscious of her body floating on top of the bed and her mind driven to some remote corner of her body, or escaped and gone flitting round the room' (p. 434). The last we hear from her consciousness is that 'it troubled her when people tried to disturb her loneliness; she wished to be alone. She wished for nothing else in the world' (p. 434).

Well – Rachel gets her wish, which is after all only the wish of a tormented mind in an afflicted body wishing for peace. The well and happy Rachel of just a few weeks earlier would not have wished it. None the less her death accords her a sort of seriousness which cannot be achieved by anyone else in the novel. Terence Hewet's anguish is briefly raised to the same status with his repeated shriek of her name as, seeing 'the table with the cups and the plates' outside her room, 'it suddenly came over him that here was a world in which he would never see Rachel again' (p. 440). But soon life comes lapping and wrapping around again, reasserting itself as it must.

This has led some commentators to interpret Rachel's death as being intended as a better alternative to a commonly happy life.[18] This can't be right. Though these critics imply the death as being willed by Rachel, Rachel really has no say in the matter. This interpretation would involve Woolf, Hardy-like, condemning her heroine to death for the sake of a moral. Woolf's business is quite other. In eschewing the conventional ending of marriage as equated with happiness, Woolf

18 See Leaska in McNees, Vol. III, p. 20; Lorna Sage, Introduction to *The Voyage Out*, Oxford World's Classics, 1992, p. xxvi.

has already prepared the reader by characterising marriage as a 'fight' (p. 380), ' "puzzling – sometimes, I think, disappointing" '(p. 385), 'painful and terrible' (p. 397), inherently unbalanced (' "There's something I can't get hold of in you. You don't want me as I want you – " ' p. 397). But she has also endorsed it, through love, and the commitment to a partnership, however faulty and combative, as one means to happiness. There is no doubt that Rachel's death is tragic in denying her, and Hewet, that ordinary happiness. But it is not that denial in itself which underpins the death as ending.

Throughout the novel Woolf turns again and again to the question of meaning and accident, randomness and causation. She pits the small lives of her characters against the largeness of nature, and shows their, sometimes pitiable, attempts to create an ordered and civilised structure, based on the London drawing-room, within a profoundly unfamiliar geography and culture. When they stray into the unknown, they carry their carapaces with them; but their adventurous intent, whilst ironised, is also applauded. In the midst of all this, Rachel contracts typhoid. Evelyn and Mrs Thornbury, in an anodyne version of the sort of philosophical discussion Hirst and Hewet have had at a more innocent time, try to make sense of it:

> 'How could one go on if there were no reason?' she [Mrs Thornbury] asked. She asked the question of someone, but she did not ask it of Evelyn. Evelyn's sobs were becoming quieter. 'There must be a reason,' she said. 'It can't only be an accident. For if it was an accident – it need never have happened.'
> Mrs Thornbury sighed deeply.
> 'But we must not let ourselves think of that,' she added, 'and let us hope that they don't either. Whatever they had done it might have been the same. These terrible illnesses – '
> 'There's no reason – I don't believe there's any reason at all!' Evelyn broke out, pulling the blind down and letting it fly back with a little snap.   [p. 443]

The sense of 'reason' here is 'meaning' as well as 'cause', but in Evelyn's cry there is also the sense of 'rationality'. In the face of such terrible events as the sudden death of a young girl with the prospect of happiness so recently before her, the world seems a place prey to unreason. Hirst might have pointed out that Rachel's death could be seen a simple matter of cause and effect. But that does not answer the question of agency, which Evelyn and Mrs Thornbury in their different ways are worrying at – and which Woolf has raised more than once.

In the end it is the 'unreason', the randomness, that Woolf wants to strike us with, to remind us that, whatever human agency we bring to bear, we cannot escape the abyss below the thin strip of pavement. Some people balance on that strip better than others, and the novel ends with the reassertion of the trivia of existence which help towards that: 'the figures of people picking up their books, their cards, their balls of wool, their work-baskets . . . on their way to bed' (p. 456). As readers we are released from the existential vertigo of the preceding pages into a welcome normality. But what we will remember of the novel is the long glimpse of 'vacancy and silence somewhere in the machine'. In that October 1929 *Diary* entry Woolf concluded: 'But I have not really laid hands on the emptiness after all' (p. 260). In *The Voyage Out* we see the beginnings of her long fictional grappling with that most fugitive of subjects.

SALLY MINOGUE

BIBLIOGRAPHY

PRIMARY SOURCES

The Voyage Out was first published by Duckworth and Co., London, 1915. The American edition (Doran, 1920) has considerable variants, from Woolf's hand. However, Woolf reverted to the Duckworth first edition for The Hogarth Press edition (as part of the Uniform Edition of Woolf's works), 1929, and that is the text used here.

Virginia Woolf, *The Voyage Out*, ed. Lorna Sage, Oxford University Press, Oxford, 1992

Virginia Woolf, *To the Lighthouse*, Wordsworth Editions, Ware, 1994

Virginia Woolf, *Moments of Being: Unpublished Autobiographical Writings* (1976), ed. Jeanne Schulkind, Triad/Granada, London, 1978

Andrew McNeillie (ed.), *The Essays of Virginia Woolf*, Vol. IV, Hogarth Press, London, 1994

Anne Olivier Bell, assisted by Andrew McNeillie (eds), *The Diary of Virginia Woolf*, 5 vols, Hogarth Press, London, 1977–84

Nigel Nicolson and Joanne Trautmann (eds), *The Letters of Virginia Woolf*, 6 vols, Hogarth Press, London, 1975–84

Leonard Woolf, *Autobiography*, 5 vols, Hogarth Press, London, 1960–9

Elinor McNees (ed.), *Virginia Woolf: Critical Assessments*, 4 vols, Helm Information, Robertsbridge, 1994. Vol. III relates to *The Voyage Out*.

BIOGRAPHY

Quentin Bell, *Virginia Woolf: A Biography*, 2 vols, Hogarth Press, London, 1972

Lyndall Gordon, *Virginia Woolf: A Writer's Life*, Oxford University Press, Oxford, 1984

Hermione Lee, *Virginia Woolf*, Chatto and Windus, London, 1996

GENERAL CRITICISM

Rachel Bowlby, *Feminist Destinations and Further Essays on Virginia Woolf*, Edinburgh University Press, Edinburgh, 1997

Julia Briggs (ed.), *Virginia Woolf: Introductions to the Major Works*, Virago Press, London, 1984

Louise A. DeSalvo, *Virginia Woolf's First Voyage: A Novel in the Making*, Macmillan, London, 1980

Louise A. DeSalvo (ed.), *'Melymbrosia' by Virginia Woolf: An Early Version of 'The Voyage Out'*, New York Public Library, Astor, Lenox and Tilden Foundations, New York, 1982

Louise A. DeSalvo, *Virginia Woolf: The Impact of Childhood Sexual Abuse on Her Life and Work*, The Women's Press, London, 1989

Jane de Gay, *Virginia Woolf's Novels and the Literary Past*, Edinburgh University Press, Edinburgh, 2007

Howard Harper, *Between Language and Silence: The Novels of Virginia Woolf*, Louisiana State University Press, Baton Rouge and London, 1982

Winifred Holtby, *Virginia Woolf: A Critical Memoir* (1932), Continuum, London, 2007

R. Majumdar and A. McLaurin (eds), *Virginia Woolf: The Critical Heritage*, Routledge and Kegan Paul, London and Boston, 1975

Laura Marcus, *Virginia Woolf*, Northcote House/British Council, Tavistock, 1997; 2nd edition 2004

James Naremore, *The World without a Self: Virginia Woolf and the Novel*, Yale University Press, New Haven and London, 1973

Linden Peach, *Virginia Woolf*, Macmillan, Critical Issues, London, 2000

Harvena Richter, *Virginia Woolf: The Inward Voyage*, Princeton University Press, 1970

Jane Wheare, *Virginia Woolf: Dramatic Novelist*, Macmillan, London, 1989

OTHER WORKS CITED

Jane Austen, *Emma*, Wordsworth Editions, Ware, 2000

Charlotte Brontë, *Villette*, Wordsworth Editions, Ware, 1999

Emily Brontë, *Wuthering Heights*, Wordsworth Editions, Ware, 1992

Joseph Conrad, *Heart of Darkness*, Wordsworth Editions, Ware, 1999

THE VOYAGE OUT

Chapter 1

As the streets that lead from the Strand to the Embankment are very narrow, it is better not to walk down them arm-in-arm. If you persist, lawyers' clerks will have to make flying leaps into the mud; young lady typists will have to fidget behind you. In the streets of London where beauty goes unregarded, eccentricity must pay the penalty, and it is better not to be very tall, to wear a long blue cloak, or to beat the air with your left hand.

One afternoon in the beginning of October when the traffic was becoming brisk a tall man strode along the edge of the pavement with a lady on his arm. Angry glances struck upon their backs. The small, agitated figures – for in comparison with this couple most people looked small – decorated with fountain pens, and burdened with despatch-boxes, had appointments to keep, and drew a weekly salary, so that there was some reason for the unfriendly stare which was bestowed upon Mr Ambrose's height and upon Mrs Ambrose's cloak. But some enchantment had put both man and woman beyond the reach of malice and unpopularity. In his case one might guess from the moving lips that it was thought; and in hers from the eyes fixed stonily straight in front of her at a level above the eyes of most that it was sorrow. It was only by scorning all she met that she kept herself from tears, and the friction of people brushing past her was evidently painful. After watching the traffic on the Embankment for a minute or two with a stoical gaze she twitched her husband's sleeve, and they crossed between the swift discharge of motor cars. When they were safe on the further side, she gently withdrew her arm from his, allowing her mouth at the same time to relax, to tremble; then tears rolled down, and leaning her elbows on the balustrade, she shielded her face from the curious. Mr Ambrose attempted consolation; he patted her shoulder; but she showed no signs of admitting him, and feeling it awkward to stand beside a grief that was greater than his, he crossed his arms behind him, and took a turn along the pavement.

The embankment juts out in angles here and there, like pulpits; instead of preachers, however, small boys occupy them, dangling string, dropping pebbles, or launching wads of paper for a cruise. With their sharp eye for eccentricity, they were inclined to think Mr Ambrose awful; but the quickest witted cried, 'Bluebeard!'[1] as he passed. In case they should proceed to tease his wife, Mr Ambrose flourished his stick at them, upon which they decided that he was grotesque merely, and four instead of one cried, 'Bluebeard!' in chorus.

Although Mrs Ambrose stood quite still, much longer than is natural, the little boys let her be. Someone is always looking into the river near Waterloo Bridge; a couple will stand there talking for half an hour on a fine afternoon; most people, walking for pleasure, contemplate for three minutes; when, having compared the occasion with other occasions, or made some sentence, they pass on. Sometimes the flats and churches and hotels of Westminster are like the outlines of Constantinople in a mist; sometimes the river is an opulent purple, sometimes mud-coloured, sometimes sparkling blue like the sea. It is always worth while to look down and see what is happening. But this lady looked neither up nor down; the only thing she had seen, since she stood there, was a circular iridescent patch slowly floating past with a straw in the middle of it. The straw and the patch swam again and again behind the tremulous medium of a great welling tear, and the tear rose and fell and dropped into the river. Then there struck close upon her ears –

> Lars Porsena of Clusium
> By the nine gods he swore – [2]

and then more faintly, as if the speaker had passed her on his walk –

> That the Great House of Tarquin
> Should suffer wrong no more.

Yes, she knew she must go back to all that, but at present she must weep. Screening her face she sobbed more steadily than she had yet done, her shoulders rising and falling with great regularity. It was this figure that her husband saw when, having reached the polished Sphinx, having entangled himself with a man selling picture postcards, he turned; the stanza instantly stopped. He came up to her, laid his hand on her shoulder, and said, 'Dearest.' His voice was supplicating. But she shut her face away from him, as much as to say, 'You can't possibly understand.'

As he did not leave her, however, she had to wipe her eyes, and to raise them to the level of the factory chimneys on the other bank. She saw also the arches of Waterloo Bridge and the carts moving across them, like the line of animals in a shooting gallery. They were seen blankly, but to see anything was of course to end her weeping and begin to walk.

'I would rather walk,' she said, her husband having hailed a cab already occupied by two city men.

The fixity of her mood was broken by the action of walking. The shooting motor cars, more like spiders in the moon than terrestrial objects, the thundering drays, the jingling hansoms, and little black broughams, made her think of the world she lived in. Somewhere up there above the pinnacles where the smoke rose in a pointed hill, her children were now asking for her, and getting a soothing reply. As for the mass of streets, squares and public buildings which parted them, she only felt at this moment how little London had done to make her love it, although thirty of her forty years had been spent in a street. She knew how to read the people who were passing her; there were the rich who were running to and from each other's houses at this hour; there were the bigoted workers driving in a straight line to their offices; there were the poor who were unhappy and rightly malignant. Already, though there was sunlight in the haze, tattered old men and women were nodding off to sleep upon the seats. When one gave up seeing the beauty that clothed things, this was the skeleton beneath.

A fine rain now made her still more dismal; vans with the odd names of those engaged in odd industries – Sprules, Manufacturer of Sawdust; Grabb, to whom no piece of waste paper comes amiss – fell flat as a bad joke; bold lovers, sheltered behind one cloak, seemed to her sordid, past their passion; the flower women, a contented company, whose talk is always worth hearing, were sodden hags; the red, yellow and blue flowers, whose heads were pressed together, would not blaze. Moreover, her husband walking with a quick rhythmic stride, jerking his free hand occasionally, was either a Viking or a stricken Nelson; the sea-gulls had changed his note.

'Ridley, shall we drive? Shall we drive, Ridley?'

Mrs Ambrose had to speak sharply; by this time he was far away.

The cab, by trotting steadily along the same road, soon withdrew them from the West End, and plunged them into London. It appeared that this was a great manufacturing place, where the people were engaged in making things, as though the West End, with its electric lamps, its vast plate-glass windows all shining yellow, its carefully-finished houses, and tiny live figures trotting on the pavement, or bowled along on wheels in the road, was the finished work. It appeared to her a very small bit of work for such an enormous factory to have made. For some reason it appeared to her as a small golden tassel on the edge of a vast black cloak.

Observing that they passed no other hansom cab, but only vans and wagons, and that not one of the thousand men and women she saw was either a gentleman or a lady, Mrs Ambrose understood that after all it is the ordinary thing to be poor, and that London is the city of innumerable poor people. Startled by this discovery and seeing herself pacing a circle all the days of her life round Piccadilly Circus she was greatly relieved to pass a building put up by the London County Council for Night Schools.

'Lord, how gloomy it is!' her husband groaned. 'Poor creatures!'

What with the misery for her children, the poor, and the rain, her mind was like a wound exposed to dry in the air.

At this point the cab stopped, for it was in danger of being crushed like an eggshell. The wide Embankment which had had room for cannonballs and squadrons, had now shrunk to a cobbled lane steaming with smells of malt and oil and blocked by wagons. While her husband read the placards pasted on the brick announcing the hours at which certain ships would sail for Scotland, Mrs Ambrose did her best to find information. From a world exclusively occupied in feeding wagons with sacks, half obliterated too in a fine yellow fog, they got neither help nor attention. It seemed a miracle when an old man approached, guessed their condition, and proposed to row them out to their ship in the little boat which he kept moored at the bottom of a flight of steps. With some hesitation they trusted themselves to him, took their places, and were soon waving up and down upon the water, London having shrunk to two lines of buildings on either side of them, square buildings and oblong buildings placed in rows like a child's avenue of bricks.

The river, which had a certain amount of troubled yellow light in it, ran with great force; bulky barges floated down swiftly escorted by tugs; police boats shot past everything; the wind went with the current. The open rowing-boat in which they sat bobbed and curtseyed across the line of traffic. In midstream the old man stayed his hands upon the oars, and as the water rushed past them, remarked that once he had taken many passengers across, where now he took scarcely any. He seemed to recall an age when his boat, moored among rushes, carried delicate feet across to lawns at Rotherhithe.

'They want bridges now,' he said, indicating the monstrous outline of the Tower Bridge. Mournfully Helen regarded him, who was putting water between her and her children. Mournfully she gazed at the ship they were approaching; anchored in the middle of the stream they could dimly read her name – *Euphrosyne*.[3]

Very dimly in the falling dusk they could see the lines of the rigging, the masts and the dark flag which the breeze blew out squarely behind.

As the little boat sidled up to the steamer, and the old man shipped his oars, he remarked, once more pointing above, that ships all the world over flew that flag the day they sailed. In the minds of both the passengers the blue flag appeared a sinister token, and this the moment for presentiments, but nevertheless they rose, gathered their things together, and climbed on deck.

Down in the saloon of her father's ship, Miss Rachel Vinrace, aged twenty-four, stood waiting her uncle and aunt nervously. To begin with, though nearly related, she scarcely remembered them; to go on with, they were elderly people, and finally, as her father's daughter, she must be in some sort prepared to entertain them. She looked forward to seeing them as civilised people generally look forward to the first sight of civilised people, as though they were of the nature of an approaching physical discomfort – a tight shoe or a draughty window. She was already unnaturally braced to receive them. As she occupied herself in laying forks severely straight by the side of knives, she heard a man's voice saying gloomily: 'On a dark night one would fall down these stairs head foremost,' to which a woman's voice added, 'And be killed.'

As she spoke the last words the woman stood in the doorway. Tall, large-eyed, draped in purple shawls, Mrs Ambrose was romantic and beautiful; not perhaps sympathetic, for her eyes looked straight and considered what they saw. Her face was much warmer than a Greek face; on the other hand it was much bolder than the face of the usual pretty Englishwoman.

'Oh, Rachel, how d'you do,' she said, shaking hands.

'How are you, dear,' said Mr Ambrose, inclining his forehead to be kissed. His niece instinctively liked his thin angular body, and the big head with its sweeping features, and the acute, innocent eyes.

'Tell Mr Pepper,' Rachel bade the servant. Husband and wife then sat down on one side of the table, with their niece opposite to them.

'My father told me to begin,' she explained. 'He is very busy with the men . . . You know Mr Pepper?'

A little man who was bent as some trees are by a gale on one side of them had slipped in. Nodding to Mr Ambrose, he shook hands with Helen.

'Draughts,' he said, erecting the collar of his coat.

'You are still rheumatic?' asked Helen. Her voice was low and seductive, though she spoke absently enough, the sight of town and river being still present to her mind.

'Once rheumatic, always rheumatic, I fear,' he replied. 'To some extent it depends on the weather, though not so much as people are apt to think.'

'One does not die of it, at any rate,' said Helen.

'As a general rule – no,' said Mr Pepper.

'Soup, Uncle Ridley?' asked Rachel.

'Thank you, dear,' he said, and, as he held his plate out, sighed audibly, 'Ah! she's not like her mother.' Helen was just too late in thumping her tumbler on the table to prevent Rachel from hearing, and from blushing scarlet with embarrassment.

'The way servants treat flowers!' she said hastily. She drew a green vase with a crinkled lip towards her, and began pulling out the tight little chrysanthemums, which she laid on the tablecloth, arranging them fastidiously side by side.

There was a pause.

'You knew Jenkinson, didn't you, Ambrose?' asked Mr Pepper across the table.

'Jenkinson of Peterhouse?[4]'

'He's dead,' said Mr Pepper.

'Ah, dear! – I knew him – ages ago,' said Ridley. 'He was the hero of the punt accident, you remember? A queer card. Married a young woman out of a tobacconist's, and lived in the Fens – never heard what became of him.'

'Drink – drugs,' said Mr Pepper with sinister conciseness. 'He left a commentary. Hopeless muddle, I'm told.'

'The man had really great abilities,' said Ridley.

'His Introduction to Jellaby holds its own still,' went on Mr Pepper, 'which is surprising, seeing how textbooks change.'

'There was a theory about the planets, wasn't there?' asked Ridley.

'A screw loose somewhere, no doubt of it,' said Mr Pepper, shaking his head.

Now a tremor ran through the table, and a light outside swerved. At the same time an electric bell rang sharply again and again.

'We're off,' said Ridley.

A slight but perceptible wave seemed to roll beneath the floor; then it sank; then another came, more perceptible. Lights slid right across the uncurtained window. The ship gave a loud melancholy moan.

'We're off!' said Mr Pepper. Other ships, as sad as she, answered her outside on the river. The chuckling and hissing of water could be plainly heard, and the ship heaved so that the steward bringing plates had to balance himself as he drew the curtain. There was a pause.

'Jenkinson of Cats[5] – d'you still keep up with him?' asked Ambrose.

'As much as one ever does,' said Mr Pepper. 'We meet annually. This year he has had the misfortune to lose his wife, which made it painful, of course.'

'Very painful,' Ridley agreed.

'There's an unmarried daughter who keeps house for him, I believe, but it's never the same, not at his age.'

Both gentlemen nodded sagely as they carved their apples.

'There was a book, wasn't there?' Ridley enquired.

'There *was* a book, but there never *will* be a book,' said Mr Pepper with such fierceness that both ladies looked up at him.

'There never will be a book, because someone else has written it for him,' said Mr Pepper with considerable acidity. 'That's what comes of putting things off, and collecting fossils, and sticking Norman arches on one's pigsties.'

'I confess I sympathise,' said Ridley with a melancholy sigh. 'I have a weakness for people who can't begin.'

'. . . The accumulations of a lifetime wasted,' continued Mr Pepper. 'He had accumulations enough to fill a barn.'

'It's a vice that some of us escape,' said Ridley. 'Our friend Miles has another work out today.'

Mr Pepper gave an acid little laugh. 'According to my calculations,' he said, 'he has produced two volumes and a half annually, which, allowing for time spent in the cradle and so forth, shows a commendable industry.'

'Yes, the old Master's saying of him has been pretty well realised,' said Ridley.

'A way they had,' said Mr Pepper. 'You know the Bruce collection? – not for publication, of course.'

'I should suppose not,' said Ridley significantly. 'For a Divine he was – remarkably free.'

'The Pump in Neville's Row, for example?' enquired Mr Pepper.

'Precisely,' said Ambrose.

Each of the ladies, being after the fashion of their sex, highly trained in promoting men's talk without listening to it, could think – about the education of children, about the use of fog sirens in an opera – without betraying herself. Only it struck Helen that Rachel was perhaps too still for a hostess, and that she might have done something with her hands.

'Perhaps – ?' she said at length, upon which they rose and left, vaguely to the surprise of the gentlemen, who had either thought them attentive or had forgotten their presence.

'Ah, one could tell strange stories of the old days,' they heard Ridley say, as he sank into his chair again. Glancing back, at the doorway, they saw Mr Pepper as though he had suddenly loosened his clothes, and had become a vivacious and malicious old ape.

Winding veils round their heads, the women walked on deck. They were now moving steadily down the river, passing the dark shapes of ships at anchor, and London was a swarm of lights with a pale yellow canopy drooping above it. There were the lights of the great theatres, the lights of the long streets, lights that indicated huge squares of domestic comfort, lights that hung high in air. No darkness would ever settle upon those lamps, as no darkness had settled upon them for hundreds of years. It seemed dreadful that the town should blaze for ever in the same spot; dreadful at least to people going away to adventure upon the sea, and beholding it as a circumscribed mound, eternally burnt, eternally scarred. From the deck of the ship the great city appeared a crouched and cowardly figure, a sedentary miser.

Leaning over the rail, side by side, Helen said, 'Won't you be cold?' Rachel replied, 'No ... How beautiful!' she added a moment later. Very little was visible – a few masts, a shadow of land here, a line of brilliant windows there. They tried to make head against the wind.

'It blows – it blows!' gasped Rachel, the words rammed down her throat. Struggling by her side, Helen was suddenly overcome by the spirit of movement, and pushed along with her skirts wrapping themselves round her knees, and both arms to her hair. But slowly the intoxication of movement died down, and the wind became rough and chilly. They looked through a chink in the blind and saw that long cigars were being smoked in the dining-room; they saw Mr Ambrose throw himself violently against the back of his chair, while Mr Pepper crinkled his cheeks as though they had been cut in wood. The ghost of a roar of laughter came out to them, and was drowned at once in the wind. In the dry yellow-lighted room Mr Pepper and Mr Ambrose were oblivious of all tumult; they were in Cambridge, and it was probably about the year 1875.

'They're old friends,' said Helen, smiling at the sight. 'Now, is there a room for us to sit in?'

Rachel opened a door.

'It's more like a landing than a room,' she said. Indeed it had nothing of the shut stationary character of a room on shore. A table was rooted in the middle, and seats were stuck to the sides. Happily the tropical suns had bleached the tapestries to a faded blue-green colour, and the mirror with its frame of shells, the work of the steward's love, when the time hung heavy in the southern seas, was quaint rather than ugly.

Twisted shells with red lips like unicorn's horns ornamented the mantelpiece, which was draped by a pall of purple plush from which depended a certain number of balls. Two windows opened on to the deck, and the light beating through them when the ship was roasted on the Amazons had turned the prints on the opposite wall to a faint yellow colour, so that 'The Coliseum' was scarcely to be distinguished from 'Queen Alexandra playing with her Spaniels'. A pair of wicker armchairs by the fireside invited one to warm one's hands at a grate full of gilt shavings; a great lamp swung above the table – the kind of lamp which makes the light of civilisation across dark fields to one walking in the country.

'It's odd that everyone should be an old friend of Mr Pepper's,' Rachel started nervously, for the situation was difficult, the room cold, and Helen curiously silent.

'I suppose you take him for granted?' said her aunt.

'He's like this,' said Rachel, lighting on a fossilised fish in a basin, and displaying it.

'I expect you're too severe,' Helen remarked.

Rachel immediately tried to qualify what she had said against her belief.

'I don't really know him,' she said, and took refuge in facts, believing that elderly people really like them better than feelings. She produced what she knew of William Pepper. She told Helen that he always called on Sundays when they were at home; he knew about a great many things – about mathematics, history, Greek, zoology, economics, and the Icelandic Sagas. He had turned Persian poetry into English prose, and English prose into Greek iambics; he was an authority upon coins; and – one other thing – oh yes, she thought it was vehicular traffic.

He was here either to get things out of the sea, or to write upon the probable course of Odysseus,[6] for Greek after all was his hobby.

'I've got all his pamphlets,' she said. 'Little pamphlets. Little yellow books.' It did not appear that she had read them.

'Has he ever been in love?' asked Helen, who had chosen a seat.

This was unexpectedly to the point.

'His heart's a piece of old shoe leather,' Rachel declared, dropping the fish. But when questioned she had to own that she had never asked him.

'I shall ask him,' said Helen. 'The last time I saw you, you were buying a piano,' she continued. 'Do you remember – the piano, the room in the attic, and the great plants with the prickles?'

'Yes, and my aunts said the piano would come through the floor, but at their age one wouldn't mind being killed in the night?' she enquired.

'I heard from Aunt Bessie not long ago,' Helen stated. 'She is afraid that you will spoil your arms if you insist upon so much practising.'

'The muscles of the forearm – and then one won't marry?'

'She didn't put it quite like that,' replied Mrs Ambrose.

'Oh, no – of course she wouldn't,' said Rachel with a sigh.

Helen looked at her. Her face was weak rather than decided, saved from insipidity by the large enquiring eyes; denied beauty, now that she was sheltered indoors, by the lack of colour and definite outline. Moreover, a hesitation in speaking, or rather a tendency to use the wrong words, made her seem more than normally incompetent for her years. Mrs Ambrose, who had been speaking much at random, now reflected that she certainly did not look forward to the intimacy of three or four weeks on board ship which was threatened. Women of her own age usually boring her, she supposed that girls would be worse. She glanced at Rachel again. Yes! how clear it was that she would be vacillating, emotional, and when you said something to her it would make no more lasting impression than the stroke of a stick upon water. There was nothing to take hold of in girls – nothing hard, permanent, satisfactory. Did Willoughby say three weeks, or did he say four? She tried to remember.

At this point, however, the door opened and a tall burly man entered the room, came forward and shook Helen's hand with an emotional kind of heartiness: Willoughby himself, Rachel's father, Helen's brother-in-law. As a great deal of flesh would have been needed to make a fat man of him, his frame being so large, he was not fat; his face was a large framework too, looking, by the smallness of the features and the glow in the hollow of the cheek, more fitted to withstand assaults of the weather than to express sentiments and emotions, or to respond to them in others.

'It is a great pleasure that you have come,' he said, 'for both of us.'

Rachel murmured in obedience to her father's glance.

'We'll do our best to make you comfortable. And Ridley. We think it an honour to have charge of him. Pepper'll have someone to contradict him – which I daren't do. You find this child grown, don't you? A young woman, eh?'

Still holding Helen's hand he drew his arm round Rachel's shoulder, thus making them come uncomfortably close, but Helen forbore to look.

'You think she does us credit?' he asked.

'Oh yes,' said Helen.

'Because we expect great things of her,' he continued, squeezing his daughter's arm and releasing her. 'But about you now.' They sat down side by side on the little sofa. 'Did you leave the children well? They'll be ready for school, I suppose. Do they take after you or Ambrose? They've got good heads on their shoulders, I'll be bound?'

At this Helen immediately brightened more than she had yet done, and explained that her son was six and her daughter ten. Everybody said that her boy was like her and her girl like Ridley. As for brains, they were quick brats, she thought, and modestly she ventured on a little story about her son – how left alone for a minute he had taken the pat of butter in his fingers, run across the room with it, and put it on the fire – merely for the fun of the thing, a feeling which she could understand.

'And you had to show the young rascal that these tricks wouldn't do, eh?'

'A child of six? I don't think they matter.'

'I'm an old-fashioned father.'

'Nonsense, Willoughby; Rachel knows better.'

Much as Willoughby would doubtless have liked his daughter to praise him she did not; her eyes were unreflecting as water, her fingers still toying with the fossilised fish, her mind absent. The elder people went on to speak of arrangements that could be made for Ridley's comfort – a table placed where he couldn't help looking at the sea, far from boilers, at the same time sheltered from the view of people passing. Unless he made this a holiday, when his books were all packed, he would have no holiday whatever; for out at Santa Marina Helen knew, by experience, that he would work all day; his boxes, she said, were packed with books.

'Leave it to me – leave it to me!' said Willoughby, obviously intending to do much more than she asked of him. But Ridley and Mr Pepper were heard fumbling at the door.

'How are you, Vinrace?' said Ridley, extending a limp hand as he came in, as though the meeting were melancholy to both, but on the whole more so to him.

Willoughby preserved his heartiness, tempered by respect. For the moment nothing was said.

'We looked in and saw you laughing,' Helen remarked. 'Mr Pepper had just told a very good story.'

'Pish. None of the stories were good,' said her husband peevishly.

'Still a severe judge, Ridley?' enquired Mr Vinrace.

'We bored you so that you left,' said Ridley, speaking directly to his wife.

As this was quite true Helen did not attempt to deny it, and her next remark, 'But didn't they improve after we'd gone?' was unfortunate, for her husband answered with a droop of his shoulders, 'If possible they got worse.'

The situation was now one of considerable discomfort for everyone concerned, as was proved by a long interval of constraint and silence. Mr Pepper, indeed, created a diversion of a kind by leaping on to his seat, both feet tucked under him, with the action of a spinster who detects a mouse, as the draught struck at his ankles. Drawn up there, sucking at his cigar, with his arms encircling his knees, he looked like the image of Buddha, and from this elevation began a discourse, addressed to nobody, for nobody had called for it, upon the unplumbed depths of ocean. He professed himself surprised to learn that although Mr Vinrace possessed ten ships, regularly plying between London and Buenos Aires, not one of them was bidden to investigate the great white monsters of the lower waters.

'No, no,' laughed Willoughby, 'the monsters of the earth are too many for me!'

Rachel was heard to sigh, 'Poor little goats!'

'If it weren't for the goats there'd be no music, my dear; music depends upon goats,' said her father rather sharply, and Mr Pepper went on to describe the white, hairless, blind monsters lying curled on the ridges of sand at the bottom of the sea, which would explode if you brought them to the surface, their sides bursting asunder and scattering entrails to the winds when released from pressure, with such considerable detail and with such show of knowledge that Ridley was disgusted and begged him to stop.

From all this Helen drew her own conclusions, which were gloomy enough. Pepper was a bore; Rachel was an unlicked girl, no doubt prolific of confidences, the very first of which would be: 'You see, I don't get on with my father.' Willoughby, as usual, loved his business and built his Empire, and between them all she would be considerably bored. Being a woman of action, however, she rose, and said that for her part she was going to bed. At the door she glanced back instinctively at Rachel, expecting that as two of the same sex they would leave the room together. Rachel rose, looked vaguely into Helen's face, and remarked with her slight stammer, 'I'm going out to t–t–triumph in the wind.'

Mrs Ambrose's worst suspicions were confirmed; she went down the passage lurching from side to side, and fending off the wall now with her right arm, now with her left; at each lurch she exclaimed emphatically, 'Damn!'

Chapter 2

Uncomfortable as the night, with its rocking movement, and salt smells, may have been, and in one case undoubtedly was, for Mr Pepper had insufficient clothes upon his bed, the breakfast next morning wore a kind of beauty. The voyage had begun, and had begun happily with a soft blue sky and a calm sea. The sense of untapped resources, things to say as yet unsaid, made the hour significant, so that in future years the entire journey perhaps would be represented by this one scene, with the sound of sirens hooting in the river the night before somehow mixing in.

The table was cheerful with apples and bread and eggs. Helen handed Willoughby the butter, and as she did so cast her eye on him and reflected, 'And she married you, and she was happy, I suppose.'

She went off on a familiar train of thought, leading on to all kinds of well-known reflections, from the old wonder, why had Theresa married Willoughby?

'Of course, one sees all that,' she thought, meaning that one sees that he is big and burly, and has a great booming voice, and a fist and a will of his own; 'but – ' here she slipped into a fine analysis of him which is best represented by one word, 'sentimental', by which she meant that he was never simple and honest about his feelings. For example, he seldom spoke of the dead, but kept anniversaries with singular pomp. She suspected him of nameless atrocities with regard to his daughter, as indeed she had always suspected him of bullying his wife. Naturally she fell to comparing her own fortunes with the fortunes of her friend, for Willoughby's wife had been perhaps the one woman Helen called friend, and this comparison often made the staple of their talk. Ridley was a scholar, and Willoughby was a man of business. Ridley was bringing out the third volume of Pindar[7] when Willoughby was launching his first ship. They built a new factory the very year the commentary on Aristotle – was it? – appeared at the University Press. 'And Rachel,' she looked at her, meaning, no doubt, to decide the argument, which was otherwise too evenly balanced, by declaring that Rachel was not comparable to her own children. 'She really might be six years old,' was all she said, however, this judgement referring to the smooth unmarked outline of the girl's face, and not condemning her otherwise, for if

Rachel were ever to think, feel, laugh or express herself, instead of dropping milk from a height as though to see what kind of drops it made, she might be interesting though never exactly pretty. She was like her mother, as the image in a pool on a still summer's day is like the vivid flushed face that hangs over it.

Meanwhile Helen herself was under examination, though not from either of her victims. Mr Pepper considered her; and his meditations, carried on while he cut his toast into bars and neatly buttered them, took him through a considerable stretch of autobiography. One of his penetrating glances assured him that he was right last night in judging that Helen was beautiful. Blandly he passed her the jam. She was talking nonsense, but not worse nonsense than people usually do talk at breakfast, the cerebral circulation, as he knew to his cost, being apt to give trouble at that hour. He went on saying 'No' to her, on principle, for he never yielded to a woman on account of her sex. And here, dropping his eyes to his plate, he became autobiographical. He had not married himself for the sufficient reason that he had never met a woman who commanded his respect. Condemned to pass the susceptible years of youth in a railway station in Bombay, he had seen only coloured women, military women, official women; and his ideal was a woman who could read Greek, if not Persian, was irreproachably fair in the face, and able to understand the small things he let fall while undressing. As it was he had contracted habits of which he was not in the least ashamed. Certain odd minutes every day went to learning things by heart; he never took a ticket without noting the number; he devoted January to Petronius,[8] February to Catullus,[9] March to the Etruscan vases perhaps; anyhow he had done good work in India, and there was nothing to regret in his life except the fundamental defects which no wise man regrets, when the present is still his. So concluding he looked up suddenly and smiled. Rachel caught his eye.

'And now you've chewed something thirty-seven times, I suppose?' she thought, but said politely aloud, 'Are your legs troubling you today, Mr Pepper?'

'My shoulder blades?' he asked, shifting them painfully. 'Beauty has no effect upon uric acid that I'm aware of,' he sighed, contemplating the round pane opposite, through which the sky and sea showed blue. At the same time he took a little parchment volume from his pocket and laid it on the table. As it was clear that he invited comment, Helen asked him the name of it. She got the name; but she got also a disquisition upon the proper method of making roads. Beginning with the Greeks, who had, he said, many difficulties to contend with, he continued with the Romans, passed to England and the right method, which speedily became the wrong method, and wound up with such a fury of denunciation directed against the road-makers of the present day in general, and the road-makers of Richmond Park in particular, where Mr Pepper had the habit of cycling every morning before breakfast, that the spoons fairly jingled against the coffee cups, and the insides of at least four rolls mounted in a heap beside Mr Pepper's plate.

'Pebbles!' he concluded, viciously dropping another bread pellet upon the heap. 'The roads of England are mended with pebbles! "With the first heavy rainfall," I've told 'em, "your road will be a swamp." Again and again my words have proved true. But d'you suppose they listen to me when I tell 'em so, when I point out the consequences, the consequences to the public purse, when I recommend 'em to read Coryphaeus?[10] No, Mrs Ambrose, you will form no just opinion of the stupidity of mankind until you have sat upon a Borough Council!' The little man fixed her with a glance of ferocious energy.

'I have had servants,' said Mrs Ambrose, concentrating her gaze. 'At this moment I have a nurse. She's a good woman as they go, but she's determined to make my children pray. So far, owing to great care on my part, they think of God as a kind of walrus; but now that my back's turned – Ridley,' she demanded, swinging round upon her husband, 'what shall we do if we find them saying the Lord's Prayer when we get home again?'

Ridley made the sound which is represented by 'Tush'. But Willoughby, whose discomfort as he listened was manifested by a slight rocking movement of his body, said awkwardly, 'Oh, surely, Helen, a little religion hurts nobody.'

'I would rather my children told lies,' she replied, and while Willoughby was reflecting that his sister-in-law was even more eccentric than he remembered, pushed her chair back and swept upstairs. In a second they heard her calling back, 'Oh, look! We're out at sea!'

They followed her on to the deck. All the smoke and the houses had disappeared, and the ship was out in a wide space of sea very fresh and clear though pale in the early light. They had left London sitting on its mud. A very thin line of shadow tapered on the horizon, scarcely thick enough to stand the burden of Paris, which nevertheless rested upon it. They were free of roads, free of mankind, and the same exhilaration at their freedom ran through them all. The ship was making her way steadily through small waves which slapped her and then fizzled like effervescing water, leaving a little border of bubbles and foam on either side. The colourless October sky above was thinly clouded as if by the trail of wood-fire smoke, and the air was wonderfully salt and brisk. Indeed it was too cold to stand still. Mrs Ambrose drew her arm within her husband's, and as they moved off it could be seen from the way in which her sloping cheek turned up to his that she had something private to communicate. They went a few paces and Rachel saw them kiss.

Down she looked into the depth of the sea. While it was slightly disturbed on the surface by the passage of the *Euphrosyne*, beneath it was green and dim, and it grew dimmer and dimmer until the sand at the bottom was only a pale blur. One could scarcely see the black ribs of wrecked ships, or the spiral towers made by the burrowings of great eels, or the smooth green-sided monsters who came by flickering this way and that.

' – And, Rachel, if anyone wants me, I'm busy till one,' said her father, enforcing his words as he often did, when he spoke to his daughter, by a smart blow upon the shoulder.

'Until one,' he repeated. 'And you'll find yourself some employment, eh? Scales, French, a little German, eh? There's Mr Pepper who knows more about separable verbs than any man in Europe, eh?' and he went off laughing. Rachel laughed, too, as indeed she had laughed ever since she could remember, without thinking it funny, but because she admired her father.

But just as she was turning with a view perhaps to finding some employment, she was intercepted by a woman who was so broad and so thick that to be intercepted by her was inevitable. The discreet tentative way in which she moved, together with her sober black dress, showed that she belonged to the lower orders; nevertheless she took up a rocklike position, looking about her to see that no gentry were near before she delivered her message, which had reference to the state of the sheets, and was of the utmost gravity.

'How ever we're to get through this voyage, Miss Rachel, I really can't tell,' she began with a shake of her head. 'There's only just sheets enough to go round, and the master's has a rotten place you could put your fingers through. And the counterpanes. Did you notice the counterpanes? I thought to myself a poor person would have been ashamed of them. The one I gave Mr Pepper was hardly fit to cover a dog . . . No, Miss Rachel, they could *not* be mended; they're only fit for dust sheets. Why, if one sewed one's finger to the bone, one would have one's work undone the next time they went to the laundry.'

Her voice in its indignation wavered as if tears were near.

There was nothing for it but to descend and inspect a large pile of linen heaped upon a table. Mrs Chailey handled the sheets as if she knew each by name, character and constitution. Some had yellow stains, others had places where the threads made long ladders; but to the ordinary eye they looked much as sheets usually do look, very chill, white, cold, and irreproachably clean.

Suddenly Mrs Chailey, turning from the subject of sheets, dismissing them entirely, clenched her fists on the top of them, and proclaimed, 'And you couldn't ask a living creature to sit where I sit!'

Mrs Chailey was expected to sit in a cabin which was large enough, but too near the boilers, so that after five minutes she could hear her heart 'go', she complained, putting her hand above it, which was a state of things that Mrs Vinrace, Rachel's mother, would never have dreamt of inflicting – Mrs Vinrace, who knew every sheet in her house, and expected of every one the best they could do, but no more.

It was the easiest thing in the world to grant another room, and the problem of sheets simultaneously and miraculously solved itself, the spots and ladders not being past cure after all, but –

'Lies! Lies! Lies!' exclaimed the mistress indignantly, as she ran up on to the deck. 'What's the use of telling me lies?'

In her anger that a woman of fifty should behave like a child and come cringing to a girl because she wanted to sit where she had not leave to sit, she did not think of the particular case, and, unpacking her music, soon forgot all about the old woman and her sheets.

Mrs Chailey folded her sheets, but her expression testified to flatness within. The world no longer cared about her, and a ship was not a home. When the lamps were lit yesterday, and the sailors went tumbling above her head, she had cried; she would cry this evening; she would cry tomorrow. It was not home. Meanwhile she arranged her ornaments in the room which she had won too easily. They were strange ornaments to bring on a sea voyage – china pugs, tea-sets in miniature, cups stamped floridly with the arms of the city of Bristol, hairpin boxes crusted with shamrock, antelopes' heads in coloured plaster, together with a multitude of tiny photographs, representing downright workmen in their Sunday best, and women holding white babies. But there was one portrait, in a gilt frame, for which a nail was needed, and before she sought it Mrs Chailey put on her spectacles and read what was written on a slip of paper at the back: 'This picture of her mistress is given to Emma Chailey by Willoughby Vinrace in gratitude for thirty years of devoted service.'

Tears obliterated the words and the head of the nail.

'So long as I can do something for your family,' she was saying, as she hammered at it, when a voice called melodiously in the passage: 'Mrs Chailey! Mrs Chailey!'

Chailey instantly tidied her dress, composed her face, and opened the door.

'I'm in a fix,' said Mrs Ambrose, who was flushed and out of breath. 'You know what gentlemen are. The chairs too high – the tables too low – there's six inches between the floor and the door. What I want's a hammer, an old quilt, and have you such a thing as a kitchen table? Anyhow, between us' – she now flung open the door of her husband's sitting-room, and revealed Ridley pacing up and down, his forehead all wrinkled, and the collar of his coat turned up.

'It's as though they'd taken pains to torment me!' he cried, stopping dead. 'Did I come on this voyage in order to catch rheumatism and pneumonia? Really one might have credited Vinrace with more sense. My dear,' Helen was on her knees under a table, 'you are only making yourself untidy, and we had much better recognise the fact that we are condemned to six weeks of unspeakable misery. To come at all was the height of folly, but now that we are here I suppose that I can face it like a man. My diseases of course will be increased – I feel already worse than I did yesterday, but we've only ourselves to thank, and the children happily – '

'Move! Move! Move!' cried Helen, chasing him from corner to corner with a chair as though he were an errant hen. 'Out of the way, Ridley, and in half an hour you'll find it ready.'

She turned him out of the room, and they could hear him groaning and swearing as he went along the passage.

'I dare say he isn't very strong,' said Mrs Chailey, looking at Mrs Ambrose compassionately, as she helped to shift and carry.

'It's books,' sighed Helen, lifting an armful of sad volumes from the floor to the shelf. 'Greek from morning to night. If ever Miss Rachel marries, Chailey, pray that she may marry a man who doesn't know his ABC.'

The preliminary discomforts and harshnesses, which generally make the first days of a sea voyage so cheerless and trying to the temper, being somehow lived through, the succeeding days passed pleasantly enough. October was well advanced, but steadily burning with a warmth that made the early months of the summer appear very young and capricious. Great tracts of the earth lay now beneath the autumn sun, and the whole of England, from the bald moors to the Cornish rocks, was lit up from dawn to sunset, and showed in stretches of yellow, green and purple. Under that illumination even the roofs of the great towns glittered. In thousands of small gardens, millions of dark-red flowers were blooming, until the old ladies who had tended them so carefully came down the paths with their scissors, snipped through their juicy stalks, and laid them upon cold stone ledges in the village church. Innumerable parties of picnickers coming home at sunset cried, 'Was there ever such a day as this?' 'It's you,' the young men whispered; 'Oh, it's you,' the young women replied. All old people and many sick people were drawn, were it only for a foot or two, into the open air, and prognosticated pleasant things about the course of the world. As for the confidences and expressions of love that were heard not only in cornfields but in lamplit rooms, where the windows opened on the garden, and men with cigars kissed women with grey hairs, they were not to be counted. Some said that the sky was an emblem of the life to come. Long-tailed birds clattered and screamed, and crossed from wood to wood, with golden eyes in their plumage.

But while all this went on by land, very few people thought about the sea. They took it for granted that the sea was calm; and there was no need, as there is in many houses when the creeper taps on the bedroom windows, for the couples to murmur before they kiss, 'Think of the ships tonight,' or, 'Thank heaven, I'm not the man in the lighthouse!' For all they imagined, the ships when they vanished on the skyline dissolved, like snow in water. The grown-up view, indeed, was not much clearer than the view of the little creatures in bathing drawers who were trotting into the foam all along the coasts of England, and scooping up buckets full of water. They saw white sails or tufts of smoke pass across the horizon, and if you had said that these were waterspouts, or the petals of white sea flowers, they would have agreed.

The people in ships, however, took an equally singular view of England. Not only did it appear to them to be an island, and a very small island, but it was a shrinking island in which people were imprisoned. One figured them first swarming about like aimless ants, and almost pressing each other over the edge; and then, as the ship withdrew, one figured them making a vain clamour, which, being unheard, either ceased or rose into a brawl. Finally, when the ship was out of sight of land, it became plain that the people of England were completely mute. The disease attacked other parts of the earth: Europe shrank, Asia shrank, Africa and America shrank, until it seemed doubtful whether the ship would ever run against any of those wrinkled little rocks again. But, on the other hand, an immense dignity had descended upon her; she was an inhabitant of the great world, which has so few inhabitants, travelling all day across an empty universe, with veils drawn before her and behind. She was more lonely than the caravan crossing the desert; she was infinitely more mysterious, moving by her own power and sustained by her own resources. The sea might give her death or some unexampled joy, and none would know of it. She was a bride going forth to her husband, a virgin unknown of men; in her vigour and purity she might be likened to all beautiful things, for as a ship she had a life of her own.

Indeed if they had not been blessed in their weather, one blue day being bowled up after another, smooth, round and flawless, Mrs Ambrose would have found it very dull. As it was, she had her embroidery frame set up on deck, with a little table by her side on which lay open a black volume of philosophy. She chose a thread from the vari-coloured tangle that lay in her lap, and sewed red into the bark of a tree, or yellow into the river torrent. She was working at a great design of a tropical river running through a tropical forest, where spotted deer would eventually browse upon masses of fruit – bananas, oranges and giant pomegranates – while a troop of naked natives whirled darts into the air. Between the stitches she looked to one side and read a sentence about the Reality of Matter, or the Nature of Good. Round her men in blue jerseys knelt and scrubbed the boards, or leant over the rails and whistled, and not far off Mr Pepper sat cutting up roots with a penknife. The rest were occupied in other parts of the ship: Ridley at his Greek – he had never found quarters more to his liking; Willoughby at his documents, for he used a voyage to work off arrears of business; and Rachel – Helen, between her sentences of philosophy, wondered sometimes what Rachel *did* do with herself? She meant vaguely to go and see. They had scarcely spoken two words to each other since that first evening; they were polite when they met, but there had been no confidence of any kind. Rachel seemed to get on very well with her father – much better, Helen thought, than she ought to – and was as ready to let Helen alone as Helen was to let her alone.

At that moment Rachel was sitting in her room doing absolutely nothing. When the ship was full this apartment bore some magnificent title and was the resort of elderly seasick ladies who left the deck to their youngsters. By virtue of the piano, and a mess of books on the floor, Rachel considered it her room, and there she would sit for hours playing very difficult music, reading a little German, or a little English when the mood took her, and doing – as at this moment – absolutely nothing.

The way she had been educated, joined to a fine natural indolence, was of course partly the reason of it, for she had been educated as the majority of well-to-do girls in the last part of the nineteenth century were educated. Kindly doctors and gentle old professors had taught her the rudiments of about ten different branches of knowledge, but they would as soon have forced her to go through one piece of drudgery thoroughly as they would have told her that her hands were dirty. The one hour or the two hours weekly passed very pleasantly, partly owing to the other pupils, partly to the fact that the window looked upon the back of a shop, where figures appeared against the red windows in winter, partly to the accidents that are bound to happen when more than two people are in the same room together. But there was no subject in the world which she knew accurately. Her mind was in the state of an intelligent man's in the beginning of the reign of Queen Elizabeth; she would believe practically anything she was told, invent reasons for anything she said. The shape of the earth, the history of the world, how trains worked, or money was invested, what laws were in force, which people wanted what, and why they wanted it, the most elementary idea of a system in modern life – none of this had been imparted to her by any of her professors or mistresses. But this system of education had one great advantage. It did not teach anything, but it put no obstacle in the way of any real talent that the pupil might chance to have. Rachel, being musical, was allowed to learn nothing but music; she became a fanatic about music. All the energies that might have gone into languages, science, or literature, that might have made her friends, or shown her the world, poured straight into music. Finding her teachers inadequate, she had practically taught herself. At the age of twenty-four she knew as much about music as most people do when they are thirty; and could play as well as nature allowed her to, which, as became daily more obvious, was a really generous allowance. If this one definite gift was surrounded by dreams and ideas of the most extravagant and foolish description, no one was any the wiser.

Her education being thus ordinary, her circumstances were no more out of the common. She was an only child and had never been bullied and laughed at by brothers and sisters. Her mother having died when she was eleven, two aunts, the sisters of her father, brought her up, and they lived for the sake of the air in a comfortable house in Richmond. She was of course brought up with excessive care, which as a child was for her health; as a girl and a young woman was for what it seems almost crude to call her morals. Until quite lately she had been completely ignorant that for women such things existed. She groped for knowledge in old books, and found it in repulsive chunks, but she did not naturally care for books and thus never troubled her head about the censorship which was exercised first by her aunts, later by her father. Friends might have told her things, but she had few of her own age – Richmond being an awkward place to reach – and, as it happened, the only girl she knew well was a religious zealot, who in the fervour of intimacy talked about God, and the best ways of taking up one's cross, a topic only fitfully interesting to one whose mind reached other stages at other times.

But lying in her chair, with one hand behind her head, the other grasping the knob on the arm, she was clearly following her thoughts intently. Her education left her abundant time for thinking. Her eyes were fixed so steadily upon a ball on the rail of the ship that she would have been startled and annoyed if anything had chanced to obscure it for a second. She had begun her meditations with a shout of laughter, caused by the following translation from *Tristan*:[11]

> In shrinking trepidation
> His shame he seems to hide,
> While to the king his relation
> He brings the corpse-like bride.
> Seems it so senseless what I say?

She cried that it did, and threw down the book. Next she had picked up Cowper's *Letters*,[12] the classic prescribed by her father which had bored her, so that one sentence chancing to say something about the smell of broom in his garden, she had thereupon seen the little hall at Richmond laden with flowers on the day of her mother's funeral, smelling so strong that now any flower-scent brought back the sickly horrible sensation; and so from one scene she passed, half-hearing, half-seeing, to another. She saw her Aunt Lucy arranging flowers in the drawing-room.

'Aunt Lucy,' she volunteered, 'I don't like the smell of broom; it reminds me of funerals.'

'Nonsense, Rachel,' Aunt Lucy replied; 'don't say such foolish things, dear. I always think it a particularly cheerful plant.'

Lying in the hot sun her mind was fixed upon the characters of her aunts, their views, and the way they lived. Indeed this was a subject that lasted her hundreds of morning walks round Richmond Park, and blotted out the trees and the people and the deer. Why did they do the things they did, and what did they feel, and what was it all about? Again she heard Aunt Lucy talking to Aunt Eleanor. She had been that morning to take up the character of a servant, 'And, of course, at half-past ten in the morning one expects to find the housemaid brushing the stairs.' How odd! How unspeakably odd! But she could not explain to herself why suddenly as her aunt spoke the whole system in which they lived had appeared before her eyes as something quite unfamiliar and inexplicable, and themselves as chairs or umbrellas dropped about here and there without any reason. She could only say with her slight stammer, 'Are you f–f–fond of Aunt Eleanor, Aunt Lucy?' to which her aunt replied, with her nervous hen-like twitter of a laugh, 'My dear child, what questions you do ask!'

'How fond? Very fond!' Rachel pursued.

'I can't say I've ever thought "how",' said Miss Vinrace. 'If one cares one doesn't think "how", Rachel,' which was aimed at the niece who had never yet 'come' to her aunts as cordially as they wished.

'But you know I care for you, don't you, dear, because you're your mother's daughter, if for no other reason, and there *are* plenty of other reasons' – and she leant over and kissed her with some emotion, and the argument was spilt irretrievably about the place like a bucket of milk.

By these means Rachel reached that stage in thinking, if thinking it can be called, when the eyes are intent upon a ball or a knob and the lips cease to move. Her efforts to come to an understanding had only hurt her aunt's feelings, and the conclusion must be that it is better not to try. To feel anything strongly was to create an abyss between oneself and others who feel strongly perhaps but differently. It was far better to play the piano and forget all the rest. The conclusion was very welcome. Let these odd men and women – her aunts, the Hunts, Ridley, Helen, Mr Pepper, and the rest – be symbols – featureless but dignified, symbols of age, of youth, of motherhood, of learning, and beautiful often as people upon the stage are beautiful. It appeared that nobody ever said a thing they meant, or ever talked of a feeling they felt, but that was what music was for. Reality dwelling in what one saw and felt, but did not talk about, one could accept a system in which things went round and round quite satisfactorily to other people without often troubling to think about it, except as something superficially strange. Absorbed by her music she accepted her lot very complacently, blazing into indignation perhaps once a fortnight, and subsiding as she subsided now. Inextricably mixed in dreamy confusion, her mind seemed to enter into communion, to be delightfully expanded and combined with the spirit of the whitish boards on deck, with the spirit of the sea, with the spirit of Beethoven Op. 112, even with the spirit of poor William Cowper there at Olney. Like a ball of thistledown it kissed the sea, rose, kissed it again, and thus rising and kissing passed finally out of sight. The rising and falling of the ball of thistledown was represented by the sudden droop forward of her own head, and when it passed out of sight she was asleep.

Ten minutes later Mrs Ambrose opened the door and looked at her. It did not surprise her to find that this was the way in which Rachel passed her mornings. She glanced round the room at the piano, at the books, at the general mess. In the first place she considered Rachel aesthetically: lying unprotected she looked somehow like a victim dropped from the claws of a bird of prey, but considered as a woman, a young woman of twenty-four, the sight gave rise to reflections. Mrs Ambrose stood thinking for at least two minutes. She then smiled, turned noiselessly away and went, lest the sleeper should waken, and there should be the awkwardness of speech between them.

Chapter 3

Early next morning there was a sound as of chains being drawn roughly overhead; the steady heart of the *Euphrosyne* slowly ceased to beat; and Helen, poking her nose above deck, saw a stationary castle upon a stationary hill. They had dropped anchor in the mouth of the Tagus,[13] and instead of cleaving new waves perpetually, the same waves kept returning and washing against the sides of the ship.

As soon as breakfast was done, Willoughby disappeared over the vessel's side, carrying a brown leather case, shouting over his shoulder that everyone was to mind and behave themselves, for he would be kept in Lisbon doing business until five o'clock that afternoon.

At about that hour he reappeared, carrying his case, professing himself tired, bothered, hungry, thirsty, cold, and in immediate need of his tea. Rubbing his hands, he told them the adventures of the day: how he had come upon poor old Jackson combing his moustache before the glass in the office, little expecting his descent; had put him through such a morning's work as seldom came his way, then treated him to a lunch of champagne and ortolans; paid a call upon Mrs Jackson, who was fatter than ever, poor woman, but asked kindly after Rachel – and O Lord, little Jackson had confessed to a confounded piece of weakness – well, well, no harm was done, he supposed, but what was the use of his giving orders if they were promptly disobeyed? He had said distinctly that he would take no passengers on this trip. Here he began searching in his pockets and eventually discovered a card, which he planked down on the table before Rachel. On it she read, 'Mr and Mrs Richard Dalloway, 23 Browne Street, Mayfair.'

'Mr Richard Dalloway,' continued Vinrace, 'seems to be a gentleman who thinks that because he was once a Member of Parliament, and his wife's the daughter of a peer, they can have what they like for the asking. They got round poor little Jackson anyhow. Said they must have passages – produced a letter from Lord Glenaway, asking me as a personal favour – overruled any objections Jackson made (I don't believe they came to much), and so there's nothing for it but to submit, I suppose.'

But it was evident that for some reason or other Willoughby was quite pleased to submit, although he made a show of growling.

The truth was that Mr and Mrs Dalloway had found themselves

stranded in Lisbon. They had been travelling on the Continent for some weeks, chiefly with a view to broadening Mr Dalloway's mind. Unable for a season, by one of the accidents of political life, to serve his country in Parliament, Mr Dalloway was doing the best he could to serve it out of Parliament. For that purpose the Latin countries did very well, although the East, of course, would have done better.

'Expect to hear of me next in Petersburg or Teheran,' he had said, turning to wave farewell from the steps of the Travellers'. But a disease had broken out in the East, there was cholera in Russia, and he was heard of, not so romantically, in Lisbon. They had been through France; he had stopped at manufacturing centres where, producing letters of introduction, he had been shown over works, and noted facts in a pocketbook. In Spain he and Mrs Dalloway had mounted mules, for they wished to understand how the peasants live. Are they ripe for rebellion, for example? Mrs Dalloway had then insisted upon a day or two at Madrid with the pictures. Finally they arrived in Lisbon and spent six days which, in a journal privately issued afterwards, they described as of 'unique interest'. Richard had audiences with ministers, and foretold a crisis at no distant date, 'the foundations of government being incurably corrupt. Yet how blame, etc.'; while Clarissa inspected the royal stables, and took several snapshots showing men now exiled and windows now broken. Among other things she photographed Fielding's grave,[14] and let loose a small bird which some ruffian had trapped, 'because one hates to think of anything in a cage where English people lie buried,' the diary stated. Their tour was thoroughly unconventional, and followed no meditated plan. The foreign correspondents of *The Times* decided their route as much as anything else. Mr Dalloway wished to look at certain guns, and was of opinion that the African coast is far more unsettled than people at home were inclined to believe. For these reasons they wanted a slow inquisitive kind of ship, comfortable, for they were bad sailors, but not extravagant, which would stop for a day or two at this port and at that, taking in coal while the Dalloways saw things for themselves. Meanwhile they found themselves stranded in Lisbon, unable for the moment to lay hands upon the precise vessel they wanted. They heard of the *Euphrosyne*, but heard also that she was primarily a cargo boat, and only took passengers by special arrangement, her business being to carry dry goods to the Amazons, and rubber home again. 'By special arrangement', however, were words of high encouragement to them, for they came of a class where almost everything was specially arranged, or could be if necessary. On this occasion all that Richard did was to write a note to Lord

Glenaway, the head of the line which bears his title; to call on poor old Jackson; to represent to him how Mrs Dalloway was so-and-so, and he had been something or other else, and what they wanted was such and such a thing. It was done. They parted with compliments and pleasure on both sides, and here, a week later, came the boat rowing up to the ship in the dusk with the Dalloways on board of it; in three minutes they were standing together on the deck of the *Euphrosyne*. Their arrival, of course, created some stir, and it was seen by several pairs of eyes that Mrs Dalloway was a tall slight woman, her body wrapped in furs, her head in veils, while Mr Dalloway appeared to be a middle-sized man of sturdy build, dressed like a sportsman on an autumnal moor. Many solid leather bags of a rich brown hue soon surrounded them, in addition to which Mr Dalloway carried a despatch box, and his wife a dressing-case suggestive of a diamond necklace and bottles with silver tops.

'It's so like Whistler!'[15] she exclaimed, with a wave towards the shore, as she shook Rachel by the hand, and Rachel had only time to look at the grey hills on one side of her before Willoughby introduced Mrs Chailey, who took the lady to her cabin.

Momentary though it seemed, nevertheless the interruption was upsetting; everyone was more or less put out by it, from Mr Grice, the steward, to Ridley himself. A few minutes later Rachel passed the smoking-room, and found Helen moving armchairs. She was absorbed in her arrangements, and on seeing Rachel remarked confidentially: 'If one can give men a room to themselves where they will sit, it's all to the good. Armchairs are *the* important things – ' She began wheeling them about. 'Now, does it still look like a bar at a railway station?'

She whipped a plush cover off a table. The appearance of the place was marvellously improved.

Again, the arrival of the strangers made it obvious to Rachel, as the hour of dinner approached, that she must change her dress; and the ringing of the great bell found her sitting on the edge of her berth in such a position that the little glass above the washstand reflected her head and shoulders. In the glass she wore an expression of tense melancholy, for she had come to the depressing conclusion, since the arrival of the Dalloways, that her face was not the face she wanted, and in all probability never would be.

However, punctuality had been impressed on her, and whatever face she had, she must go in to dinner.

These few minutes had been used by Willoughby in sketching to the Dalloways the people they were to meet, and checking them upon his fingers.

'There's my brother-in-law, Ambrose, the scholar (I dare say you've heard his name), his wife, my old friend Pepper, a very quiet fellow, but knows everything, I'm told. And that's all. We're a very small party. I'm dropping them on the coast.'

Mrs Dalloway, with her head a little on one side, did her best to recollect Ambrose – was it a surname? – but failed. She was made slightly uneasy by what she had heard. She knew that scholars married anyone – girls they met at farms on reading parties; or little suburban women who said disagreeably, 'Of course I know it's my husband you want; not *me.*'

But Helen came in at that point, and Mrs Dalloway saw with relief that though slightly eccentric in appearance, she was not untidy, held herself well, and her voice had restraint in it, which she held to be the sign of a lady. Mr Pepper had not troubled to change his neat ugly suit.

'But after all,' Clarissa thought to herself as she followed Vinrace in to dinner, '*everyone's* interesting really.'

When seated at the table she had some need of that assurance, chiefly because of Ridley, who came in late, looked decidedly unkempt, and took to his soup in profound gloom.

An imperceptible signal passed between husband and wife, meaning that they grasped the situation and would stand by each other loyally. With scarcely a pause Mrs Dalloway turned to Willoughby and began: 'What I find so tiresome about the sea is that there are no flowers in it. Imagine fields of hollyhocks and violets in mid-ocean! How divine!'

'But somewhat dangerous to navigation,' boomed Richard, in the bass, like the bassoon to the flourish of his wife's violin. 'Why, weeds can be bad enough, can't they, Vinrace? I remember crossing in the *Mauretania* once, and saying to the Captain – Richards – did you know him? – "Now tell me what perils you really dread most for your ship, Captain Richards?" expecting him to say icebergs, or derelicts, or fog, or something of that sort. Not a bit of it. I've always remembered his answer. "*Sedgius aquatici,*" he said, which I take to be a kind of duckweed.'

Mr Pepper looked up sharply, and was about to put a question when Willoughby continued: 'They've an awful time of it – those captains! Three thousand souls on board!'

'Yes, indeed,' said Clarissa. She turned to Helen with an air of profundity. 'I'm convinced people are wrong when they say it's work that wears one; it's responsibility. That's why one pays one's cook more than one's housemaid, I suppose.'

'According to that, one ought to pay one's nurse double; but one doesn't,' said Helen.

'No; but think what a joy to have to do with babies, instead of saucepans!' said Mrs Dalloway, looking with more interest at Helen, a probable mother.

'I'd much rather be a cook than a nurse,' said Helen. 'Nothing would induce me to take charge of children.'

'Mothers always exaggerate,' said Ridley. 'A well-bred child is no responsibility. I've travelled all over Europe with mine. You just wrap 'em up warm and put 'em in the rack.'

Helen laughed at that. Mrs Dalloway exclaimed, looking at Ridley: 'How like a father! My husband's just the same. And then one talks of the equality of the sexes!'

'Does one?' said Mr Pepper.

'Oh, some do!' cried Clarissa. 'My husband had to pass an irate lady every afternoon last session who said nothing else, I imagine.'

'She sat outside the House; it was very awkward,' said Dalloway. 'At last I plucked up courage and said to her, "My good creature, you're only in the way where you are. You're hindering me, and you're doing no good to yourself." '

'And then she caught him by the coat, and would have scratched his eyes out – ' Mrs Dalloway put in.

'Pooh – that's been exaggerated,' said Richard. 'No, I pity them, I confess. The discomfort of sitting on those steps must be awful.'

'Serve them right,' said Willoughby curtly.

'Oh, I'm entirely with you there,' said Dalloway. 'Nobody can condemn the utter folly and futility of such behaviour more than I do; and as for the whole agitation, well! may I be in my grave before a woman has the right to vote in England! That's all I say.'[16]

The solemnity of her husband's assertion made Clarissa grave.

'It's unthinkable,' she said. 'Don't tell me you're a suffragist?' she turned to Ridley.

'I don't care a fig one way or t'other,' said Ambrose. 'If any creature is so deluded as to think that a vote does him or her any good, let him have it. He'll soon learn better.'

'You're not a politician, I see,' she smiled.

'Goodness, no,' said Ridley.

'I'm afraid your husband won't approve of me,' said Dalloway aside, to Mrs Ambrose. She suddenly recollected that he had been in Parliament.

'Don't you ever find it rather dull?' she asked, not knowing exactly what to say.

Richard spread his hands before him, as if inscriptions were to be read in the palms of them.

'If you ask me whether I ever find it rather dull,' he said, 'I am bound to say yes; on the other hand, if you ask me what career do you consider on the whole, taking the good with the bad, the most enjoyable and enviable, not to speak of its more serious side, of all careers, for a man, I am bound to say, "The politician's." '

'The Bar or politics, I agree,' said Willoughby. 'You get more run for your money.'

'All one's faculties have their play,' said Richard. 'I may be treading on dangerous ground; but what I feel about poets and artists in general is this: on your own lines, you can't be beaten – granted; but off your own lines – puff – one has to make allowances. Now, I shouldn't like to think that anyone had to make allowances for me.'

'I don't quite agree, Richard,' said Mrs Dalloway. 'Think of Shelley. I feel that there's almost everything one wants in *Adonais*.'[17]

'Read *Adonais* by all means,' Richard conceded. 'But whenever I hear of Shelley I repeat to myself the words of Matthew Arnold,[18] "What a set! What a set!" '

This roused Ridley's attention. 'Matthew Arnold? A detestable prig!' he snapped.

'A prig – granted,' said Richard; 'but, I think a man of the world. That's where my point comes in. We politicians doubtless seem to you' (he grasped somehow that Helen was the representative of the arts) 'a gross commonplace set of people; but we see both sides; we may be clumsy, but we do our best to get a grasp of things. Now your artists *find* things in a mess, shrug their shoulders, turn aside to their visions – which I grant may be very beautiful – and *leave* things in a mess. Now that seems to me evading one's responsibilities. Besides, we aren't all born with the artistic faculty.'

'It's dreadful,' said Mrs Dalloway, who, while her husband spoke, had been thinking. 'When I'm with artists I feel so intensely the delights of shutting oneself up in a little world of one's own, with pictures and music and everything beautiful, and then I go out into the streets and the first child I meet with its poor, hungry, dirty little face makes me turn round and say, "No, I *can't* shut myself up – I *won't* live in a world of my own. I should like to stop all the painting and writing and music until this kind of thing exists no longer." Don't you feel,' she wound up, addressing Helen, 'that life's a perpetual conflict?'

Helen considered for a moment. 'No,' she said. 'I don't think I do.'

There was a pause, which was decidedly uncomfortable. Mrs Dalloway then gave a little shiver, and asked whether she might have her fur cloak brought to her. As she adjusted the soft brown fur about her neck a fresh topic struck her. 'I own,' she said, 'that I shall never forget the *Antigone*.[19] I saw it at Cambridge years ago, and it's haunted me ever since. Don't you think it's quite the most modern thing you ever saw?' she asked Ridley. 'It seemed to me I'd known twenty Clytemnestras. Old Lady Ditchling for one. I don't know a word of Greek, but I could listen to it for ever – '

Here Mr Pepper struck up:

πολλὰ τὰ δεινὰ κοὐδὲν ἀν-
θρώπον δεινότερον πέλει.
τοῦτο καὶ πολιοῦ πέραν
πόντου χειμερίῳ νότῳ
χωρεῖ, περιβρυχίοισι
περῶν ὑπ' οἴδμασι.

Mrs Dalloway looked at him with compressed lips.

'I'd give ten years of my life to know Greek,' she said, when he had done.

'I could teach you the alphabet in half an hour,' said Ridley, 'and you'd read Homer in a month. I should think it an honour to instruct you.'

Helen, engaged with Mr Dalloway and the habit, now fallen into decline, of quoting Greek in the House of Commons, noted, in the great commonplace book that lies open beside us as we talk, the fact that all men, even men like Ridley, really prefer women to be fashionable.

Clarissa exclaimed that she could think of nothing more delightful. For an instant she saw herself in her drawing-room in Browne Street with a Plato[20] open on her knees – Plato in the original Greek. She could not help believing that a real scholar, if specially interested, could slip Greek into her head with scarcely any trouble.

Ridley engaged her to come tomorrow.

'If only your ship is going to treat us kindly!' she exclaimed, drawing Willoughby into play. For the sake of guests, and these were distinguished, Willoughby was ready with a bow of his head to vouch for the good behaviour even of the waves.

'I'm dreadfully bad; and my husband's not very good,' sighed Clarissa.

'I am never sick,' Richard explained. 'At least, I have only been actually sick once,' he corrected himself. 'That was crossing the Channel. But a choppy sea, I confess, or still worse, a swell, makes me distinctly uncomfortable. The great thing is never to miss a meal. You look at the food, and you say, "I can't"; you take a mouthful, and Lord knows how you're going to swallow it; but persevere, and you often settle the attack for good. My wife's a coward.'

They were pushing back their chairs. The ladies were hesitating at the doorway.

'I'd better show the way,' said Helen, advancing.

Rachel followed. She had taken no part in the talk; no one had spoken to her; but she had listened to every word that was said. She had looked from Mrs Dalloway to Mr Dalloway, and from Mr Dalloway back again. Clarissa, indeed, was a fascinating spectacle. She wore a white dress and a long glittering necklace. What with her clothes, and her arch delicate face, which showed exquisitely pink beneath hair turning grey, she was astonishingly like an eighteenth-century masterpiece – a Reynolds or a Romney.[21] She made Helen and the others look coarse and slovenly beside her. Sitting lightly upright she seemed to be dealing with the world as she chose; the enormous solid globe spun round this way and that beneath her fingers. And her husband! Mr Dalloway rolling that rich deliberate voice was even more impressive. He seemed to come from the humming oily centre of the machine where the polished rods are sliding, and the pistons thumping; he grasped things so firmly but so loosely; he made the others appear like old maids cheapening remnants. Rachel followed in the wake of the matrons, as if in a trance; a curious scent of violets came back from Mrs Dalloway, mingling with the soft rustling of her skirts, and the tinkling of her chains. As she followed, Rachel thought with supreme self-abasement, taking in the whole course of her life and the lives of all her friends, 'She said we lived in a world of our own. It's true. We're perfectly absurd.'

'We sit in here,' said Helen, opening the door of the saloon.

'You play?' said Mrs Dalloway to Mrs Ambrose, taking up the score of *Tristan* which lay on the table.

'My niece does,' said Helen, laying her hand on Rachel's shoulder.

'Oh, how I envy you!' Clarissa addressed Rachel for the first time. 'D'you remember this? Isn't it divine?' She played a bar or two with ringed fingers upon the page.

'And then Tristan goes like this, and Isolde – oh! – it's all too thrilling! Have you been to Bayreuth?'[22]

'No, I haven't,' said Rachel.

'Then that's still to come. I shall never forget my first *Parsifal* [23] – a grilling August day, and those fat old German women, come in their stuffy high frocks, and then the dark theatre, and the music beginning, and one couldn't help sobbing. A kind man went and fetched me water, I remember; and I could only cry on his shoulder! It caught me here' (she touched her throat). 'It's like nothing else in the world! But where's your piano?'

'It's in another room,' Rachel explained.

'But you will play to us?' Clarissa entreated. 'I can't imagine anything nicer than to sit out in the moonlight and listen to music – only that sounds too like a schoolgirl! You know,' she said, turning to Helen, 'I don't think music's altogether good for people – I'm afraid not.'

'Too great a strain?' asked Helen.

'Too emotional, somehow,' said Clarissa. 'One notices it at once when a boy or girl takes up music as a profession. Sir William Broadley told me just the same thing. Don't you hate the kind of attitudes people go into over Wagner – like this – ' She cast her eyes to the ceiling, clasped her hands, and assumed a look of intensity. 'It really doesn't mean that they appreciate him; in fact, I always think it's the other way round. The people who really care about an art are always the least affected. D'you know Henry Philips, the painter?' she asked.

'I have seen him,' said Helen.

'To look at, one might think he was a successful stockbroker, and not one of the greatest painters of the age. That's what I like.'

'There are a great many successful stockbrokers, if you like looking at them,' said Helen.

Rachel wished vehemently that her aunt would not be so perverse.

'When you see a musician with long hair, don't you know instinctively that he's bad?' Clarissa asked, turning to Rachel. 'Watts[24] and Joachim[25] – they looked just like you and me.'

'And how much nicer they'd have looked with curls!' said Helen. 'The question is, are you going to aim at beauty or are you not?'

'Cleanliness!' said Clarissa, 'I do want a man to look clean!'

'By cleanliness you really mean well-cut clothes,' said Helen.

'There's something one knows a gentleman by,' said Clarissa, 'but one can't say what it is.'

'Take my husband now, does he look like a gentleman?'

The question seemed to Clarissa in extraordinarily bad taste. 'One of the things that can't be said,' she would have put it. She could find no answer, but a laugh.

'Well, anyhow,' she said, turning to Rachel, 'I shall insist upon your playing to me tomorrow.'

There was that in her manner that made Rachel love her.

Mrs Dalloway hid a tiny yawn, a mere dilation of the nostrils.

'D'you know,' she said, 'I'm extraordinarily sleepy. It's the sea air. I think I shall escape.'

A man's voice, which she took to be that of Mr Pepper, strident in discussion, and advancing upon the saloon, gave her the alarm.

'Good-night – good-night!' she said. 'Oh, I know my way – do pray for calm! Good-night!'

Her yawn must have been the image of a yawn. Instead of letting her mouth droop, dropping all her clothes in a bunch as though they depended on one string, and stretching her limbs to the utmost end of her berth, she merely changed her dress for a dressing-gown, with innumerable frills, and wrapping her feet in a rug, sat down with a writing-pad on her knee. Already this cramped little cabin was the dressing-room of a lady of quality. There were bottles containing liquids; there were trays, boxes, brushes, pins. Evidently not an inch of her person lacked its proper instrument. The scent which had intoxicated Rachel pervaded the air. Thus established, Mrs Dalloway began to write. A pen in her hands became a thing one caressed paper with, and she might have been stroking and tickling a kitten as she wrote:

Picture us, my dear, afloat in the very oddest ship you can imagine. It's not the ship, so much as the people. One does come across queer sorts as one travels. I must say I find it hugely amusing. There's the manager of the line – called Vinrace – a nice big Englishman, doesn't say much – you know the sort. As for the rest – they might have come trailing out of an old number of *Punch*. They're like people playing croquet in the 'sixties. How long they've all been shut up in this ship I don't know – years and years I should say – but one feels as though one had boarded a little separate world, and they'd never been on shore, or done ordinary things in their lives. It's what I've always said about literary people – they're far the hardest of any to get on with. The worst of it is, these people – a man and his wife and a niece – might have been, one feels, just like everybody else, if they hadn't got swallowed up by Oxford or Cambridge or some such place and been made cranks of. The man's really delightful (if he'd cut his nails), and the woman has quite a fine face, only she dresses, of course, in a potato sack, and wears her hair like a Liberty shopgirl's. They talk about art, and think us such poops for dressing in the evening. However, I can't help that; I'd rather die than come in to dinner without changing – wouldn't you? It matters ever so much more than the soup. (It's odd how things like that *do* matter so much more than what's generally supposed to matter. I'd rather have my head cut off than wear flannel next the skin.) Then there's the nice shy girl – poor thing – I wish one could rake her out before it's too late. She has quite nice eyes and hair, only, of course, she'll get funny too. We ought to start a society for broadening the minds of the young – much more useful than missionaries, Hester! Oh, I'd forgotten there's a dreadful little thing called Pepper. He's just like his name. He's indescribably insignificant, and rather queer in his temper, poor dear. It's like sitting down to dinner with an ill-conditioned fox-terrier, only one can't comb him out, and sprinkle him with powder, as one would one's dog. It's a pity, sometimes, one can't treat people like dogs! The great comfort is that we're away from newspapers, so that Richard will have a real holiday this time. Spain wasn't a holiday . . .

'You coward!' said Richard, almost filling the room with his sturdy figure.

'I did my duty at dinner!' cried Clarissa.

'You've let yourself in for the Greek alphabet, anyhow.'

'Oh, my dear! Who *is* Ambrose?'

'I gather that he was a Cambridge don; lives in London now, and edits classics.'

'Did you ever see such a set of cranks? The woman asked me if I thought her husband looked like a gentleman!'

'It was hard to keep the ball rolling at dinner, certainly,' said Richard. 'Why is it that the women, in that class, are so much queerer than the men?'

'They're not half bad-looking, really – only – they're so odd!'

They both laughed, thinking of the same things, so that there was no need to compare their impressions.

'I see I shall have quite a lot to say to Vinrace,' said Richard. 'He knows Sutton and all that set. He can tell me a good deal about the conditions of shipbuilding in the North.'

'Oh, I'm glad. The men always *are* so much better than the women.'

'One always has something to say to a man certainly,' said Richard. 'But I've no doubt you'll chatter away fast enough about the babies, Clarice.'

'Has she got children? She doesn't look like it somehow.'

'Two. A boy and girl.'

A pang of envy shot through Mrs Dalloway's heart.

'We *must* have a son, Dick,' she said.

'Good Lord, what opportunities there are now for young men!' said Dalloway, for his talk had set him thinking. 'I don't suppose there's been so good an opening since the days of Pitt.'

'And it's yours!' said Clarissa.

'To be a leader of men,' Richard soliloquised. 'It's a fine career. My God – what a career!'

The chest slowly curved beneath his waistcoat.

'D'you know, Dick, I can't help thinking of England,' said his wife meditatively, leaning her head against his chest. 'Being on this ship seems to make it so much more vivid – what it really means to be English. One thinks of all we've done, and our navies, and the people in India and Africa, and how we've gone on century after century, sending out boys from little country villages – and of men like you, Dick, and it makes one feel as if one couldn't bear *not* to be English! Think of the light burning over the House,[26] Dick! When I stood on deck just now I seemed to see it. It's what one means by London.'

'It's the continuity,' said Richard sententiously. A vision of English history, King following King, Prime Minister Prime Minister and Law Law, had come over him while his wife spoke. He ran his mind along the line of conservative policy, which went steadily from Lord Salisbury to Alfred,[27] and gradually enclosed, as though it were a lasso that opened and caught things, enormous chunks of the habitable globe.

'It's taken a long time, but we've pretty nearly done it,' he said; 'it remains to consolidate.'

'And these people don't see it!' Clarissa exclaimed.

'It takes all sorts to make a world,' said her husband. 'There would never be a government if there weren't an opposition.'

'Dick, you're better than I am,' said Clarissa. 'You see round, where I only see *there*.' She pressed a point on the back of his hand.

'That's my business, as I tried to explain at dinner.'

'What I like about you, Dick,' she continued, 'is that you're always the same, and I'm a creature of moods.'

'You're a pretty creature, anyhow,' he said, gazing at her with deeper eyes.

'You think so, do you? Then kiss me.'

He kissed her passionately, so that her half-written letter slid to the ground. Picking it up, he read it without asking leave.

'Where's your pen?' he said; and added in his little masculine hand:

R. D. *loquitur*:[28] Clarice has omitted to tell you that she looked exceedingly pretty at dinner, and made a conquest by which she has bound herself to learn the Greek alphabet. I will take this occasion of adding that we are both enjoying ourselves in these outlandish parts, and only wish for the presence of our friends (yourself and

John, to wit) to make the trip perfectly enjoyable as it promises to be instructive . . .

Voices were heard at the end of the corridor. Mrs Ambrose was speaking low; William Pepper was remarking in his definite and rather acid voice, 'That is the type of lady with whom I find myself distinctly out of sympathy. She – '

But neither Richard nor Clarissa profited by the verdict, for directly it seemed likely that they would overhear, Richard crackled a sheet of paper.

'I often wonder,' Clarissa mused in bed, over the little white volume of Pascal [29] which went with her everywhere, 'whether it is really good for a woman to live with a man who is morally her superior, as Richard is mine. It makes one so dependent. I suppose I feel for him what my mother and women of her generation felt for Christ. It just shows that one can't do without *something*.' She then fell into a sleep, which was as usual extremely sound and refreshing, but visited by fantastic dreams of great Greek letters stalking round the room, when she woke up and laughed to herself, remembering where she was and that the Greek letters were real people, lying asleep not many yards away. Then, thinking of the black sea outside tossing beneath the moon, she shuddered, and thought of her husband and the others as companions on the voyage. The dreams were not confined to her indeed, but went from one brain to another. They all dreamt of each other that night, as was natural, considering how thin the partitions were between them, and how strangely they had been lifted off the earth to sit next each other in mid-ocean, and see every detail of each other's faces, and hear whatever they chanced to say.

Chapter 4

Next morning Clarissa was up before anyone else. She dressed, and was out on deck, breathing the fresh air of a calm morning and making the circuit of the ship for the second time, when she ran straight into the lean person of Mr Grice, the steward. She apologised, and at the same time asked him to enlighten her: what were those shiny brass stands for, half glass on the top? She had been wondering, and could not guess. When he had done explaining, she cried enthusiastically: 'I do think that to be a sailor must be the finest thing in the world!'

'And what d'you know about it?' said Mr Grice, kindling in a strange manner. 'Pardon me. What does any man or woman brought up in England know about the sea? They profess to know; but they don't.'

The bitterness with which he spoke was ominous of what was to come. He led her off to his own quarters, and, sitting on the edge of a brass-bound table, looking uncommonly like a seagull, with her white tapering body and thin alert face, Mrs Dalloway had to listen to the tirade of a fanatical man. Did she realise, to begin with, what a very small part of the world the land was? How peaceful, how beautiful, how benignant in comparison the sea? The deep waters could sustain Europe unaided if every earthly animal died of the plague tomorrow. Mr Grice recalled dreadful sights which he had seen in the richest city of the world – men and women standing in line hour after hour to receive a mug of greasy soup. 'And I thought of the good flesh down here waiting and asking to be caught. I'm not exactly a Protestant, and I'm not a Catholic, but I could almost pray for the days of popery to come again – because of the fasts.'

As he talked he kept opening drawers and moving little glass jars. Here were the treasures which the great ocean had bestowed upon him – pale fish in greenish liquids, blobs of jelly with streaming tresses, fish with lights in their heads, they lived so deep.

'They have swum about among bones,' Clarissa sighed.

'You're thinking of Shakespeare,' said Mr Grice, and taking down a copy from a shelf well lined with books, recited in an emphatic nasal voice:

'Full fathom five thy father lies . . .'[30]

'A grand fellow, Shakespeare,' he said, replacing the volume.

Clarissa was so glad to hear him say so.

'Which is your favourite play? I wonder if it's the same as mine?'

'*Henry the Fifth*,' said Mr Grice.

'Joy!' cried Clarissa. 'It is!'

Hamlet was what you might call too introspective for Mr Grice, the sonnets too passionate; Henry the Fifth was to him the model of an English gentleman. But his favourite reading was Huxley,[31] Herbert Spencer[32] and Henry George;[33] while Emerson[34] and Thomas Hardy[35] he read for relaxation. He was giving Mrs Dalloway his views upon the present state of England when the breakfast bell rang so imperiously that she had to tear herself away, promising to come back and be shown his seaweeds.

The party, which had seemed so odd to her the night before, was already gathered round the table, still under the influence of sleep, and therefore uncommunicative, but her entrance sent a little flutter like a breath of air through them all.

'I've had the most interesting talk of my life!' she exclaimed, taking her seat beside Willoughby. 'D'you realise that one of your men is a philosopher and a poet?'

'A very interesting fellow – that's what I always say,' said Willoughby, distinguishing Mr Grice. 'Though Rachel finds him a bore.'

'He's a bore when he talks about currents,' said Rachel. Her eyes were full of sleep, but Mrs Dalloway still seemed to her wonderful.

'I've never met a bore yet!' said Clarissa.

'And I should say the world was full of them!' exclaimed Helen. But her beauty, which was radiant in the morning light, took the contrariness from her words.

'I agree that it's the worst one can possibly say of anyone,' said Clarissa. 'How much rather one would be a murderer than a bore!' she added, with her usual air of saying something profound. 'One can fancy liking a murderer. It's the same with dogs. Some dogs are awful bores, poor dears.'

It happened that Richard was sitting next to Rachel. She was curiously conscious of his presence and appearance – his well-cut clothes, his crackling shirt-front, his cuffs with blue rings round them, and the square-tipped, very clean fingers with the red stone on the little finger of the left hand.

'We had a dog who was a bore and knew it,' he said, addressing her in cool, easy tones. 'He was a Skye terrier, one of those long chaps, with little feet poking out from their hair like – like caterpillars – no, like sofas I should say. Well, we had another dog at the same time, a black brisk animal – a Schipperke, I think, you call them. You can't imagine a greater contrast. The Skye so slow and deliberate, looking up at you like some old gentleman in the club, as much as to say, "You don't really mean it, do you?" and the Schipperke as quick as a knife. I liked the Skye best, I must confess. There was something pathetic about him.'

The story seemed to have no climax.

'What happened to him?' Rachel asked.

'That's a very sad story,' said Richard, lowering his voice and peeling an apple. 'He followed my wife in the car one day and got run over by a brute of a cyclist.'

'Was he killed?' asked Rachel.

But Clarissa at her end of the table had overheard.

'Don't talk of it!' she cried. 'It's a thing I can't bear to think of to this day.'

Surely the tears stood in her eyes?

'That's the painful thing about pets,' said Mr Dalloway; 'they die. The first sorrow I can remember was for the death of a dormouse. I regret to say that I sat upon it. Still, that didn't make one any the less sorry. Here lies the duck that Samuel Johnson sat on, eh?[36] I was big for my age.

'Then we had canaries,' he continued, 'a pair of ring-doves, a lemur, and at one time a martin.'

'Did you live in the country?' Rachel asked him.

'We lived in the country for six months of the year. When I say "we" I mean four sisters, a brother, and myself. There's nothing like coming of a large family. Sisters particularly are delightful.'

'Dick, you were horribly spoilt!' cried Clarissa across the table.

'No, no. Appreciated,' said Richard.

Rachel had other questions on the tip of her tongue; or rather one enormous question, which she did not in the least know how to put into words. The talk appeared too airy to admit of it.

'Please tell me – everything.' That was what she wanted to say. He had drawn apart one little chink and showed astonishing treasures. It seemed to her incredible that a man like that should be willing to talk to her. He had sisters and pets, and once lived in the country. She stirred her tea round and round; the bubbles which swam and clustered in the cup seemed to her like the union of their minds.

The talk meanwhile raced past her, and when Richard suddenly stated in a jocular tone of voice, 'I'm sure Miss Vinrace, now, has secret leanings towards Catholicism,' she had no idea what to answer, and Helen could not help laughing at the start she gave.

However, breakfast was over and Mrs Dalloway was rising. 'I always think religion's like collecting beetles,' she said, summing up the discussion as she went up the stairs with Helen. 'One person has a passion for black beetles; another hasn't; it's no good arguing about it. What's *your* black beetle now?'

'I suppose it's my children,' said Helen.

'Ah – that's different,' Clarissa breathed. 'Do tell me. You have a boy, haven't you? Isn't it detestable, leaving them?'

It was as though a blue shadow had fallen across a pool. Their eyes became deeper, and their voices more cordial. Instead of joining them as they began to pace the deck, Rachel was indignant with the prosperous matrons, who made her feel outside their world and motherless, and turning back, she left them abruptly. She slammed the door of her room, and pulled out her music. It was all old music – Bach and Beethoven, Mozart and Purcell – the pages yellow, the engraving rough to the finger. In three minutes she was deep in a very difficult, very classical fugue in A, and over her face came a queer remote impersonal expression of complete absorption and anxious satisfaction. Now she stumbled; now she faltered and had to play the same bar twice over; but an invisible line seemed to string the notes together, from which rose a shape, a building. She was so far absorbed in this work, for it was really difficult to find how all these sounds should stand together, and drew upon the whole of her faculties, that she never heard a knock at the door. It was burst impulsively open, and Mrs Dalloway stood in the room leaving the door open, so that a strip of the white deck and of the blue sea appeared through the opening. The shape of the Bach fugue crashed to the ground.

'Don't let me interrupt,' Clarissa implored. 'I heard you playing, and I couldn't resist. I adore Bach!'

Rachel flushed and fumbled her fingers in her lap. She stood up awkwardly.

'It's too difficult,' she said.

'But you were playing quite splendidly! I ought to have stayed outside.'

'No,' said Rachel.

She slid *Cowper's Letters* and *Wuthering Heights*[37] out of the armchair, so that Clarissa was invited to sit there

'What a dear little room!' she said, looking round. 'Oh, *Cowper's Letters*! I've never read them. Are they nice?'

'Rather dull,' said Rachel.

'He wrote awfully well, didn't he?' said Clarissa; ' – if one likes that kind of thing – finished his sentences and all that. *Wuthering Heights*! Ah – that's more in my line. I really couldn't exist without the Brontës! Don't you love them? Still, on the whole, I'd rather live without them than without Jane Austen.'[38]

Lightly and at random though she spoke, her manner conveyed an extraordinary degree of sympathy and desire to befriend.

'Jane Austen? I don't like Jane Austen,' said Rachel.

'You monster!' Clarissa exclaimed. 'I can only just forgive you. Tell me why?'

'She's so – so – well, so like a tight plait,' Rachel floundered.

'Ah – I see what you mean. But I don't agree. And you won't when you're older. At your age I only liked Shelley. I can remember sobbing over him in the garden.

> He has outsoared the shadow of our night,
> Envy and calumny and hate and pain –

you remember?

> Can touch him not and torture not again
> From the contagion of the world's slow stain.

How divine! – and yet what nonsense!'

She looked lightly round the room. 'I always think it's *living*, not dying, that counts. I really respect some snuffy old stockbroker who's gone on adding up column after column all his days, and trotting back to his villa at Brixton with some old pug dog he worships, and a dreary little wife sitting at the end of the table, and going off to Margate for a fortnight – I assure you I know heaps like that – well, they seem to me *really* nobler than poets whom everyone worships, just because they're geniuses and die young. But I don't expect *you* to agree with me!'

She pressed Rachel's shoulder.

'Um–m–m – ' she went on quoting – ' "Unrest which men miscall delight" – [39] when you're my age you'll see that the world is *crammed* with delightful things. I think young people make such a mistake about that – not letting themselves be happy. I sometimes think that happiness is the only thing that counts. I don't know you well enough to say, but I should guess you might be a little inclined to – when one's young and attractive – I'm going to say it! – *every*thing's at one's feet.' She glanced round as much as to say, 'not only a few stuffy books and Bach'.

'I long to ask questions,' she continued. 'You interest me so much. If I'm impertinent, you must just box my ears.'

'And I – I want to ask questions,' said Rachel with such earnestness that Mrs Dalloway had to check her smile.

'D'you mind if we walk?' she said. 'The air's so delicious.'

She snuffed it like a racehorse as they shut the door and stood on deck.

'Isn't it good to be alive?' she exclaimed, and drew Rachel's arm within hers.

'Look, look! How exquisite!'

The shores of Portugal were beginning to lose their substance; but the land was still the land, though at a great distance. They could distinguish the little towns that were sprinkled in the folds of the hills, and the smoke rising faintly. The towns appeared to be very small in comparison with the great purple mountains behind them.

'Honestly, though,' said Clarissa, having looked, 'I don't like views. They're too inhuman.' They walked on.

'How odd it is!' she continued impulsively. 'This time yesterday we'd never met. I was packing in a stuffy little room in the hotel. We know absolutely nothing about each other – and yet – I feel as if I *did* know you!'

'You have children – your husband was in Parliament?'

'You've never been to school, and you live – ?'

'With my aunts at Richmond.'

'Richmond?'

'You see, my aunts like the park. They like the quiet.'

'And you don't! I understand!' Clarissa laughed.

'I like walking in the park alone; but not – with the dogs,' she finished.

'No; and some people *are* dogs; aren't they?' said Clarissa, as if she had guessed a secret. 'But not every one – oh no, not every one.'

'Not every one,' said Rachel, and stopped.

'I can quite imagine you walking alone,' said Clarissa: 'and thinking – in a little world of your own. But how you will enjoy it – some day!'

'I shall enjoy walking with a man – is that what you mean?' said Rachel, regarding Mrs Dalloway with her large enquiring eyes.

'I wasn't thinking of a man particularly,' said Clarissa. 'But you will.'

'No. I shall never marry,' Rachel determined.

'I shouldn't be so sure of that,' said Clarissa. Her sidelong glance told Rachel that she found her attractive although she was inexplicably amused.

'Why do people marry?' Rachel asked.

'That's what you're going to find out,' Clarissa laughed.

Rachel followed her eyes and found that they rested, for a second, on the robust figure of Richard Dalloway, who was engaged in striking a match on the sole of his boot; while Willoughby expounded something, which seemed to be of great interest to them both.

'There's nothing like it,' she concluded. 'Do tell me about the Ambroses. Or am I asking too many questions?'

'I find you easy to talk to,' said Rachel.

The short sketch of the Ambroses was, however, somewhat perfunctory, and contained little but the fact that Mr Ambrose was her uncle.

'Your mother's brother?'

When a name has dropped out of use, the lightest touch upon it tells. Mrs Dalloway went on: 'Are you like your mother?'

'No; she was different,' said Rachel.

She was overcome by an intense desire to tell Mrs Dalloway things she had never told anyone – things she had not realised herself until this moment.

'I am lonely,' she began. 'I want – ' She did not know what she wanted, so that she could not finish the sentence; but her lip quivered.

But it seemed that Mrs Dalloway was able to understand without words.

'I know,' she said, actually putting one arm round Rachel's shoulder. 'When I was your age I wanted too. No one understood until I met Richard. He gave me all I wanted. He's man and woman as well.' Her eyes rested upon Mr Dalloway, leaning upon the rail, still talking. 'Don't think I say that because I'm his wife – I see his faults more clearly than I see anyone else's. What one wants in the person one lives with is that they should keep one at one's best. I often wonder what I've done to be so happy!' she exclaimed, and a tear slid down her cheek. She wiped it away, squeezed Rachel's hand, and exclaimed: 'How good life is!' At that moment, standing out in the fresh breeze, with the sun upon the waves, and Mrs Dalloway's hand upon her arm, it seemed indeed as if life which had been unnamed before was infinitely wonderful, and too good to be true.

Here Helen passed them, and seeing Rachel arm in arm with a comparative stranger, looking excited, was amused, but at the same time slightly irritated. But they were immediately joined by Richard, who had enjoyed a very interesting talk with Willoughby and was in a sociable mood.

'Observe my panama,' he said, touching the brim of his hat. 'Are you aware, Miss Vinrace, how much can be done to induce fine weather by appropriate headdress? I have determined that it is a hot summer day; I warn you that nothing you can say will shake me. Therefore I am going to sit down. I advise you to follow my example.' Three chairs in a row invited them to be seated.

Leaning back, Richard surveyed the waves.

'That's a very pretty blue,' he said. 'But there's a little too much of it. Variety is essential to a view. Thus, if you have hills you ought to have a river; if a river, hills. The best view in the world in my opinion is that from Boars Hill[40] on a fine day – it must be a fine day, mark you. A rug? – oh, thank you, my dear . . . in that case you have also the advantage of associations – the Past.'

'D'you want to talk, Dick, or shall I read aloud?'

Clarissa had fetched a book with the rugs.

'*Persuasion*,'[41] announced Richard, examining the volume.

'That's for Miss Vinrace,' said Clarissa. 'She can't bear our beloved Jane.'

'That – if I may say so – is because you have not read her,' said Richard. 'She is incomparably the greatest female writer we possess.

'She is the greatest,' he continued, 'and for this reason: she does not attempt to write like a man. Every other woman does; on that account, I don't read 'em.

'Produce your instances, Miss Vinrace,' he went on, joining his finger-tips. 'I'm ready to be converted.'

He waited, while Rachel vainly tried to vindicate her sex from the slight he put upon it.

'I'm afraid he's right,' said Clarissa. 'He generally is – the wretch!'

'I brought *Persuasion*,' she went on, 'because I thought it was a little less threadbare than the others – though, Dick, it's no good *your* pretending to know Jane by heart, considering that she always sends you to sleep!'

'After the labours of legislation, I deserve sleep,' said Richard.

'You're not to think about those guns,' said Clarissa, seeing that his eye, passing over the waves, still sought the land meditatively, 'or about navies, or empires, or anything.' So saying she opened the book and began to read: ' "Sir Walter Elliott, of Kellynch Hall, in Somersetshire, was a man who, for his own amusement, never took up any book but the *Baronetage*" – don't you know Sir Walter? – "There he found occupation for an idle hour, and consolation in a distressed one." She does write well, doesn't she? "There – " ' She read on in a light humorous voice. She was determined that Sir Walter should take her husband's mind off the guns of Britain, and divert him in an exquisite, quaint, sprightly, and slightly ridiculous world. After a time it appeared that the sun was sinking in that world, and the points becoming softer. Rachel looked up to see what caused the change. Richard's eyelids were closing and opening; opening and closing. A loud nasal breath announced that he no longer considered appearances, that he was sound asleep.

'Triumph!' Clarissa whispered at the end of a sentence. Suddenly she raised her hand in protest. A sailor hesitated; she gave the book to Rachel, and stepped lightly to take the message – 'Mr Grice wished to know if it was convenient,' etc. She followed him. Ridley, who had prowled unheeded, started forward, stopped, and, with a gesture of disgust, strode off to his study. The sleeping politician was left in Rachel's charge. She read a sentence, and took a look at him. In sleep he looked like a coat hanging at the end of a bed; there were all the wrinkles, and the sleeves and trousers kept their shape though no longer filled out by legs and arms. You can then best judge the age and state of the coat. She looked him all over until it seemed to her that he must protest.

He was a man of forty perhaps; and here there were lines round his eyes, and there curious clefts in his cheeks. Slightly battered he appeared, but dogged and in the prime of life.

'Sisters and a dormouse and some canaries,' Rachel murmured, never taking her eyes off him. 'I wonder, I wonder – ' she ceased, her chin upon her hand, still looking at him. A bell chimed behind them, and Richard raised his head. Then he opened his eyes which wore for a second the queer look of a short-sighted person's whose spectacles are lost. It took him a moment to recover from the impropriety of having snored, and possibly grunted, before a young lady. To wake and find oneself left alone with one was also slightly disconcerting.

'I suppose I've been dozing,' he said. 'What's happened to everyone? Clarissa?'

'Mrs Dalloway has gone to look at Mr Grice's fish,' Rachel replied.

'I might have guessed,' said Richard. 'It's a common occurrence. And how have you improved the shining hour? Have you become a convert?'

'I don't think I've read a line,' said Rachel.

'That's what I always find. There are too many things to look at. I find nature very stimulating myself. My best ideas have come to me out of doors.'

'When you were walking?'

'Walking – riding – yachting – I suppose the most momentous conversations of my life took place while perambulating the great court at Trinity.[42] I was at both universities.[43] It was a fad of my father's. He thought it broadening to the mind. I think I agree with him. I can remember – what an age ago it seems! – settling the basis of a future state with the present Secretary for India. We thought ourselves very wise. I'm not sure we weren't. We were happy, Miss Vinrace, and we were young – gifts which make for wisdom.'

'Have you done what you said you'd do?' she asked.

'A searching question! I answer – Yes and No. If on the one hand I have not accomplished what I set out to accomplish – which of us does! – on the other I can fairly say this: I have not lowered my ideal.'

He looked resolutely at a seagull, as though his ideal flew on the wings of the bird.

'But,' said Rachel, 'what *is* your ideal?'

'There you ask too much, Miss Vinrace,' said Richard playfully.

She could only say that she wanted to know, and Richard was sufficiently amused to answer.

'Well, how shall I reply? In one word – Unity. Unity of aim, of dominion, of progress. The dispersion of the best ideas over the greatest area.'

'The English?'

'I grant that the English seem, on the whole, whiter than most men, their records cleaner. But, good Lord, don't run away with the idea that I don't see the drawbacks – horrors – unmentionable things done in our very midst! I'm under no illusions. Few people, I suppose, have fewer illusions than I have. Have you ever been in a factory, Miss Vinrace! – No, I suppose not – I may say I hope not.'

As for Rachel, she had scarcely walked through a poor street, and always under the escort of father, maid or aunts.

'I was going to say that if you'd ever seen the kind of thing that's going on round you, you'd understand what it is that makes me and men like me politicians. You asked me a moment ago whether I'd done what I set out to do. Well, when I consider my life, there is one fact I admit that I'm proud of; owing to me some thousands of girls in Lancashire – and many thousands to come after them – can spend an hour every day in the open air which their mothers had to spend over their looms. I'm prouder of that, I own, than I should be of writing Keats – and Shelley into the bargain!'

It became painful to Rachel to be one of those who write Keats and Shelley. She liked Richard Dalloway, and warmed as he warmed. He seemed to mean what he said.

'I know nothing!' she exclaimed.

'It's far better that you should know nothing,' he said paternally, 'and you wrong yourself, I'm sure. You play very nicely, I'm told, and I've no doubt you've read heaps of learned books.'

Elderly banter would no longer check her.

'You talk of unity,' she said. 'You ought to make me understand.'

'I never allow my wife to talk politics,' he said seriously. 'For this reason. It is impossible for human beings, constituted as they are, both to fight and to have ideals. If I have preserved mine, as I am thankful to say that in great measure I have, it is due to the fact that I have been able to come home to my wife in the evening and to find that she has spent her day in calling, music, play with the children, domestic duties – what you will; her illusions have not been destroyed. She gives me courage to go on. The strain of public life is very great,' he added.

This made him appear a battered martyr, parting every day with some of the finest gold, in the service of mankind.

'I can't think,' Rachel exclaimed, 'how anyone does it!'

'Explain, Miss Vinrace,' said Richard. 'This is a matter I want to clear up.'

His kindness was genuine, and she determined to take the chance he gave her, although to talk to a man of such worth and authority made her heart beat.

'It seems to me like this,' she began, doing her best first to recollect and then to expose her shivering private visions.

'There's an old widow in her room, somewhere, let us suppose in the suburbs of Leeds.'

Richard bent his head to show that he accepted the widow.

'In London you're spending your life talking, writing things, getting bills through, missing what seems natural. The result of it all is that she goes to her cupboard and finds a little more tea, a few lumps of sugar, or a little less tea and a newspaper. Widows all over the country I admit do this. Still, there's the mind of the widow – the affections; those you leave untouched. But you waste you own.'

'If the widow goes to her cupboard and finds it bare,' Richard answered, 'her spiritual outlook we may admit will be affected. If I may pick holes in your philosophy, Miss Vinrace, which has its merits, I would point out that a human being is not a set of compartments, but an organism. Imagination, Miss Vinrace; use your imagination; that's where you young Liberals fail. Conceive the world as a whole. Now for your second point; when you assert that in trying to set the house in order for the benefit of the young generation I am wasting my higher capabilities, I totally disagree with you. I can conceive no more exalted aim – to be the citizen of the Empire. Look at it in this way, Miss

Vinrace: conceive the state as a complicated machine; we citizens are parts of that machine; some fulfil more important duties; others (perhaps I am one of them) serve only to connect some obscure parts of the mechanism, concealed from the public eye. Yet if the meanest screw fails in its task, the proper working of the whole is imperilled.'

It was impossible to combine the image of a lean black widow, gazing out of her window, and longing for someone to talk to, with the image of a vast machine, such as one sees at South Kensington,[44] thumping, thumping, thumping. The attempt at communication had been a failure.

'We don't seem to understand each other,' she said.

'Shall I say something that will make you very angry?' he replied.

'It won't,' said Rachel.

'Well, then; no woman has what I may call the political instinct. You have very great virtues; I am the first, I hope, to admit that; but I have never met a woman who even saw what is meant by statesmanship. I am going to make you still more angry. I hope that I never shall meet such a woman. Now, Miss Vinrace, are we enemies for life?'

Vanity, irritation, and a thrusting desire to be understood, urged her to make another attempt.

'Under the streets, in the sewers, in the wires, in the telephones, there is something alive; is that what you mean? In things like dustcarts, and men mending roads? You feel that all the time when you walk about London, and when you turn on a tap and the water comes?'

'Certainly,' said Richard. 'I understand you to mean that the whole of modern society is based upon cooperative effort. If only more people would realise that, Miss Vinrace, there would be fewer of your old widows in solitary lodgings!'

Rachel considered.

'Are you a Liberal or are you a Conservative?' she asked.

'I call myself a Conservative for convenience's sake,' said Richard, smiling. 'But there is more in common between the two parties than people generally allow.'

There was a pause, which did not come on Rachel's side from any lack of things to say; as usual she could not say them, and was further confused by the fact that the time for talking probably ran short. She was haunted by absurd jumbled ideas – how, if one went back far enough, everything perhaps was intelligible; everything was in common; for the mammoths who pastured in the fields of Richmond High Street had turned into paving stones, and boxes full of ribbon, and her aunts.

'Did you say you lived in the country when you were a child?' she asked.

Crude as her manners seemed to him, Richard was flattered. There could be no doubt that her interest was genuine.

'I did,' he smiled.

'And what happened?' she asked. 'Or do I ask too many questions?'

'I'm flattered, I assure you. But – let me see – what happened? Well, riding, lessons, sisters. There was an enchanted rubbish heap, I remember, where all kinds of queer things happened. Odd, what things impress children! I can remember the look of the place to this day. It's a fallacy to think that children are happy. They're not; they're unhappy. I've never suffered so much as I did when I was a child.'

'Why?' she asked.

'I didn't get on well with my father,' said Richard shortly. 'He was a very able man, but hard. Well – it makes one determined not to sin in that way oneself. Children never forget injustice. They forgive heaps of things grown-up people mind; but that sin is the unpardonable sin. Mind you – I dare say I was a difficult child to manage; but when I think what I was ready to give! No, I was more sinned against than sinning. And then I went to school, where I did very fairly well; and and then, as I say, my father sent me to both universities . . . D'you know, Miss Vinrace, you've made me think? How little, after all, one can tell anybody about one's life! Here I sit; there you sit; both, I doubt not, chock-full of the most interesting experiences, ideas, emotions; yet how communicate? I've told you what every second person you meet might tell you.'

'I don't think so,' she said. 'It's the way of saying things, isn't it, not the things?'

'True,' said Richard. 'Perfectly true.' He paused. 'When I look back over my life – I'm forty-two – what are the great facts that stand out? What were the revelations, if I may call them so? The misery of the poor and – ' (he hesitated and pitched over) 'love!'

Upon that word he lowered his voice; it was a word that seemed to unveil the skies for Rachel.

'It's an odd thing to say to a young lady,' he continued. 'But have you any idea what – what I mean by that? No, of course not. I don't use the word in a conventional sense. I use it as young men use it. Girls are kept very ignorant, aren't they? Perhaps it's wise – perhaps – You *don't* know?'

He spoke as if he had lost consciousness of what he was saying.

'No; I don't,' she said, scarcely speaking above her breath.

'Warships, Dick! Over there! Look!' Clarissa, released from Mr Grice, appreciative of all his seaweeds, skimmed towards them, gesticulating.

She had sighted two sinister grey vessels, low in the water, and bald as bone, one closely following the other with the look of eyeless beasts seeking their prey. Consciousness returned to Richard instantly.

'By George!' he exclaimed, and stood shielding his eyes.

'Ours, Dick?' said Clarissa.

'The Mediterranean Fleet,' he answered.

'The *Euphrosyne* was slowly dipping her flag. Richard raised his hat. Convulsively Clarissa squeezed Rachel's hand.

'Aren't you glad to be English!' she said.

The warships drew past, casting a curious effect of discipline and sadness upon the waters, and it was not until they were again invisible that people spoke to each other naturally. At lunch the talk was all of valour and death, and the magnificent qualities of British admirals. Clarissa quoted one poet, Willoughby quoted another. Life on board a man-of-war was splendid, so they agreed, and sailors, whenever one met them, were quite especially nice and simple.

This being so, no one liked it when Helen remarked that it seemed to her as wrong to keep sailors as to keep a zoo, and that as for dying on a battlefield, surely it was time we ceased to praise courage – 'or to write bad poetry about it,' snarled Pepper.

But Helen was really wondering why Rachel, sitting silent, looked so queer and flushed.

Chapter 5

She was not able to follow up her observations, however, or to come to any conclusion, for by one of those accidents which are liable to happen at sea, the whole course of their lives was now put out of order.

Even at tea the floor rose beneath their feet and pitched too low again, and at dinner the ship seemed to groan and strain as though a lash were descending. She who had been a broad-backed dray horse, upon whose hindquarters pierrots might waltz, became a colt in a field. The plates slanted away from the knives, and Mrs Dalloway's face blanched for a second as she helped herself and saw the potatoes roll this way and that. Willoughby, of course, extolled the virtues of his ship, and quoted what had been said of her by experts and distinguished passengers, for he loved his own possessions. Still, dinner was uneasy, and directly the ladies were alone Clarissa owned that she would be better off in bed, and went, smiling bravely.

Next morning the storm was on them, and no politeness could ignore it. Mrs Dalloway stayed in her room. Richard faced three meals, eating valiantly at each; but at the third, certain glazed asparagus swimming in oil finally conquered him.

'That beats me,' he said, and withdrew.

'Now we are alone once more,' remarked William Pepper, looking round the table; but no one was ready to engage him in talk, and the meal ended in silence.

On the following day they met – but as flying leaves meet in the air. Sick they were not; but the wind propelled them hastily into rooms, violently downstairs. They passed each other gasping on deck; they shouted across tables. They wore fur coats; and Helen was never seen without a bandanna on her head. For comfort they retreated to their cabins, where with tightly wedged feet they let the ship bounce and tumble. Their sensations were the sensations of potatoes in a sack on a galloping horse. The world outside was merely a violent grey tumult. For two days they had a perfect rest from their old emotions. Rachel had just enough consciousness to suppose herself a donkey on the summit of a moor in a hailstorm, with its coat blown into furrows; then she became a wizened tree, perpetually driven back by the salt Atlantic gale.

Helen, on the other hand, staggered to Mrs Dalloway's door, knocked, could not be heard for the slamming of doors and the battering of wind, and entered.

There were basins, of course. Mrs Dalloway lay half-raised on a pillow, and did not open her eyes. Then she murmured, 'Oh, Dick, is that you?'

Helen shouted – for she was thrown against the washstand – 'How are you?'

Clarissa opened one eye. It gave her an incredibly dissipated appearance. 'Awful!' she gasped. Her lips were white inside.

Planting her feet wide, Helen contrived to pour champagne into a tumbler with a toothbrush in it.

'Champagne,' she said.

'There's a toothbrush in it,' murmured Clarissa, and smiled; it might have been the contortion of one weeping. She drank.

'Disgusting,' she whispered, indicating the basins. Relics of humour still played over her face like moonshine.

'Want more?' Helen shouted. Speech was again beyond Clarissa's reach. The wind laid the ship shivering on her side. Pale agonies crossed Mrs Dalloway in waves. When the curtains flapped, grey lights puffed across her. Between the spasms of the storm, Helen made the curtain fast, shook the pillows, stretched the bedclothes, and smoothed the hot nostrils and forehead with cold scent.

'You *are* good!' Clarissa gasped. 'Horrid mess!'

She was trying to apologise for white underclothes fallen and scattered on the floor. For one second she opened a single eye, and saw that the room was tidy.

'That's nice,' she gasped.

Helen left her; far, far away she knew that she felt a kind of liking for Mrs Dalloway. She could not help respecting her spirit and her desire, even in the throes of sickness, for a tidy bedroom. Her petticoats, however, rose above her knees.

Quite suddenly the storm relaxed its grasp. It happened at tea; the expected paroxysm of the blast gave out just as it reached its climax and dwindled away, and the ship instead of taking the usual plunge went steadily. The monotonous order of plunging and rising, roaring and relaxing, was interfered with, and everyone at table looked up and felt something loosen within them. The strain was slackened and human feelings began to peep again, as they do when daylight shows at the end of a tunnel.

'Try a turn with me,' Ridley called across to Rachel.

'Foolish!' cried Helen, but they went stumbling up the ladder. Choked by the wind their spirits rose with a rush, for on the skirts of all the grey tumult was a misty spot of gold. Instantly the world dropped into shape; they were no longer atoms flying in the void, but people riding a triumphant ship on the back of the sea. Wind and space were banished; the world floated like an apple in a tub, and the mind of man, which had been unmoored also, once more attached itself to the old beliefs.

Having scrambled twice round the ship and received many sound cuffs from the wind, they saw a sailor's face positively shine golden. They looked, and beheld a complete yellow circle of sun; next minute it was traversed by sailing stands of cloud, and then completely hidden. By breakfast the next morning, however, the sky was swept clean, the waves, although steep, were blue, and after their view of the strange underworld, inhabited by phantoms, people began to live among teapots and loaves of bread with greater zest than ever.

Richard and Clarissa, however, still remained on the borderland. She did not attempt to sit up; her husband stood on his feet, contemplated his waistcoat and trousers, shook his head, and then lay down again. The inside of his brain was still rising and falling like the sea on the stage. At four o'clock he woke from sleep and saw the sunlight make a vivid angle across the red plush curtains and the grey tweed trousers. The ordinary world outside slid into his mind, and by the time he was dressed he was an English gentleman again.

He stood beside his wife. She pulled him down to her by the lapel of his coat, kissed him, and held him fast for a minute.

'Go and get a breath of air, Dick,' she said. 'You look quite washed out . . . How nice you smell! . . . And be polite to that woman. She was so kind to me.'

Thereupon Mrs Dalloway turned to the cool side of her pillow, terribly flattened but still invincible.

Richard found Helen talking to her brother-in-law, over two dishes of yellow cake and smooth bread and butter.

'You look very ill!' she exclaimed on seeing him. 'Come and have some tea.'

He remarked that the hands that moved about the cups were beautiful.

'I hear you've been very good to my wife,' he said. 'She's had an awful time of it. You came in and fed her with champagne. Were you among the saved yourself?'

'I? Oh, I haven't been sick for twenty years – seasick, I mean.'

'There are three stages of convalescence, I always say,' broke in the hearty voice of Willoughby. 'The milk stage, the bread-and-butter stage, and the roast-beef stage. I should say you were at the bread-and-butter stage.' He handed him the plate.

'Now, I should advise a hearty tea, then a brisk walk on deck; and by dinner-time you'll be clamouring for beef, eh?' He went off laughing, excusing himself on the score of business.

'What a splendid fellow he is!' said Richard. 'Always keen on something.'

'Yes,' said Helen, 'he's always been like that.'

'This is a great undertaking of his,' Richard continued. 'It's a business that won't stop with ships, I should say. We shall see him in Parliament, or I'm much mistaken. He's the kind of man we want in Parliament – the man who has done things.'

But Helen was not much interested in her brother-in-law.

'I expect your head's aching, isn't it?' she asked, pouring a fresh cup.

'Well, it is,' said Richard. 'It's humiliating to find what a slave one is to one's body in this world. D'you know, I can never work without a kettle on the hob. As often as not I don't drink tea, but I must feel that I can if I want to.'

'That's very bad for you,' said Helen.

'It shortens one's life; but I'm afraid, Mrs Ambrose, we politicians must make up our minds to that at the outset. We've got to burn the candle at both ends, or – '

'You've cooked your goose!' said Helen brightly.

'We can't make you take us seriously, Mrs Ambrose,' he protested. 'May I ask how you've spent your time? Reading – philosophy?' (He saw the black book.) 'Metaphysics and fishing!' he exclaimed. 'If I had to live again I believe I should devote myself to one or the other.' He began turning the pages.

' "Good, then, is indefinable," ' he read out. 'How jolly to think that's going on still! "So far as I know there is only one ethical writer, Professor Henry Sidgwick,[45] who has clearly recognised and stated this fact." That's just the kind of thing we used to talk about when we were boys. I can remember arguing until five in the morning with Duffy – now Secretary for India – pacing round and round those cloisters until we decided it was too late to go to bed, and we went for a ride instead. Whether we ever came to any conclusion – that's another matter. Still, it's the arguing that counts. It's things like that that stand out in life. Nothing's been quite so vivid since. It's the philosophers, it's the scholars,' he continued, 'they're the people who pass the torch, who keep the light burning by which we live. Being a politician doesn't necessarily blind one to that, Mrs Ambrose.'

'No. Why should it?' said Helen. 'But can you remember if your wife takes sugar?'

She lifted the tray and went off with it to Mrs Dalloway.

Richard twisted a muffler twice round his throat and struggled up on deck. His body, which had grown white and tender in a dark room, tingled all over in the fresh air. He felt himself a man undoubtedly in the prime of life. Pride glowed in his eye as he let the wind buffet him and stood firm. With his head slightly lowered he sheered round corners, strode uphill, and met the blast. There was a collision. For a second he could not see what the body was he had run into. 'Sorry. Sorry.' It was Rachel who apologised. They both laughed, too much blown about to speak. She drove open the door of her room and stepped into its calm. In order to speak to her, it was necessary that Richard should follow. They stood in a whirlpool of wind; papers began flying round in circles, the door crashed to, and they tumbled, laughing, into chairs. Richard sat upon Bach.

'My word! What a tempest!' he exclaimed.

'Fine, isn't it?' said Rachel. Certainly the struggle and wind had given her a decision she lacked; red was in her cheeks, and her hair was down.

'Oh, what fun!' he cried. 'What am I sitting on? Is this your room? How jolly!'

'There – sit there,' she commanded. *Cowper* slid once more.

'How jolly to meet again,' said Richard. 'It seems an age. *Cowper's Letters*? . . . Bach? . . . *Wuthering Heights*? . . . Is this where you meditate on the world, and then come out and pose poor politicians with questions? In the intervals of seasickness I've thought a lot of our talk. I assure you, you made me think.'

'I made you think! But why?'

'What solitary icebergs we are, Miss Vinrace! How little we can communicate! There are lots of things I should like to tell you about – to hear your opinion of. Have you ever read Burke?'[46]

'Burke?' she repeated. 'Who was Burke?'

'No? Well, then I shall make a point of sending you a copy. *The Speech on the French Revolution – The American Rebellion*? Which shall it be, I wonder?' He noted something in his pocketbook. 'And then you must write and tell me what you think of it. This reticence – this isolation – that's what's the matter with modern life! Now, tell me about yourself. What are your interests and occupations? I should imagine that you were a person with very strong interests. Of course you are! Good God! When I think of the age we live in, with its opportunities and possibilities, the mass of things to be done and enjoyed – why haven't we ten lives instead of one? But about yourself?'

'You see, I'm a woman,' said Rachel.

'I know – I know,' said Richard, throwing his head back, and drawing his fingers across his eyes. 'How strange to be a woman! A young and beautiful woman,' he continued sententiously, 'has the whole world at her feet. That's true, Miss Vinrace. You have an inestimable power – for good or for evil. What couldn't you do – ' he broke off.

'What?' asked Rachel.

'You have beauty,' he said. The ship lurched. Rachel fell slightly forward. Richard took her in his arms and kissed her. Holding her tight, he kissed her passionately, so that she felt the hardness of his body and the roughness of his cheek printed upon hers. She fell back in her chair, with tremendous beats of the heart, each of which sent black waves across her eyes.

He clasped his forehead in his hands. 'You tempt me,' he said. The tone of his voice was terrifying. He seemed choked in fright. They were both trembling.

Rachel stood up and went. Her head was cold, her knees shaking, and the physical pain of the emotion was so great that she could only keep herself moving above the great leaps of her heart. She leant upon the rail of the ship, and gradually ceased to feel, for a chill of body and mind crept over her. Far out between the waves little black-and-white seabirds were riding. Rising and falling with smooth and graceful movements in the hollows of the waves they seemed singularly detached and unconcerned.

'You're peaceful,' she said. She became peaceful too, at the same time possessed with a strange exultation. Life seemed to hold infinite possibilities she had never guessed at. She leant upon the rail and looked over the troubled grey waters, where the sunlight was fitfully scattered upon the crests of the waves, until she was cold and absolutely calm again. Nevertheless something wonderful had happened.

At dinner, however, she did not feel exalted, but merely uncomfortable, as if she and Richard had seen something together which is hidden in ordinary life, so that they did not like to look at each other. Richard slid his eyes over her uneasily once, and never looked at her again. Formal platitudes were manufactured with effort, but Willoughby was kindled.

'Beef for Mr Dalloway!' he shouted. 'Come now – after that walk you're at the beef stage, Dalloway!'

Wonderful masculine stories followed about Bright[47] and Disraeli[48] and coalition governments, wonderful stories which made the people at the dinner-table seem featureless and small. After dinner, sitting alone with Rachel under the great swinging lamp, Helen was struck by her pallor. It once more occurred to her that there was something strange in the girl's behaviour.

'You look tired. Are you tired?' she asked.

'Not tired,' said Rachel. 'Oh, yes, I suppose I am tired.'

Helen advised bed, and she went, not seeing Richard again. She must have been very tired for she fell asleep at once, but after an hour or two of dreamless sleep, she dreamt. She dreamt that she was walking down a long tunnel, which grew so narrow by degrees that she could touch the damp bricks on either side. At length the tunnel opened and became a vault; she found herself trapped in it, bricks meeting her wherever she turned, alone with a little deformed man who squatted on the floor gibbering, with long nails. His face was pitted and like the face of an animal. The wall behind him oozed with damp, which collected into drops and slid down. Still and cold as death she lay, not daring to move, until she broke the agony by tossing herself across the bed, and woke crying, 'Oh!'

Light showed her the familiar things: her clothes, fallen off the chair; the water jug gleaming white; but the horror did not go at once. She felt herself pursued, so that she got up and actually locked her door. A voice moaned for her; eyes desired her. All night long barbarian men harassed the ship; they came scuffling down the passages, and stopped to snuffle at her door. She could not sleep again.

Chapter 6

'That's the tragedy of life – as I always say!' said Mrs Dalloway. 'Beginning things and having to end them. Still, I'm not going to let *this* end, if you're willing.' It was the morning, the sea was calm, and the ship once again was anchored not far from another shore.

She was dressed in her long fur cloak, with the veils wound around her head, and once more the rich boxes stood on top of each other so that the scene of a few days back seemed to be repeated.

'D'you suppose we shall ever meet in London?' said Ridley ironically. 'You'll have forgotten all about me by the time you step out there.'

He pointed to the shore of the little bay, where they could now see the separate trees with moving branches.

'How horrid you are!' she laughed. 'Rachel's coming to see me anyhow – the instant you get back,' she said, pressing Rachel's arm. 'Now – you've no excuse!'

With a silver pencil she wrote her name and address on the flyleaf of *Persuasion*, and gave the book to Rachel. Sailors were shouldering the luggage, and people were beginning to congregate. There were Captain Cobbold, Mr Grice, Willoughby, Helen, and an obscure grateful man in a blue jersey.

'Oh, it's time,' said Clarissa. 'Well, goodbye. I *do* like you,' she murmured as she kissed Rachel. People in the way made it unnecessary for Richard to shake Rachel by the hand; he managed to look at her very stiffly for a second before he followed his wife down the ship's side.

The boat separating from the vessel made off towards the land, and for some minutes Helen, Ridley and Rachel leant over the rail, watching. Once Mrs Dalloway turned and waved; but the boat steadily grew smaller and smaller until it ceased to rise and fall, and nothing could be seen save two resolute backs.

'Well, that's over,' said Ridley after a long silence. 'We shall never see *them* again,' he added, turning to go to his books. A feeling of emptiness and melancholy came over them; they knew in their hearts that it was over, and that they had parted for ever, and the knowledge filled them with far greater depression than the length of their acquaintance seemed to justify. Even as the boat pulled away they could feel other sights and sounds beginning to take the place of the Dalloways, and the feeling was so unpleasant that they tried to resist it. For so, too, would they be forgotten.

In much the same way as Mrs Chailey downstairs was sweeping the withered rose leaves off the dressing-table, so Helen was anxious to make things straight again after the visitors had gone. Rachel's obvious languor and listlessness made her an easy prey, and indeed Helen had devised a kind of trap. That something had happened she now felt pretty certain; moreover, she had come to think that they had been strangers long enough; she wished to know what the girl was like, partly of course because Rachel showed no disposition to be known. So, as they turned from the rail, she said: 'Come and talk to me instead of practising,' and led the way to the sheltered side where the deckchairs were stretched in the sun. Rachel followed her indifferently. Her mind was absorbed by Richard; by the extreme strangeness of what had happened, and by a thousand feelings of which she had not been conscious before. She made scarcely any attempt to listen to what Helen was saying, as Helen indulged in commonplaces to begin with. While Mrs Ambrose arranged her embroidery, sucked her silk, and threaded her needle, she lay back gazing at the horizon.

'Did you like those people?' Helen asked her casually.

'Yes,' she replied blankly.

'You talked to him, didn't you?'

She said nothing for a minute.

'He kissed me,' she said without any change of tone.

Helen started, looked at her, but could not make out what she felt.

'M–m–m'yes,' she said, after a pause. 'I thought he was that kind of man.'

'What kind of man?' said Rachel.

'Pompous and sentimental.'

'I like him,' said Rachel.

'So you really didn't mind?'

For the first time since Helen had known her Rachel's eyes lit up brightly.

'I did mind,' she said vehemently. 'I dreamt. I couldn't sleep.'

'Tell me what happened,' said Helen. She had to keep her lips from twitching as she listened to Rachel's story. It was poured out abruptly with great seriousness and no sense of humour.

'We talked about politics. He told me what he had done for the poor somewhere. I asked him all sorts of questions. He told me about his own life. The day before yesterday, after the storm, he came in to see me. It happened then, quite suddenly. He kissed me. I don't know why.'

As she spoke she grew flushed. 'I was a good deal excited,' she continued. 'But I didn't mind till afterwards; when – ' she paused, and saw the figure of the bloated little man again – 'I became terrified.'

From the look in her eyes it was evident she was again terrified. Helen was really at a loss what to say. From the little she knew of Rachel's upbringing she supposed that she had been kept entirely ignorant as to the relations of men with women. With a shyness which she felt with women and not with men she did not like to explain simply what these are. Therefore she took the other course and belittled the whole affair.

'Oh, well,' she said, 'he was a silly creature, and if I were you, I'd think no more about it.'

'No,' said Rachel, sitting bolt upright, 'I shan't do that. I shall think about it all day and all night until I find out exactly what it does mean.'

'Don't you ever read?' Helen asked tentatively.

'*Cowper's Letters* – that kind of thing. Father gets them for me or my aunts.'

Helen could hardly restrain herself from saying out loud what she thought of a man who brought up his daughter so that at the age of twenty-four she scarcely knew that men desired women and was terrified by a kiss. She had good reason to fear that Rachel had made herself incredibly ridiculous.

'You don't know many men?' she asked.

'Mr Pepper,' said Rachel ironically.

'So no one's ever wanted to marry you?'

'No,' she answered ingenuously.

Helen reflected that as, from what she had said, Rachel certainly would think these things out, it might be as well to help her.

'You oughtn't to be frightened,' she said. 'It's the most natural thing in the world. Men will want to kiss you, just as they'll want to marry you. The pity is to get things out of proportion. It's like noticing the noises people make when they eat, or men spitting; or, in short, any small thing that gets on one's nerves.'

Rachel seemed to be inattentive to these remarks.

'Tell me,' she said suddenly, 'what are those women in Piccadilly?'

'In Piccadilly? They are prostituted,' said Helen.

'It *is* terrifying – it *is* disgusting,' Rachel asserted, as if she included Helen in the hatred.

'It is,' said Helen. 'But – '

'I did like him,' Rachel mused, as if speaking to herself. 'I wanted to talk to him; I wanted to know what he'd done. The women in Lancashire – '

It seemed to her as she recalled their talk that there was something lovable about Richard, good in their attempted friendship, and strangely piteous in the way they had parted.

The softening of her mood was apparent to Helen.

'You see,' she said, 'you must take things as they are; and if you want friendship with men you must run risks. Personally,' she continued, breaking into a smile, 'I think it's worth it; I don't mind being kissed; I'm rather jealous, I believe, that Mr Dalloway kissed you and didn't kiss me. Though,' she added, 'he bored me considerably.'

But Rachel did not return the smile or dismiss the whole affair, as Helen meant her to. Her mind was working very quickly, inconsistently and painfully. Helen's words hewed down great blocks which had stood there always, and the light which came in was cold. After sitting for a time with fixed eyes, she burst out: 'So that's why I can't walk alone!'

By this new light she saw her life for the first time as a creeping hedged-in thing, driven cautiously between high walls, here turned aside, there plunged in darkness, made dull and crippled for ever – her life that was the only chance she had – a thousand words and actions became plain to her.

'Because men are brutes! I hate men!' she exclaimed.

'I thought you said you liked him?' said Helen.

'I liked him, and I liked being kissed,' she answered, as if that only added more difficulties to her problem.

Helen was surprised to see how genuine both shock and problem were, but she could think of no way of easing the difficulty except by going on talking. She wanted to make her niece talk, and so to understand why this rather dull, kindly, plausible politician had made so deep an impression on her, for surely at the age of twenty-four this was not natural.

'And did you like Mrs Dalloway too?' she asked.

As she spoke she saw Rachel redden; for she remembered silly things she had said, and also it occurred to her that she treated this exquisite woman rather badly, for Mrs Dalloway had said that she loved her husband.

'She was quite nice, but a thimble-pated creature,' Helen continued. 'I never heard such nonsense! Chitter-chatter-chitter-chatter – fish and the Greek alphabet – never listened to a word anyone said – chock-full of idiotic theories about the way to bring up children – I'd far rather talk to him any day. He was pompous, but he did at least understand what was said to him.'

The glamour insensibly faded a little both from Richard and Clarissa.

They had not been so wonderful after all, then, in the eyes of a mature person.

'It's very difficult to know what people are like,' Rachel remarked, and Helen saw with pleasure that she spoke more naturally. 'I suppose I was taken in.'

There was little doubt about that according to Helen, but she restrained herself and said aloud: 'One has to make experiments.'

'And they *were* nice,' said Rachel. 'They were extraordinarily interesting.' She tried to recall the image of the world as a live thing that Richard had given her, with drains like nerves, and bad houses like patches of diseased skin. She recalled his watch-words – Unity – Imagination – and saw again the bubbles meeting in her teacup as he spoke of sisters and canaries, boyhood and his father, her small world becoming wonderfully enlarged.

'But all people don't seem to you equally interesting, do they?' asked Mrs Ambrose.

Rachel explained that most people had hitherto been symbols; but that when they talked to one they ceased to be symbols, and became – 'I could listen to them for ever!' she exclaimed. She then jumped up, disappeared downstairs for a minute, and came back with a fat red book.

'*Who's Who*,' she said, laying it upon Helen's knee and turning the pages. 'It gives short lives of people – for instance: "Sir Roland Beal: born 1852; parents from Moffatt; educated at Rugby; passed first into Royal Engineers; married 1878 the daughter of T. Fishwick; served in the Bechuanaland Expedition 1884–85 (honourably mentioned). Clubs: United Service, Naval and Military. Recreations: an enthusiastic curler." '

Sitting on the deck at Helen's feet she went on turning the pages and reading biographies of bankers, writers, clergymen, sailors, surgeons, judges, professors, statesmen, editors, philanthropists, merchants and actresses; what clubs they belonged to, where they lived, what games they played, and how many acres they owned.

She became absorbed in the book.

Helen meanwhile stitched at her embroidery and thought over the things they had said. Her conclusion was that she would very much like to show her niece, if it were possible, how to live, or as she put it, how to be a reasonable person. She thought that there must be something wrong in this confusion between politics and kissing politicians, and that an elder person ought to be able to help.

'I quite agree,' she said, 'that people are very interesting; only – '
Rachel, putting her finger between the pages, looked up enquiringly.

'Only I think you ought to discriminate,' she ended. 'It's a pity to be intimate with people who are – well, rather second-rate, like the Dalloways, and to find it out later.'

'But how does one know?' Rachel asked.

'I really can't tell you,' replied Helen candidly, after a moment's thought. 'You'll have to find out for yourself. But try and – Why don't you call me Helen?' she added. ' "Aunt" is a horrid name. I never liked my aunts.'

'I should like to call you Helen,' Rachel answered.

'D'you think me very unsympathetic?'

Rachel reviewed the points which Helen had certainly failed to understand; they arose chiefly from the difference of nearly twenty years in age between them, which made Mrs Ambrose appear too humorous and cool in a matter of such moment.

'No,' she said. 'Some things you don't understand, of course.'

'Of course,' Helen agreed. 'So now you can go ahead and be a person on your own account,' she added.

The vision of her own personality, of herself as a real everlasting thing, different from anything else, unmergeable, like the sea or the wind, flashed into Rachel's mind, and she became profoundly excited at the thought of living.

'I can by m-m-myself,' she stammered, 'in spite of you, in spite of the Dalloways, and Mr Pepper, and father, and my aunts, in spite of these?' She swept her hand across a whole page of statesmen and soldiers.

'In spite of them all,' said Helen gravely. She then put down her needle, and explained a plan which had come into her head as they talked. Instead of wandering on down the Amazons until she reached some sulphurous tropical port, where one had to lie within doors all day beating off insects with a fan, the sensible thing to do surely was to spend the season with them in their villa by the seaside, where among other advantages Mrs Ambrose herself would be at hand to – 'After all, Rachel,' she broke off, 'it's silly to pretend that because there's twenty years' difference between us we therefore can't talk to each other like human beings.'

'No; because we like each other,' said Rachel.

'Yes,' Mrs Ambrose agreed.

That fact, together with other facts, had been made clear by their twenty minutes' talk, although how they had come to these conclusions they could not have said.

However they were come by, they were sufficiently serious to send Mrs Ambrose a day or two later in search of her brother-in-law. She found him sitting in his room working, applying a stout blue pencil authoritatively to bundles of filmy paper. Papers lay to left and to right of him, there were great envelopes so gorged with papers that they spilt papers on to the table. Above him hung a photograph of a woman's head. The need of sitting absolutely still before a cockney photographer had given her lips a queer little pucker, and her eyes for the same reason looked as though she thought the whole situation ridiculous. Nevertheless it was the head of an individual and interesting woman, who would no doubt have turned and laughed at Willoughby if she could have caught his eye; but when he looked up at her he sighed profoundly. In his mind this work of his, the great factories at Hull which showed like mountains at night, the ships that crossed the ocean punctually, the schemes for combining this and that and building up a solid mass of industry, was all an offering to her; he laid his success at her feet; and was always thinking how to educate his daughter so that Theresa might be glad. He was a very ambitious man; and although he had not been particularly kind to her while she lived, as Helen thought, he now believed that she watched him from heaven, and inspired what was good in him.

Mrs Ambrose apologised for the interruption, and asked whether she might speak to him about a plan of hers. Would he consent to leave his daughter with them when they landed, instead of taking her on up the Amazons?

'We would take great care of her,' she added, 'and we should really like it.'

Willoughby looked very grave and carefully laid aside his papers.

'She's a good girl,' he said at length. 'There is a likeness?' – he nodded his head at the photograph of Theresa and sighed. Helen looked at Theresa pursing up her lips before the cockney photographer. It suggested her in an absurd human way, and she felt an intense desire to share some joke.

'She's the only thing that's left to me,' sighed Willoughby. 'We go on year after year without talking about these things – ' He broke off. 'But it's better so. Only life's very hard.'

Helen was sorry for him, and patted him on the shoulder, but she felt uncomfortable when her brother-in-law expressed his feelings, and took refuge in praising Rachel, and explaining why she thought her plan might be a good one.

'True,' said Willoughby when she had done. 'The social conditions are bound to be primitive. I should be out a good deal. I agreed because she wished it. And of course I have complete confidence in you . . . You see, Helen,' he continued, becoming confidential, 'I want to bring her up as her mother would have wished. I don't hold with these modern views – any more than you do, eh? She's a nice quiet girl, devoted to her music – a little less of *that* would do no harm. Still, it's kept her happy, and we lead a very quiet life at Richmond. I should like her to begin to see more people. I want to take her about with me when I get home. I've half a mind to rent a house in London, leaving my sisters at Richmond, and take her to see one or two people who'd be kind to her for my sake. I'm beginning to realise,' he continued, stretching himself out, 'that all this is tending to Parliament, Helen. It's the only way to get things done as one wants them done. I talked to Dalloway about it. In that case, of course, I should want Rachel to be able to take more part in things. A certain amount of entertaining would be necessary – dinners, an occasional evening party. One's constituents like to be fed, I believe. In all these ways Rachel could be of great help to me. So,' he wound up, 'I should be very glad, if we arrange this visit (which must be upon a business footing, mind), if you could see your way to helping my girl, bringing her out – she's a little shy now – making a woman of her, the kind of woman her mother would have liked her to be,' he ended, jerking his head at the photograph.

Willoughby's selfishness, though consistent as Helen saw with real affection for his daughter, made her determined to have the girl to stay with her, even if she had to promise a complete course of instruction in the feminine graces. She could not help laughing at the notion of it – Rachel a Tory hostess! – and marvelling as she left him at the astonishing ignorance of a father.

Rachel, when consulted, showed less enthusiasm than Helen could have wished. One moment she was eager, the next doubtful. Visions of a great river, now blue, now yellow in the tropical sun and crossed by bright birds, now white in the moon, now deep in shade with moving trees and canoes sliding out from the tangled banks, beset her. Helen promised a river. Then she did not want to leave her father. That feeling seemed genuine too, but in the end Helen prevailed, although when she had won her case she was beset by doubts, and more than once regretted the impulse which had entangled her with the fortunes of another human being.

Chapter 7

From a distance the *Euphrosyne* looked very small. Glasses were turned upon her from the decks of great liners, and she was pronounced a tramp, a cargo-boat, or one of those wretched little passenger steamers where people rolled about among the cattle on deck. The insect-like figures of Dalloways, Ambroses and Vinraces were also derided, both from the extreme smallness of their persons and the doubt which only strong glasses could dispel as to whether they were really live creatures or only lumps on the rigging. Mr Pepper with all his learning had been mistaken for a cormorant, and then, as unjustly, transformed into a cow. At night, indeed, when the waltzes were swinging in the saloon, and gifted passengers reciting, the little ship – shrunk to a few beads of light out among the dark waves, and one high in air upon the masthead – seemed something mysterious and impressive to heated partners resting from the dance. She became a ship passing in the night – an emblem of the loneliness of human life, an occasion for queer confidences and sudden appeals for sympathy.

On and on she went, by day and by night, following her path, until one morning broke and showed the land. Losing its shadow-like appearance it became first cleft and mountainous, next coloured grey and purple, next scattered with white blocks which gradually separated themselves, and then, as the progress of the ship acted upon the view like a field-glass of increasing power, became streets of houses. By nine o'clock, the *Euphrosyne* had taken up her position in the middle of a great bay; she dropped her anchor; immediately, as if she were a recumbent giant requiring examination, small boats came swarming about her. She rang with cries; men jumped on to her; her deck was thumped by feet. The lonely little island was invaded from all quarters at once, and after four weeks of silence it was bewildering to hear human speech. Mrs Ambrose alone heeded none of this stir. She was pale with suspense while the boat with mailbags was making towards them. Absorbed in her letters she did not notice that she had left the *Euphrosyne*, and felt no sadness when the ship lifted up her voice and bellowed thrice like a cow separated from its calf.

'The children are well!' she exclaimed. Mr Pepper, who sat opposite with a great mound of bag and rug upon his knees, said, 'Gratifying.'

Rachel, to whom the end of the voyage meant a complete change of perspective, was too much bewildered by the approach of the shore to realise what children were well or why it was gratifying. Helen went on reading.

Moving very slowly, and rearing absurdly high over each wave, the little boat was now approaching a white crescent of sand. Behind this was a deep green valley, with distinct hills on either side. On the slope of the right-hand hill white houses with brown roofs were settled, like nesting sea-birds, and at intervals cypresses striped the hill with black bars. Mountains whose sides were flushed with red, but whose crowns were bald, rose as a pinnacle, half-concealing another pinnacle behind it. The hour being still early, the whole view was exquisitely light and airy; the blues and greens of sky and tree were intense but not sultry. As they drew nearer and could distinguish details, the effect of the earth with its minute objects and colours and different forms of life was overwhelming after four weeks of the sea, and kept them silent.

'Three hundred years odd,' said Mr Pepper meditatively at length.

As nobody said, 'What?' he merely extracted a bottle and swallowed a pill. The piece of information that died within him was to the effect that three hundred years ago five Elizabethan barques had anchored where the *Euphrosyne* now floated. Half-drawn up upon the beach lay an equal number of Spanish galleons, unmanned, for the country was still a virgin land behind a veil. Slipping across the water, the English sailors bore away bars of silver, bales of linen, timbers of cedar wood, golden crucifixes knobbed with emeralds. When the Spaniards came down from their drinking, a fight ensued, the two parties churning up the sand, and driving each other into the surf. The Spaniards, bloated with fine living upon the fruits of the miraculous land, fell in heaps; but the hardy Englishmen, tawny with sea-voyaging, hairy for lack of razors, with muscles like wire, fangs greedy for flesh and fingers itching for gold, dispatched the wounded, drove the dying into the sea and soon reduced the natives to a state of superstitious wonderment. Here a settlement was made; women were imported; children grew. All seemed to favour the expansion of the British Empire, and had there been men like Richard Dalloway in the time of Charles I, the map would undoubtedly be red where it is now an odious green. But it must be supposed that the political mind of that age lacked imagination, and, merely for want of a few thousand pounds and a few thousand men, the spark died that should have been a conflagration. From the interior came Indians with subtle poisons, naked bodies and painted idols; from the sea came vengeful Spaniards and rapacious Portuguese; exposed to all these enemies (though the climate proved wonderfully kind and the earth abundant) the English dwindled away and all but disappeared. Somewhere about the middle of the seventeenth century a single sloop watched its season and slipped out by night, bearing within it all that was left of the great British colony, a few men, a few women, and perhaps a dozen dusky children. English history then denies all knowledge of the place. Owing to one cause and another civilisation shifted its centre to a spot some four or five hundred miles to the south, and today Santa Marina is not much larger than it was three hundred years ago. In population it is a happy compromise, for Portuguese fathers wed Indian mothers, and their children intermarry with the Spanish. Although they get their ploughs from Manchester, they make their coats from their own sheep, their silk from their own worms, and their furniture from their own cedar trees, so that in arts and industries the place is still much where it was in Elizabethan days.

The reasons which had drawn the English across the sea to found a small colony within the last ten years are not so easily described, and will never perhaps be recorded in history books. Granted facility of travel, peace, good trade and so on, there was besides a kind of dissatisfaction among the English with the older countries and the enormous accumulations of carved stone, stained glass and rich brown painting which they offered to the tourist. The movement in search of something new was of course infinitely small, affecting only a handful of well-to-do people. It began by a few schoolmasters serving their passage out to South America as the pursers of tramp steamers. They returned in time for the summer term, when their stories of the splendours and hardships of life at sea, the humours of sea-captains, the wonders of night and dawn, and the marvels of the place delighted outsiders, and sometimes found their way into print. The country itself taxed all their powers of description, for they said it was much bigger than Italy, and really nobler than Greece. Again, they declared that the natives were strangely beautiful, very big in stature, dark, passionate, and quick to seize the knife. The place seemed new and full of new forms of beauty, in proof of which they showed handkerchiefs which the women had worn round their heads, and primitive carvings coloured bright greens and blues. Somehow or other, as fashions do, the fashion spread; an old monastery was quickly turned into a hotel, while a famous line of steamships altered its route for the convenience of passengers.

Oddly enough it happened that the least satisfactory of Helen Ambrose's brothers had been sent out years before to make his fortune, at any rate to keep clear of racehorses, in the very spot which had now become so popular. Often, leaning upon the column in the verandah, he had watched the English ships with English schoolmasters for pursers steaming into the bay. Having at length earned enough to take a holiday, and being sick of the place, he proposed to put his villa, on the slope of the mountain, at his sister's disposal. She, too, had been a little stirred by the talk of a new world, where there was always sun and never a fog, which went on around her, and the chance, when they were planning where to spend the winter out of England, seemed too good to be missed. For these reasons she determined to accept Willoughby's offer of free passages on his ship, to place the children with their grandparents, and to do the thing thoroughly while she was about it.

Taking seats in a carriage drawn by long-tailed horses with pheasants' feathers erect between their ears, the Ambroses, Mr Pepper and Rachel rattled out of the harbour. The day increased in heat as they drove up the hill. The road passed through the town, where men seemed to be beating brass and crying 'Water', where the passage was blocked by mules and cleared by whips and curses, where the women walked barefoot, their heads balancing baskets, and cripples hastily displayed mutilated members; it issued among steep green fields, not so green but that the earth showed through. Great trees now shaded all but the centre of the road, and a mountain stream, so shallow and so swift that it plaited itself into strands as it ran, raced along the edge. Higher they went, until Ridley and Rachel walked behind; next they turned along a lane scattered with stones, where Mr Pepper raised his stick and silently indicated a shrub, bearing among sparse leaves a voluminous purple blossom; and at a rickety canter the last stage of the way was accomplished.

The villa was a roomy white house, which, as is the case with most continental houses, looked to an English eye frail, ramshackle, and absurdly frivolous, more like a pagoda in a tea-garden than a place where one slept. The garden called urgently for the services of a gardener. Bushes waved their branches across the paths, and the blades of grass, with spaces of earth between them, could be counted. In the circular piece of ground in front of the verandah were two cracked vases, from which red flowers drooped, with a stone fountain between them, now parched in the sun. The circular garden led to a long garden, where the gardener's shears had scarcely been, unless now and then, when he cut a bough of blossom for his beloved. A few tall trees shaded it, and round bushes with waxlike flowers mobbed their heads together in a row. A garden smoothly laid with turf, divided by thick hedges, with raised beds of bright flowers, such as we keep within walls in England, would have been out of place upon the side of this bare hill. There was no ugliness to shut out, and the villa looked straight across the shoulder of a slope, ribbed with olive trees, to the sea.

The indecency of the whole place struck Mrs Chailey forcibly. There were no blinds to shut out the sun, nor was there any furniture to speak of for the sun to spoil. Standing in the bare stone hall, and surveying a staircase of superb breadth, but cracked and carpetless, she further ventured the opinion that there were rats, as large as terriers at home, and that if one put one's foot down with any force one would come through the floor. As for hot water – at this point her investigations left her speechless.

'Poor creature!' she murmured to the sallow Spanish servant-girl who came out with the pigs and hens to receive them, 'no wonder you hardly look like a human being!' Maria accepted the compliment with an exquisite Spanish grace. In Chailey's opinion they would have done better to stay on board an English ship, but none knew better than she that her duty commanded her to stay.

When they were settled in, and in train to find daily occupation, there was some speculation as to the reasons which induced Mr Pepper to stay, taking up his lodging in the Ambroses' house. Efforts had been made for some days before landing to impress upon him the advantages of the Amazons.

'That great stream!' Helen would begin, gazing as if she saw a visionary cascade, 'I've a good mind to go with you myself, Willoughby – only I can't. Think of the sunsets and the moonrises – I believe the colours are unimaginable.'

'There are wild peacocks,' Rachel hazarded.

'And marvellous creatures in the water,' Helen asserted.

'One might discover a new reptile,' Rachel continued.

'There's certain to be a revolution, I'm told,' Helen urged.

The effect of these subterfuges was a little dashed by Ridley, who, after regarding Pepper for some moments, sighed aloud, 'Poor fellow!' and inwardly speculated upon the unkindness of women.

He stayed, however, in apparent contentment for six days, playing with a microscope and a notebook in one of the many sparsely furnished sitting-rooms, but on the evening of the seventh day, as they sat at dinner, he appeared more restless than usual. The dinner-table was set between two long windows which were left uncurtained by Helen's orders. Darkness fell as sharply as a knife in this climate, and the town then sprang out in circles and lines of bright dots beneath them.

Buildings which never showed by day showed by night, and the sea flowed right over the land judging by the moving lights of the steamers. The sight fulfilled the same purpose as an orchestra in a London restaurant, and silence had its setting. William Pepper observed it for some time; he put on his spectacles to contemplate the scene.

'I've identified the big block to the left,' he observed, and pointed with his fork at a square formed by several rows of lights. 'One should infer that they can cook vegetables,' he added.

'An hotel?' said Helen.

'Once a monastery,' said Mr Pepper.

Nothing more was said then, but, the day after, Mr Pepper returned from a midday walk, and stood silently before Helen who was reading in the verandah.

'I've taken a room over there,' he said.

'You're not going?' she exclaimed.

'On the whole – yes,' he remarked. 'No private cook *can* cook vegetables.'

Knowing his dislike of questions, which she to some extent shared, Helen asked no more. Still, an uneasy suspicion lurked in her mind that William was hiding a wound. She flushed to think that her words, or her husband's, or Rachel's had penetrated and stung. She was half-moved to cry, 'Stop, William; explain!' and would have returned to the subject at luncheon if William had not shown himself inscrutable and chill, lifting fragments of salad on the point of his fork, with the gesture of a man pronging seaweed, detecting gravel, suspecting germs.

'If you all die of typhoid I won't be responsible!' he snapped.

'If you die of dullness, neither will I,' Helen echoed in her heart.

She reflected that she had never yet asked him whether he had been in love. They had got further and further from that subject instead of drawing nearer to it, and she could not help feeling it a relief when William Pepper, with all his knowledge, his microscope, his notebooks, his genuine kindliness and good sense, but a certain dryness of soul, took his departure. Also she could not help feeling it sad that friendships should end thus, although in this case to have the room empty was something of a comfort, and she tried to console herself with the reflection that one never knows how far other people feel the things they might be supposed to feel.

Chapter 8

The next few months passed away, as many years can pass away, without definite events, and yet, if suddenly disturbed, it would be seen that such months or years had a character unlike others. The three months which had passed had brought them to the beginning of March. The climate had kept its promise, and the change of season from winter to spring had made very little difference, so that Helen, who was sitting in the drawing-room with a pen in her hand, could keep the windows open though a great fire of logs burnt on one side of her. Below, the sea was still blue and the roofs still brown and white, though the day was fading rapidly. It was dusk in the room, which, large and empty at all times, now appeared larger and emptier than usual. Her own figure, as she sat writing with a pad on her knee, shared the general effect of size and lack of detail, for the flames which ran along the branches, suddenly devouring little green tufts, burnt intermittently and sent irregular illuminations across her face and the plaster walls. There were no pictures on the walls but here and there boughs laden with heavy-petalled flowers spread widely against them. Of the books fallen on the bare floor and heaped upon the large table, it was only possible in this light to trace the outline.

Mrs Ambrose was writing a very long letter. Beginning 'Dear Bernard', it went on to describe what had been happening in the Villa San Gervasio during the past three months, as, for instance, that they had had the British Consul to dinner, and had been taken over a Spanish man-of-war, and had seen a great many processions and religious festivals, which were so beautiful that Mrs Ambrose couldn't conceive why, if people must have a religion, they didn't all become Roman Catholics. They had made several expeditions though none of any length. It was worth coming if only for the sake of the flowering trees which grew wild quite near the house, and the amazing colours of sea and earth. The earth, instead of being brown, was red, purple, green. 'You won't believe me,' she added, 'there is no colour like it in England.' She adopted, indeed, a condescending tone towards that poor island, which was now advancing chilly crocuses and nipped violets in nooks, in copses, in cosy corners, tended by rosy old gardeners in mufflers, who were always touching their hats and bobbing obsequiously. She went on to deride the islanders themselves. Rumours of London all in a ferment over a General Election had reached them even out here. 'It seems incredible,' she went on, 'that people should care whether Asquith is in or Austen Chamberlin out,[49] and while you scream yourselves hoarse about politics you let the only people who are trying for something good starve or simply laugh at them. When have you ever encouraged a living artist? Or bought his best work? Why are you all so ugly and so servile? Here the servants are human beings. They talk to one as if they were equals. As far as I can tell there are no aristocrats.'

Perhaps it was the mention of aristocrats that reminded her of Richard Dalloway and Rachel, for she ran on with the same penful to describe her niece.

'It's an odd fate that has put me in charge of a girl,' she wrote, 'considering that I have never got on well with women, or had much to do with them. However, I must retract some of the things that I have said against them. If they were properly educated I don't see why they shouldn't be much the same as men – as satisfactory I mean; though, of course, very different. The question is, how should one educate them. The present method seems to me abominable. This girl, though twenty-four, had never heard that men desired women, and, until I explained it, did not know how children were born. Her ignorance upon other matters as important' (here Mrs Ambrose's letter may not be quoted) . . . 'was complete. It seems to me not merely foolish but criminal to bring people up like that. Let alone the suffering to them, it explains why women are what they are – the wonder is they're no worse. I have taken it upon myself to enlighten her, and now, though still a good deal prejudiced and liable to exaggerate, she is more or less a reasonable human being. Keeping them ignorant, of course, defeats its own object, and when they begin to understand they take it all much too seriously. My brother-in-law really deserved a catastrophe – which he won't get. I now pray for a young man to come to my help; someone, I mean, who would talk to her openly, and prove how absurd most of her ideas about life are. Unluckily such men seem almost as rare as the women. The English colony certainly doesn't provide one: artists, merchants, cultivated people – they are stupid, conventional, and flirtatious . . . ' She ceased, and with her pen in her hand sat looking into the fire, making the logs into caves and mountains, for it had grown too dark to go on writing. Moreover, the house began to stir as the hour of dinner approached; she could hear the plates being chinked in the dining-room next door, and Chailey instructing the Spanish girl where to put things down in vigorous English. The bell rang; she rose, met Ridley and Rachel outside, and they all went in to dinner.

Three months had made but little difference in the appearance either of Ridley or Rachel; yet a keen observer might have thought that the girl was more definite and self-confident in her manner than before. Her skin was brown, her eyes certainly brighter, and she attended to what was said as though she might be going to contradict it. The meal began with the comfortable silence of people who are quite at their ease together. Then Ridley, leaning on his elbow and looking out of the window, observed that it was a lovely night.

'Yes,' said Helen. She added, 'The season's begun,' looking at the lights beneath them. She asked Maria in Spanish whether the hotel was not filling up with visitors. Maria informed her with pride that there would come a time when it was positively difficult to buy eggs – the shopkeepers would not mind what prices they asked; they would get them, at any rate, from the English.

'That's an English steamer in the bay,' said Rachel, looking at a triangle of lights below. 'She came in early this morning.'

'Then we may hope for some letters and send ours back,' said Helen.

For some reason the mention of letters always made Ridley groan, and the rest of the meal passed in a brisk argument between husband and wife as to whether he was or was not wholly ignored by the entire civilised world.

'Considering the last batch,' said Helen, 'you deserve beating. You were asked to lecture, you were offered a degree, and some silly woman praised not only your books but your beauty – she said he was what Shelley would have been if Shelley had lived to fifty-five and grown a beard. Really, Ridley, I think you're the vainest man I know,' she ended, rising from the table, 'which I may tell you is saying a good deal.'

Finding her letter lying before the fire she added a few lines to it, and then announced that she was going to take the letters now – Ridley must bring his – and Rachel?

'I hope you've written to your aunts? It's high time.'

The women put on cloaks and hats, and after inviting Ridley to come with them, which he emphatically refused to do, exclaiming that Rachel he expected to be a fool, but Helen surely knew better, they turned to go. He stood over the fire gazing into the depths of the looking-glass, and compressing his face into the likeness of a commander surveying a field of battle, or a martyr watching the flames lick his toes, rather than that of a secluded professor.

Helen laid hold of his beard.

'Am I a fool?' she said.

'Let me go, Helen.'

'Am I a fool?' she repeated.

'Vile woman!' he exclaimed, and kissed her.

'We'll leave you to your vanities,' she called back as they went out of the door.

It was a beautiful evening, still light enough to see a long way down the road, though the stars were coming out. The pillar-box was let into a high yellow wall where the lane met the road, and having dropped the letters into it, Helen was for turning back.

'No, no,' said Rachel, taking her by the wrist. 'We're going to see life. You promised.'

'Seeing life' was the phrase they used for their habit of strolling through the town after dark. The social life of Santa Marina was carried on almost entirely by lamplight, which the warmth of the nights and the scents culled from flowers made pleasant enough. The young women, with their hair magnificently swept in coils, a red flower behind the ear, sat on the doorsteps, or issued out on to balconies, while the young men ranged up and down beneath, shouting up a greeting from time to time and stopping here and there to enter into amorous talk. At the open windows merchants could be seen making up the day's account, and older women lifting jars from shelf to shelf. The streets were full of people, men for the most part, who interchanged their views of the world as they walked, or gathered round the wine-tables at the street corner, where an old cripple was twanging his guitar strings, while a poor girl cried her passionate song in the gutter. The two Englishwomen excited some friendly curiosity, but no one molested them.

Helen sauntered on, observing the different people in their shabby clothes, who seemed so careless and so natural, with satisfaction.

'Just think of the Mall tonight!'[50] she exclaimed at length. 'It's the fifteenth of March. Perhaps there's a Court.'[51] She thought of the crowd waiting in the cold spring air to see the grand carriages go by. 'It's very cold, if it's not raining,' she said. 'First there are men selling picture postcards; then there are wretched little shop-girls with round bandboxes; then there are bank clerks in tail coats; and then – any number of dressmakers. People from South Kensington drive up in a hired fly; officials have a pair of bays; earls, on the other hand, are allowed one footman to stand up behind; dukes have two; royal dukes – so I was told – have three; the king, I suppose, can have as many as he likes. And the people believe in it!'

Out here it seemed as though the people of England must be shaped in the body like the kings and queens, knights and pawns of the chessboard, so strange were their differences, so marked and so implicitly believed in.

They had to part in order to circumvent a crowd.

'They believe in God,' said Rachel as they regained each other. She meant that the people in the crowd believed in Him; for she remembered the crosses with bleeding plaster figures that stood where footpaths joined, and the inexplicable mystery of a service in a Roman Catholic church. 'We shall never understand!' she sighed.

They had walked some way and it was now night, but they could see a large iron gate a little way farther down the road on their left.

'Do you mean to go right up to the hotel?' Helen asked.

Rachel gave the gate a push; it swung open, and, seeing no one about and judging that nothing was private in this country, they walked straight on. An avenue of trees ran along the road, which was completely straight. The trees suddenly came to an end; the road turned a corner, and they found themselves confronted by a large square building. They had come out upon the broad terrace which ran round the hotel and were only a few feet distant from the windows. A row of long windows opened almost to the ground. They were all of them uncurtained, and all brilliantly lighted, so that they could see everything inside. Each window revealed a different section of the life of the hotel. They drew into one of the broad columns of shadow which separated the windows and gazed in. They found themselves just outside the dining-room. It was being swept; a waiter was eating a bunch of grapes with his leg across the corner of a table. Next door was the kitchen, where they were washing up; white cooks were dipping their arms into cauldrons, while the waiters made their meal voraciously off broken meats, sopping up the gravy with bits of crumb. Moving on, they became lost in a plantation of bushes, and then suddenly found themselves outside the drawing-room, where the ladies and gentlemen, having dined well, lay back in deep armchairs, occasionally speaking or turning over the pages of magazines. A thin woman was flourishing up and down the piano.

'What is a dahabeeyah,[52] Charles?' the distinct voice of a widow, seated in an armchair by the window, asked her son.

It was the end of the piece, and his answer was lost in the general clearing of throats and tapping of knees.

'They're all old in this room,' Rachel whispered.

Creeping on, they found that the next window revealed two men in shirt-sleeves playing billiards with two young ladies.

'He pinched my arm!' the plump young woman cried, as she missed her stroke.

'Now you two – no ragging,' the young man with the red face, who was marking, reproved them.

'Take care or we shall be seen,' whispered Helen, plucking Rachel by the arm. Incautiously her head had risen to the middle of the window.

Turning the corner they came to the largest room in the hotel, which was supplied with four windows, and was called the Lounge, although it was really a hall. Hung with armour and native embroideries, furnished with divans and screens, which shut off convenient corners, the room was less formal than the others, and was evidently the haunt of youth. Signor Rodriguez, whom they knew to be the manager of the hotel, stood quite near them in the doorway surveying the scene – the gentlemen lounging in chairs, the couples leaning over coffee-cups, the game of cards in the centre under profuse clusters of electric light. He was congratulating himself upon the enterprise which had turned the refectory, a cold stone room with pots on trestles, into the most comfortable room in the house. The hotel was very full, and proved his wisdom in decreeing that no hotel can flourish without a lounge.

The people were scattered about in couples or parties of four, and either they were actually better acquainted, or the informal room made their manners easier. Through the open window came an uneven humming sound like that which rises from a flock of sheep pent within hurdles at dusk. The card-party occupied the centre of the foreground.

Helen and Rachel watched them play for some minutes without being able to distinguish a word. Helen was observing one of the men intently. He was a lean, somewhat cadaverous man of about her own age, whose profile was turned to them, and he was the partner of a highly-coloured girl, obviously English by birth.

Suddenly, in the strange way in which some words detach themselves from the rest, they heard him say quite distinctly: 'All you want is practice, Miss Warrington; courage and practice – one's no good without the other.'

'Hughling Elliot! Of course!' Helen exclaimed. She ducked her head immediately, for at the sound of his name he looked up. The game went on for a few minutes, and was then broken up by the approach of a wheeled chair, containing a voluminous old lady who paused by the table and said: 'Better luck tonight, Susan?'

'All the luck's on our side,' said a young man who until now had kept his back turned to the window. He appeared to be rather stout, and had a thick crop of hair.

'Luck, Mr Hewet?' said his partner, a middle-aged lady with spectacles. 'I assure you, Mrs Paley, our success is due solely to our brilliant play.'

'Unless I go to bed early I get practically no sleep at all,' Mrs Paley was heard to explain, as if to justify her seizure of Susan, who got up and proceeded to wheel the chair to the door.

'They'll get someone else to take my place,' she said cheerfully. But she was wrong. No attempt was made to find another player, and after the young man had built three stories of a card-house, which fell down, the players strolled off in different directions.

Mr Hewet turned his full face towards the window. They could see that he had large eyes obscured by glasses; his complexion was rosy, his lips clean-shaven; and, seen among ordinary people, it appeared to be an interesting face. He came straight towards them, but his eyes were fixed not upon the eavesdroppers but upon a spot where the curtain hung in folds.

'Asleep?' he said.

Helen and Rachel started to think that someone had been sitting near to them unobserved all the time. There were legs in the shadow. A melancholy voice issued from above them.

'Two women,' it said.

A scuffling was heard on the gravel. The women had fled. They did not stop running until they felt certain that no eye could penetrate the darkness and the hotel was only a square shadow in the distance, with red holes regularly cut in it.

Chapter 9

An hour passed, and the downstairs rooms at the hotel grew dim and were almost deserted, while the little boxlike squares above them were brilliantly irradiated. Some forty or fifty people were going to bed. The thump of jugs set down on the floor above could be heard and the clink of china, for there was not as thick a partition between the rooms as one might wish, so Miss Allan, the elderly lady who had been playing bridge, determined, giving the wall a smart rap with her knuckles. It was only matchboard, she decided, run up to make many little rooms of one large one. Her grey petticoats slipped to the ground, and, stooping, she folded her clothes with neat, if not loving fingers, screwed her hair into a plait, wound her father's great gold watch, and opened the complete works of Wordsworth. She was reading *The Prelude*,[53] partly because she always read *The Prelude* abroad, and partly because she was engaged in writing a short *Primer of English Literature – Beowulf*[54] *to Swinburne*[55] – which would have a paragraph on Wordsworth. She was deep in the fifth book, stopping indeed to pencil a note, when a pair of boots dropped, one after another, on the floor above her. She looked up and speculated. Whose boots were they, she wondered. She then became aware of a swishing sound next door – a woman, clearly, putting away her dress. It was succeeded by a gentle tapping sound, such as that which accompanies hairdressing. It was very difficult to keep her attention fixed upon *The Prelude*. Was it Susan Warrington tapping? She forced herself, however, to read to the end of the book, when she placed a mark between the pages, sighed contentedly, and then turned out the light.

Very different was the room through the wall, though as like in shape as one egg-box is like another. As Miss Allan read her book, Susan Warrington was brushing her hair. Ages have consecrated this hour, and the most majestic of all domestic actions, to talk of love between women; but Miss Warrington being alone could not talk; she could only look with extreme solicitude at her own face in the glass. She turned her head from side to side, tossing heavy locks now this way now that; and then withdrew a pace or two, and considered herself seriously.

'I'm nice-looking,' she determined. 'Not pretty – possibly,' she drew herself up a little. 'Yes – most people would say I was handsome.'

She was really wondering what Arthur Venning would say she was.

Her feeling about him was decidedly queer. She would not admit to herself that she was in love with him or that she wanted to marry him, yet she spent every minute when she was alone in wondering what he thought of her, and in comparing what they had done today with what they had done the day before.

'He didn't ask me to play, but he certainly followed me into the hall,' she meditated, summing up the evening. She was thirty years of age, and owing to the number of her sisters and the seclusion of life in a country parsonage had as yet had no proposal of marriage. The hour of confidences was often a sad one, and she had been known to jump into bed, treating her hair unkindly, feeling herself overlooked by life in comparison with others. She was a big, well-made woman, the red lying upon her cheeks in patches that were too well defined, but her serious anxiety gave her a kind of beauty.

She was just about to pull back the bedclothes when she exclaimed, 'Oh, but I'm forgetting,' and went to her writing-table. A brown volume lay there stamped with the figure of the year. She proceeded to write in the square ugly hand of a mature child, as she wrote daily year after year, keeping the diaries though she seldom looked at them.

A.M. – Talked to Mrs H. Elliot about country neighbours. She knows the Manns; also the Selby-Carroways. How small the world is! Like her. Read a chapter of *Miss Appleby's Adventure* to Aunt E.

P.M. – Played lawn-tennis with Mr Perrott and Evelyn M. Don't *like* Mr P. Have a feeling that he is not 'quite', though clever certainly. Beat them. Day splendid, view wonderful. One gets used to no trees, though much too bare at first. Cards after dinner. Aunt E. cheerful, though twingy, she says. *Mem.: Ask about damp sheets.*

She knelt in prayer, and then lay down in bed, tucking the blankets comfortably about her, and in a few minutes her breathing showed that she was asleep. With its profoundly peaceful sighs and hesitations it resembled that of a cow standing up to its knees all night through in the long grass.

A glance into the next room revealed little more than a nose, prominent above the sheets. Growing accustomed to the darkness, for the windows were open and showed grey squares with splinters of starlight, one could distinguish a lean form, terribly like the body of a dead person, the body indeed of William Pepper, asleep too. Thirty-six, thirty-seven, thirty-eight – here were three Portuguese men of business, asleep presumably, since a snore came with the regularity of a great ticking clock. Thirty-nine was a corner room, at the end of the passage, but late though it was – 'One' struck gently downstairs – a line of light under the door showed that someone was still awake.

'How late you are, Hugh!' a woman, lying in bed, said in a peevish but solicitous voice. Her husband was brushing his teeth, and for some moments did not answer.

'You should have gone to sleep,' he replied. 'I was talking to Thornbury.'

'But you know that I never can sleep when I'm waiting for you,' she said.

To that he made no answer, but only remarked, 'Well then, we'll turn out the light.' They were silent.

The faint but penetrating pulse of an electric bell could now be heard in the corridor. Old Mrs Paley, having woken hungry but without her spectacles, was summoning her maid to find the biscuit-box. The maid having answered the bell, drearily respectful even at this hour though muffled in a mackintosh, the passage was left in silence. Downstairs all was empty and dark; but on the upper floor a light still burnt in the room where the boots had dropped so heavily above Miss Allan's head. Here was the gentleman who, a few hours previously, in the shade of the curtain, had seemed to consist entirely of legs. Deep in an armchair he was reading the third volume of Gibbon's *History of the Decline and Fall of Rome*[56] by candlelight. As he read he knocked the ash automatically, now and again, from his cigarette and turned the page, while a whole procession of splendid sentences entered his capacious brow and went marching through his brain in order. It seemed likely that this process might continue for an hour or more, until the entire regiment had shifted its quarters, had not the door opened and the young man who was inclined to be stout come in with large naked feet.

'Oh, Hirst, what I forgot to say was – '

'Two minutes,' said Hirst, raising his finger.

He safely stowed away the last words of the paragraph.

'What was it you forgot to say?' he asked.

'D'you think you *do* make enough allowance for feelings?' asked Mr Hewet. He had again forgotten what he had meant to say.

After intense contemplation of the immaculate Gibbon, Mr Hirst smiled at the question of his friend. He laid aside his book and considered.

'I should call yours a singularly untidy mind,' he observed. 'Feelings? Aren't they just what we do allow for? We put love up there, and all the rest somewhere down below.' With his left hand he indicated the top of a pyramid, and with his right the base. 'But you didn't get out of bed to tell me that,' he added severely.

'I got out of bed,' said Hewet vaguely, 'merely to talk I suppose.'

'Meanwhile I shall undress,' said Hirst. When naked of all but his shirt, and bent over the basin, Mr Hirst no longer impressed one with the majesty of his intellect, but with the pathos of his young yet ugly body, for he stooped, and he was so thin that there were dark lines between the different bones of his neck and shoulders.

'Women interest me,' said Hewet, who, sitting on the bed with his chin resting on his knees, paid no attention to the undressing of Mr Hirst.

'They're so stupid,' said Hirst. 'You're sitting on my pyjamas.'

'I suppose they *are* stupid?' Hewet wondered.

'There can't be two opinions about that, I imagine,' said Hirst, hopping briskly across the room, 'unless you're in love – that fat woman Warrington?' he enquired.

'Not one fat woman – all fat women,' Hewet sighed.

'The women I saw tonight were not fat,' said Hirst, who was taking advantage of Hewet's company to cut his toenails.

'Describe them,' said Hewet.

'You know I can't describe things!' said Hirst. 'They were much like other women, I should think. They always are.'

'No; that's where we differ,' said Hewet. 'I say everything's different. No two people are in the least the same. Take you and me now.'

'So I used to think once,' said Hirst. 'But now they're all types. Don't take us – take this hotel. You could draw circles round the whole lot of them, and they'd never stray outside.'

('You can kill a hen by doing that'), Hewet murmured.

'Mr Hughling Elliot, Mrs Hughling Elliot, Miss Allan, Mr and Mrs Thornbury – one circle,' Hirst continued. 'Miss Warrington, Mr Arthur Venning, Mr Perrott, Evelyn M. another circle; then there are a whole lot of natives; finally ourselves.'

'Are we all alone in our circle?' asked Hewet.

'Quite alone,' said Hirst. 'You try to get out, but you can't. You only make a mess of things by trying.'

'I'm not a hen in a circle,' said Hewet. 'I'm a dove on a tree-top.'

'I wonder if this is what they call an ingrowing toenail?' said Hirst, examining the big toe on his left foot.

'I flit from branch to branch,' continued Hewet. 'The world is profoundly pleasant.' He lay back on the bed, upon his arms.

'I wonder if it's really nice to be as vague as you are?' asked Hirst, looking at him. 'It's the lack of continuity – that's what's so odd about you,' he went on. 'At the age of twenty-seven, which is nearly thirty, you seem to have drawn no conclusions. A party of old women excites you still as though you were three.'

Hewet contemplated the angular young man who was neatly brushing the rims of his toenails into the fireplace in silence for a moment.

'I respect you, Hirst,' he remarked.

'I envy you – some things,' said Hirst. 'One: your capacity for not thinking; two: people like you better than they like me. Women like you, I suppose.'

'I wonder whether that isn't really what matters most?' said Hewet. Lying now flat on the bed he waved his hand in vague circles above him.

'Of course it is,' said Hirst. 'But that's not the difficulty. The difficulty is, isn't it, to find an appropriate object?'

'There are no female hens in your circle?' asked Hewet.

'Not the ghost of one,' said Hirst.

Although they had known each other for three years Hirst had never yet heard the true story of Hewet's loves. In general conversation it was taken for granted that they were many, but in private the subject was allowed to lapse. The fact that he had money enough to do no work, and that he had left Cambridge after two terms owing to a difference with the authorities, and had then travelled and drifted, made his life strange at many points where his friends' lives were much of a piece.

'I don't see your circles – I don't see them,' Hewet continued. 'I see a thing like a teetotum[57] spinning in and out – knocking into things – dashing from side to side – collecting numbers – more and more and more, till the whole place is thick with them. Round and round they go – out there, over the rim – out of sight.'

His fingers showed that the waltzing teetotums had spun over the edge of the counterpane and fallen off the bed into infinity.

'Could you contemplate three weeks alone in this hotel?' asked Hirst, after a moment's pause.

Hewet proceeded to think.

'The truth of it is that one never is alone, and one never is in company,' he concluded.

'Meaning?' said Hirst.

'Meaning? Oh, something about bubbles – auras – what d'you call 'em? You can't see my bubble; I can't see yours; all we see of each other is a speck, like the wick in the middle of that flame. The flame goes about with us everywhere; it's not ourselves exactly, but what we feel; the world is short, or people mainly; all kinds of people.'

'A nice streaky bubble yours must be!' said Hirst.

'And supposing my bubble could run into someone else's bubble – '

'And they both burst?' put in Hirst.

'Then – then – then – ' pondered Hewet, as if to himself, 'it would be an e–nor–mous world,' he said, stretching his arms to their full width, as though even so they could hardly clasp the billowy universe, for when he was with Hirst he always felt unusually sanguine and vague.

'I don't think you altogether as foolish as I used to, Hewet,' said Hirst. 'You don't know what you mean but you try to say it.'

'But aren't you enjoying yourself here?' asked Hewet.

'On the whole – yes,' said Hirst. 'I like observing people. I like looking at things. This country is amazingly beautiful. Did you notice how the top of the mountain turned yellow tonight? Really we must take our lunch and spend the day out. You're getting disgustingly fat.' He pointed at the calf of Hewet's bare leg.

'We'll get up an expedition,' said Hewet energetically. 'We'll ask the entire hotel. We'll hire donkeys and – '

'Oh, Lord!' said Hirst, 'do shut it! I can see Miss Warrington and Miss Allan and Mrs Elliot and the rest squatting on the stones and quacking, "How jolly!" '

'We'll ask Venning and Perrott and Miss Murgatroyd – everyone we can lay hands on,' went on Hewet. 'What's the name of the little old grasshopper with the eyeglasses? Pepper? – Pepper shall lead us.'

'Thank God, you'll never get the donkeys,' said Hirst.

'I must make a note of that,' said Hewet, slowly dropping his feet to the floor. 'Hirst escorts Miss Warrington; Pepper advances alone on a white ass; provisions equally distributed – or shall we hire a mule? The matrons – there's Mrs Paley, by Jove! – share a carriage.'

'That's where you'll go wrong,' said Hirst. 'Putting virgins among matrons.'

'How long should you think that an expedition like that would take, Hirst?' asked Hewet.

'From twelve to sixteen hours I would say,' said Hirst. 'The time usually occupied by a first confinement.'

'It will need considerable organisation,' said Hewet. He was now padding softly round the room, and stopped to stir the books on the table. They lay heaped one upon another.

'We shall want some poets too,' he remarked. 'Not Gibbon; no; d'you happen to have *Modern Love*[58] or *John Donne*[59]? You see, I contemplate pauses when people get tired of looking at the view, and then it would be nice to read something rather difficult aloud.'

'Mrs Paley *will* enjoy herself,' said Hirst.

'Mrs Paley will enjoy it certainly,' said Hewet. 'It's one of the saddest things I know – the way elderly ladies cease to read poetry. And yet how appropriate this is:

> I speak as one who plumbs
>   Life's dim profound,
> One who at length can sound
>   Clear views and certain.
> But – after love what comes?
>   A scene that lours,
> A few sad vacant hours,
>   And then, the curtain.[60]

I dare say Mrs Paley is the only one of us who can really understand that.'

'We'll ask her,' said Hirst. 'Please, Hewet, if you must go to bed, draw my curtain. Few things distress me more than the moonlight.'

Hewet retreated, pressing the poems of Thomas Hardy beneath his arm, and in their beds next door to each other both the young men were soon asleep.

Between the extinction of Hewet's candle and the rising of a dusky Spanish boy who was the first to survey the desolation of the hotel in the early morning, a few hours of silence intervened. One could almost hear a hundred people breathing deeply, and however wakeful and restless it would have been hard to escape sleep in the middle of so much sleep. Looking out of the windows, there was only darkness to be seen. All over the shadowed half of the world people lay prone, and a few flickering lights in empty streets marked the places where their cities were built. Red and yellow omnibuses were crowding each other in Piccadilly; sumptuous women were rocking at a standstill; but here in the darkness an owl flitted from tree to tree, and when the breeze lifted the branches the moon flashed as if it were a torch. Until all people should awake again the houseless animals were abroad, the tigers and the stags, and the elephants coming down in the darkness to drink at pools. The wind at night blowing over the hills and woods was purer and fresher than the wind by day, and the earth, robbed of detail, more mysterious than the earth coloured and divided by roads and fields. For six hours this profound beauty existed, and then as the east grew whiter and whiter the ground swam to the surface, the roads were revealed, the smoke rose and the people stirred, and the sun shone upon the windows of the hotel at Santa Marina until they were uncurtained, and the gong blaring all through the house gave notice of breakfast.

Directly breakfast was over, the ladies as usual circled vaguely, picking up papers and putting them down again, about the hall.

'And what are you going to do today?' asked Mrs Elliot drifting up against Miss Warrington.

Mrs Elliot, the wife of Hughling the Oxford don, was a short woman, whose expression was habitually plaintive. Her eyes moved from thing to thing as though they never found anything sufficiently pleasant to rest upon for any length of time.

'I'm going to try to get Aunt Emma out into the town,' said Susan. 'She's not seen a thing yet.'

'I call it so spirited of her at her age,' said Mrs Elliot, 'coming all this way from her own fireside.'

'Yes, we always tell her she'll die on board ship,' Susan replied. 'She was born on one,' she added.

'In the old days,' said Mrs Elliot, 'a great many people were. I always pity the poor women so! We've got a lot to complain of!' She shook her head. Her eyes wandered about the table, and she remarked irrelevantly, 'The poor little Queen of Holland![61] Newspaper reporters practically, one may say, at her bedroom door!'

'Were you talking of the Queen of Holland?' said the pleasant voice of Miss Allan, who was searching for the thick pages of *The Times* among a litter of thin foreign sheets.

'I always envy anyone who lives in such an excessively flat country,' she remarked.

'How very strange!' said Mrs Elliot. 'I find a flat country so depressing.'

'I'm afraid you can't be very happy here then, Miss Allan,' said Susan.

'On the contrary,' said Miss Allan, 'I am exceedingly fond of mountains.' Perceiving *The Times* at some distance, she moved off to secure it.

'Well, I must find my husband,' said Mrs Elliot, fidgeting away.

'And I must go to my aunt,' said Miss Warrington, and taking up the duties of the day they moved away.

Whether the flimsiness of foreign sheets and the coarseness of their type is any proof of frivolity and ignorance, there is no doubt that English people scarce consider news read there as news, any more than a programme bought from a man in the street inspires confidence in what it says. A very respectable elderly pair, having inspected the long tables of newspapers, did not think it worth their while to read more than the headlines.

'The debate on the fifteenth should have reached us by now,' Mrs Thornbury murmured. Mr Thornbury, who was beautifully clean and had red rubbed into his handsome worn face like traces of paint on a weather-beaten wooden figure, looked over his glasses and saw that Miss Allan had *The Times*.

The couple therefore sat themselves down in armchairs and waited.

'Ah, there's Mr Hewet,' said Mrs Thornbury. 'Mr Hewet,' she continued, 'do come and sit by us. I was telling my husband how much you reminded me of a dear old friend of mine – Mary Umpleby. She was a most delightful woman, I assure you. She grew roses. We used to stay with her in the old days.'

'No young man likes to have it said that he resembles an elderly spinster,' said Mr Thornbury.

'On the contrary,' said Mr Hewet, 'I always think it a compliment to remind people of someone else. But Miss Umpleby – why did she grow roses?'

'Ah, poor thing,' said Mrs Thornbury, 'that's a long story. She had gone through dreadful sorrows. At one time I think she would have lost her senses if it hadn't been for her garden. The soil was very much against her – a blessing in disguise; she had to be up at dawn – out in all weathers. And then there are creatures that eat roses. But she triumphed. She always did. She was a brave soul.' She sighed deeply but at the same time with resignation.

'I did not realise that I was monopolising the paper,' said Miss Allan, coming up to them.

'We were so anxious to read about the debate,' said Mrs Thornbury, accepting it on behalf of her husband. 'One doesn't realise how interesting a debate can be until one has sons in the navy. My interests are equally balanced, though; I have sons in the army too; and one son who makes speeches at the Union – my baby!'

'Hirst would know him, I expect,' said Hewet.

'Mr Hirst has such an interesting face,' said Mrs Thornbury. 'But I feel one ought to be very clever to talk to him. Well, William?' she enquired, for Mr Thornbury grunted.

'They're making a mess of it,' said Mr Thornbury. He had reached the second column of the report, a spasmodic column, for the Irish members [62] had been brawling three weeks ago at Westminster over a question of naval efficiency. After a disturbed paragraph or two, the column of print once more ran smoothly.

'You have read it?' Mrs Thornbury asked Miss Allan.

'No, I am ashamed to say I have only read about the discoveries in Crete,' said Miss Allan.

'Oh, but I would give so much to realise the ancient world!' cried Mrs

Thornbury. 'Now that we old people are alone – we're on our second honeymoon – I am really going to put myself to school again. After all we are *founded* on the past, aren't we, Mr Hewet? My soldier son says that there is still a great deal to be learnt from Hannibal.[63] One ought to know so much more than one does. Somehow when I read the paper, I begin with the debates first, and, before I've done, the door always opens – we're a very large party at home – and so one never does think enough about the ancients and all they've done for us. But *you* begin at the beginning, Miss Allan.'

'When I think of the Greeks I think of them as naked black men,' said Miss Allan, 'which is quite incorrect, I'm sure.'

'And you, Mr Hirst?' said Mrs Thornbury, perceiving that the gaunt young man was near. 'I'm sure you read everything.'

'I confine myself to cricket and crime,' said Hirst. 'The worst of coming from the upper classes,' he continued, 'is that one's friends are never killed in railway accidents.'

Mr Thornbury threw down the paper, and emphatically dropped his eyeglasses. The sheets fell in the middle of the group, and were eyed by them all.

'It's not gone well?' asked his wife solicitously.

Hewet picked up one sheet and read, 'A lady was walking yesterday in the streets of Westminster when she perceived a cat in the window of a deserted house. The famished animal – '

'I shall be out of it anyway,' Mr Thornbury interrupted peevishly.

'Cats are often forgotten,' Miss Allan remarked.

'Remember, William, the Prime Minister has reserved his answer,' said Mrs Thornbury.

'At the age of eighty, Mr Joshua Harris of Eeles Park, Brondesbury, has had a son,' said Hirst.

' . . . The famished animal, which had been noticed by workmen for some days, was rescued, but – by Jove! it bit the man's hand to pieces!'

'Wild with hunger, I suppose,' commented Miss Allan.

'You're all neglecting the chief advantage of being abroad,' said Mr Hughling Elliot, who had joined the group. 'You might read your news in French, which is equivalent to reading no news at all.'

Mr Elliot had a profound knowledge of Coptic,[64] which he concealed as far as possible, and quoted French phrases so exquisitely that it was hard to believe that he could also speak the ordinary tongue. He had an immense respect for the French.

'Coming?' he asked the two young men. 'We ought to start before it's really hot.'

'I beg of you not to walk in the heat, Hugh,' his wife pleaded, giving him an angular parcel enclosing half a chicken and some raisins.

'Hewet will be our barometer,' said Mr Elliot. 'He will melt before I shall.' Indeed, if so much as a drop had melted off his spare ribs, the bones would have lain bare.

The ladies were left alone now, surrounding *The Times* which lay upon the floor. Miss Allan looked at her father's watch. 'Ten minutes to eleven,' she observed.

'Work?' asked Mrs Thornbury.

'Work,' replied Miss Allan.

'What a fine creature she is!' murmured Mrs Thornbury, as the square figure in its manly coat withdrew.

'And I'm sure she has a hard life,' sighed Mrs Elliot.

'Oh, it *is* a hard life,' said Mrs Thornbury. 'Unmarried women – earning their livings – it's the hardest life of all.'

'Yet she seems pretty cheerful,' said Mrs Elliot.

'It must be very interesting,' said Mrs Thornbury. 'I envy her her knowledge.'

'But that isn't what women want,' said Mrs Elliot.

'I'm afraid it's all a great many can hope to have,' sighed Mrs Thornbury. 'I believe that there are more of us than ever now. Sir Harley Lethbridge was telling me only the other day how difficult it is to find boys for the navy – partly because of their teeth, it is true. And I have heard young women talk quite openly of – '

'Dreadful, dreadful!' exclaimed Mrs Elliot. 'The crown, as one may call it, of a woman's life. I, who know what it is to be childless – ' she sighed and ceased.

'But we must not be hard,' said Mrs Thornbury. 'The conditions are so much changed since I was a young woman.'

'Surely *maternity* does not change,' said Mrs Elliot.

'In some ways we can learn a great deal from the young,' said Mrs Thornbury. 'I learn so much from my own daughters.'

'I believe that Hughling really doesn't mind,' said Mrs Elliot. 'But then he has his work.'

'Women without children can do so much for the children of others,' observed Mrs Thornbury gently.

'I sketch a great deal,' said Mrs Elliot, 'but that isn't really an occupation. It's so disconcerting to find girls just beginning doing better than one does oneself! And nature's difficult – very difficult!'

'Are there not institutions – clubs – that you could help?' asked Mrs Thornbury.

'They are so exhausting,' said Mrs Elliot. 'I look strong, because of my colour; but I'm not; the youngest of eleven never is.'

'If the mother is careful before,' said Mrs Thornbury judicially, 'there is no reason why the size of the family should make any difference. And there is no training like the training that brothers and sisters give each other. I am sure of that. I have seen it with my own children. My eldest boy Ralph, for instance – '

But Mrs Elliot was inattentive to the elder lady's experience, and her eyes wandered about the hall.

'My mother had two miscarriages, I know,' she said suddenly. 'The first because she met one of those great dancing bears – they shouldn't be allowed; the other – it was a horrid story – our cook had a child and there was a dinner party. So I put my dyspepsia down to that.'

'And a miscarriage is so much worse than a confinement,' Mrs Thornbury murmured absent-mindedly, adjusting her spectacles and picking up *The Times*. Mrs Elliot rose and fluttered away.

When she had heard what one of the million voices speaking in the paper had to say, and noticed that a cousin of hers had married a clergyman at Minehead – ignoring the drunken women, the golden animals of Crete, the movements of battalions, the dinners, the reforms, the fires, the indignant, the learned and benevolent, Mrs Thornbury went upstairs to write a letter for the mail.

The paper lay directly beneath the clock, the two together seeming to represent stability in a changing world. Mr Perrott passed through; Mr Venning poised for a second on the edge of a table. Mrs Paley was wheeled past. Susan followed. Mr Venning strolled after her. Portuguese military families, their clothes suggesting late rising in untidy bedrooms, trailed across, attended by confidential nurses carrying noisy children. As midday drew on, and the sun beat straight upon the roof, an eddy of great flies droned in a circle; iced drinks were served under the palms; the long blinds were pulled down with a shriek, turning all the light yellow. The clock now had a silent hall to tick in, and an audience of four or five somnolent merchants. By degrees white figures with shady hats came in at the door, admitting a wedge of the hot summer day, and shutting it out again. After resting in the dimness for a minute, they went upstairs. Simultaneously, the clock wheezed one, and the gong sounded, beginning softly, working itself into a frenzy, and ceasing. There was a pause. Then all those who had gone upstairs came down; cripples came, planting both feet on the same step lest they should slip; prim little girls came, holding the nurse's finger; fat old men came still buttoning waistcoats. The gong had been sounded in the garden, and by degrees recumbent figures rose and strolled in to eat, since the time had come for them to feed again. There were pools and bars of shade in the garden even at midday, where two or three visitors could lie working or talking at their ease.

Owing to the heat of the day, luncheon was generally a silent meal, when people observed their neighbours and took stock of any new faces there might be, hazarding guesses as to who they were and what they did. Mrs Paley, although well over seventy and crippled in the legs, enjoyed her food and the peculiarities of her fellow-beings. She was seated at a small table with Susan.

'I shouldn't like to say what *she* is!' she chuckled, surveying a tall woman dressed conspicuously in white, with paint in the hollows of her cheeks, who was always late, and always attended by a shabby female follower, at which remark Susan blushed, and wondered why her aunt said such things.

Lunch went on methodically, until each of the seven courses was left in fragments and the fruit was merely a toy, to be peeled and sliced as a child destroys a daisy, petal by petal. The food served as an extinguisher upon any faint flame of the human spirit that might survive the midday heat, but Susan sat in her room afterwards, turning over and over the delightful fact that Mr Venning had come to her in the garden, and had sat there quite half an hour while she read aloud to her aunt. Men and women sought different corners where they could lie unobserved, and from two to four it might be said without exaggeration that the hotel was inhabited by bodies without souls. Disastrous would have been the result if a fire or a death had suddenly demanded something heroic of human nature, but tragedies come in the hungry hours. Towards four o'clock the human spirit again began to lick the body, as a flame licks a black promontory of coal. Mrs Paley felt it unseemly to open her toothless jaw so widely, though there was no one near, and Mrs Elliot surveyed her round flushed face anxiously in the looking-glass.

Half an hour later, having removed the traces of sleep, they met each other in the hall, and Mrs Paley observed that she was going to have her tea.

'You like your tea too, don't you?' she said, and invited Mrs Elliot, whose husband was still out, to join her at a special table which she had placed for her under a tree.

'A little silver goes a long way in this country,' she chuckled.

She sent Susan back to fetch another cup.

'They have such excellent biscuits here,' she said, contemplating a plateful. 'Not sweet biscuits, which I don't like – dry biscuits . . . Have you been sketching?'

'Oh, I've done two or three little daubs,' said Mrs Elliot, speaking rather louder than usual. 'But it's so difficult after Oxfordshire, where there are so many trees. The light's so strong here. Some people admire it, I know, but I find it very fatiguing.'

'I really don't need cooking, Susan,' said Mrs Paley, when her niece returned. 'I must trouble you to move me.' Everything had to be moved. Finally the old lady was placed so that the light wavered over her, as though she were a fish in a net. Susan poured out tea, and was just remarking that they were having hot weather in Wiltshire too, when Mr Venning asked whether he might join them.

'It's so nice to find a young man who doesn't despise tea,' said Mrs Paley, regaining her good humour. 'One of my nephews the other day asked for a glass of sherry – at five o'clock! I told him he could get it at the public house round the corner, but not in my drawing-room.'

'I'd rather go without lunch than tea,' said Mr Venning. 'That's not strictly true. I want both.'

Mr Venning was a dark young man, about thirty-two years of age, very slapdash and confident in his manner, although at this moment obviously a little excited. His friend Mr Perrott was a barrister, and as Mr Perrott refused to go anywhere without Mr Venning it was necessary, when Mr Perrott came to Santa Marina about a Company, for Mr Venning to come too. He was a barrister also, but he loathed a profession which kept him indoors over books, and directly his widowed mother died he was going, so he confided to Susan, to take up flying seriously, and become partner in a large business for making aeroplanes. The talk rambled on. It dealt, of course, with the beauties and singularities of the place, the streets, the people, and the quantities of unowned yellow dogs.

'Don't you think it dreadfully cruel the way they treat dogs in this country?' asked Mrs Paley.

'I'd have 'em all shot,' said Mr Venning.

'Oh, but the darling puppies,' said Susan.

'Jolly little chaps,' said Mr Venning. 'Look here, you've got nothing to eat.' A great wedge of cake was handed Susan on the point of a trembling knife. Her hand trembled too as she took it.

'I have such a dear dog at home,' said Mrs Elliot.

'My parrot can't stand dogs,' said Mrs Paley, with the air of one making a confidence. 'I always suspect that he (or she) was teased by a dog when I was abroad.'

'You didn't get far this morning, Miss Warrington,' said Mr Venning.

'It was hot,' she answered. Their conversation became private, owing to Mrs Paley's deafness and the long sad history which Mrs Elliot had embarked upon of a wire-haired terrier, white with just one black spot, belonging to an uncle of hers, which had committed suicide. 'Animals do commit suicide,' she sighed, as if she asserted a painful fact.

'Couldn't we explore the town this evening?' Mr Venning suggested.

'My aunt – ' Susan began.

'You deserve a holiday,' he said. 'You're always doing things for other people.'

'But that's my life,' she said, under cover of refilling the teapot.

'That's no one's life,' he returned, 'no young person's. You'll come?'

'I should like to come,' she murmured.

At this moment Mrs Elliot looked up and exclaimed, 'Oh, Hugh! He's bringing someone,' she added.

'He would like some tea,' said Mrs Paley. 'Susan, run and get some cups – there are the two young men.'

'We're thirsting for tea,' said Mr Elliot. 'You know Mr Ambrose, Hilda? We met on the hill.'

'He dragged me in,' said Ridley, 'or I should have been ashamed. I'm dusty and dirty and disagreeable.' He pointed to his boots which were white with dust, while a dejected flower drooping in his button-hole, like an exhausted animal over a gate, added to the effect of length and untidiness. He was introduced to the others. Mr Hewet and Mr Hirst brought chairs, and tea began again, Susan pouring cascades of water from pot to pot, always cheerfully, and with the competence of long use.

'My wife's brother,' Ridley explained to Hilda, whom he failed to remember, 'has a house here, which he has lent us. I was sitting on a rock thinking of nothing at all when Elliot started up like a fairy in a pantomime.'

'Our chicken got into the salt,' Hewet said dolefully to Susan. 'Nor is it true that bananas include moisture as well as sustenance.'

Hirst was already drinking.

'We've been cursing you,' said Ridley in answer to Mrs Elliot's kind enquiries about his wife. 'You tourists eat up all the eggs, Helen tells me. That's an eyesore too' – he nodded his head at the hotel. 'Disgusting luxury, I call it. We live with pigs in the drawing-room.'

'The food is not at all what it ought to be, considering the price,' said Mrs Paley seriously. 'But unless one goes to a hotel where is one to go to?'

'Stay at home,' said Ridley. 'I often wish I had! Everyone ought to stay at home. But, of course, they won't.'

Mrs Paley conceived a certain grudge against Ridley, who seemed to be criticising her habits after an acquaintance of five minutes.

'I believe in foreign travel myself,' she stated, 'if one knows one's native land, which I think I can honestly say I do. I should not allow any one to travel until they had visited Kent and Dorsetshire – Kent for the hops, and Dorsetshire for its old stone cottages. There is nothing to compare with them here.'

'Yes – I always think that some people like the flat and other people like the downs,' said Mrs Elliot rather vaguely.

Hirst, who had been eating and drinking without interruption, now lit a cigarette, and observed, 'Oh, but we're all agreed by this time that nature's a mistake. She's either very ugly, appallingly uncomfortable, or absolutely terrifying. I don't know which alarms me most – a cow or a tree. I once met a cow in a field by night. The creature looked at me. I assure you it turned my hair grey. It's a disgrace that the animals should be allowed to go at large.'

'And what did the cow think of *him*?' Venning mumbled to Susan, who immediately decided in her own mind that Mr Hirst was a dreadful young man, and that although he had such an air of being clever he probably wasn't as clever as Arthur, in the ways that really matter.

'Wasn't it Wilde[65] who discovered the fact that nature makes no allowance for hip-bones?' enquired Hughling Elliot. He knew by this time exactly what scholarships and distinction Hirst enjoyed, and had formed a very high opinion of his capacities.

But Hirst merely drew his lips together very tightly and made no reply.

Ridley conjectured that it was now permissible for him to take his leave. Politeness required him to thank Mrs Elliot for his tea, and to add, with a wave of his hand, 'You must come up and see us.'

The wave included both Hirst and Hewet, and Hewet answered, 'I should like it immensely.'

The party broke up, and Susan, who had never felt so happy in her life, was just about to start for her walk in the town with Arthur, when Mrs Paley beckoned her back. She could not understand from the book how Double Demon patience is played; and suggested that if they sat down and worked it out together it would fill up the time nicely before dinner.

Chapter 10

Among the promises which Mrs Ambrose had made her niece should she stay was a room cut off from the rest of the house, large, private – a room in which she could play, read, think, defy the world, a fortress as well as a sanctuary. Rooms, she knew, became more like worlds than rooms at the age of twenty-four. Her judgement was correct, and when she shut the door Rachel entered an enchanted place, where the poets sang and things fell into their right proportions. Some days after the vision of the hotel by night she was sitting alone, sunk in an armchair, reading a brightly-covered red volume lettered on the back *Works of Henrik Ibsen*.[66] Music was open on the piano, and books of music rose in two jagged pillars on the floor; but for the moment music was deserted.

Far from looking bored or absent-minded, her eyes were concentrated almost sternly upon the page, and from her breathing, which was slow but repressed, it could be seen that her whole body was constrained by the working of her mind. At last she shut the book sharply, lay back, and drew a deep breath, expressive of the wonder which always marks the transition from the imaginary world to the real world.

'What I want to know,' she said aloud, 'is this: What is the truth? What's the truth of it all?' She was speaking partly as herself, and partly as the heroine of the play she had just read. The landscape outside, because she had seen nothing but print for the space of two hours, now appeared amazingly solid and clear, but although there were men on the hill washing the trunks of olive trees with a white liquid, for the moment she herself was the most vivid thing in it – an heroic statue in the middle of the foreground, dominating the view. Ibsen's plays always left her in that condition. She acted them for days at a time, greatly to Helen's amusement; and then it would be Meredith's turn and she became Diana of the Crossways.[67] But Helen was aware that it was not all acting, and that some sort of change was taking place in the human being. When Rachel became tired of the rigidity of her pose on the back of the chair, she turned round, slid comfortably down into it, and gazed out over the furniture through the window opposite which opened on the garden. (Her mind wandered away from Nora, but she went on thinking of things that the book suggested to her, of women and life.)

During the three months she had been here she had made up considerably, as Helen meant she should, for time spent in interminable walks round sheltered gardens, and the household gossip of her aunts. But Mrs Ambrose would have been the first to disclaim any influence, or indeed any belief that to influence was within her power. She saw her less shy, and less serious, which was all to the good, and the violent leaps and the interminable mazes which had led to that result were usually not even guessed at by her. Talk was the medicine she trusted to, talk about everything, talk that was free, unguarded, and as candid as a habit of talking with men made natural in her own case. Nor did she encourage those habits of unselfishness and amiability founded upon insincerity which are put at so high a value in mixed households of men and women. She desired that Rachel should think, and for this reason offered books and discouraged too entire a dependence upon Bach and Beethoven and Wagner. But when Mrs Ambrose would have suggested Defoe,[68] Maupassant,[69] or some spacious chronicle of family life, Rachel chose modern books, books in shiny yellow covers, books with a great deal of gilding on the back, which were tokens in her aunt's eyes of harsh wrangling and disputes about facts which had no such importance as the moderns claimed for them. But she did not interfere. Rachel read what she chose, reading with the curious literalness of one to whom written sentences are unfamiliar, and handling words as though they were made of wood, separately of great importance, and possessed of shapes like tables or chairs. In this way she came to conclusions, which had to be remodelled according to the adventures of the day, and were indeed recast as liberally as anyone could desire, leaving always a small grain of belief behind them.

Ibsen was succeeded by a novel such as Mrs Ambrose detested, whose purpose was to distribute the guilt of a woman's downfall upon the right shoulders; a purpose which was achieved, if the reader's discomfort were any proof of it. She threw the book down, looked out of the window, turned away from the window, and relapsed into an armchair.

The morning was hot, and the exercise of reading left her mind contracting and expanding like the mainspring of a clock. The sounds in the garden outside joined with the clock, and the small noises of midday, which one can ascribe to no definite cause, in a regular rhythm. It was all very real, very big, very impersonal, and after a moment or two she began to raise her first finger and to let it fall on the arm of her chair so as to bring back to herself some consciousness of her own existence. She was next overcome by the unspeakable queerness of the fact that she should be sitting in an armchair, in the morning, in the middle of the world. Who were the people moving in the house – moving things from one place to another? And life, what was that? It was only a light passing over the surface and vanishing, as in time she would vanish, though the furniture in the room would remain. Her dissolution became so complete that she could not raise her finger any more, and sat perfectly still, listening and looking always at the same spot. It became stranger and stranger. She was overcome with awe that things should exist at all ... She forgot that she had any fingers to raise ... The things that existed were so immense and so desolate ... She continued to be conscious of these vast masses of substance for a long stretch of time, the clock still ticking in the midst of the universal silence.

'Come in,' she said mechanically, for a string in her brain seemed to be pulled by a persistent knocking at the door. With great slowness the door opened and a tall human being came towards her, holding out her arm and saying: 'What am I to say to this?'

The utter absurdity of a woman coming into a room with a piece of paper in her hand amazed Rachel.

'I don't know what to answer, or who Terence Hewet is,' Helen continued, in the toneless voice of a ghost. She put a paper before Rachel on which were written the incredible words:

DEAR MRS AMBROSE – I am getting up a picnic for next Friday, when we propose to start at eleven-thirty if the weather is fine, and to make the ascent of Monte Rosa. It will take some time, but the view should be magnificent. It would give me great pleasure if you and Miss Vinrace would consent to be of the party.

Yours sincerely,

TERENCE HEWET

Rachel read the words aloud to make herself believe in them. For the same reason she put her hand on Helen's shoulder.

'Books – books – books,' said Helen, in her absent-minded way. 'More new books – I wonder what you find in them ... '

For the second time Rachel read the letter, but to herself. This time, instead of seeming vague as ghosts, each word was astonishingly prominent; they came out as the tops of mountains come through a mist. *Friday – eleven-thirty – Miss Vinrace*. The blood began to run in her veins; she felt her eyes brighten.

'We must go,' she said, rather surprising Helen by her decision. 'We must certainly go' – such was the relief of finding that things still happened, and indeed they appeared the brighter for the mist surrounding them.

'Monte Rosa – that's the mountain over there, isn't it?' said Helen; 'but Hewet – who's he? One of the young men Ridley met, I suppose. Shall I say yes, then? It may be dreadfully dull.'

She took the letter back and went, for the messenger was waiting for her answer.

The party which had been suggested a few nights ago in Mr Hirst's bedroom had taken shape and was the source of great satisfaction to Mr Hewet, who had seldom used his practical abilities, and was pleased to find them equal to the strain. His invitations had been universally accepted, which was the more encouraging as they had been issued against Hirst's advice to people who were very dull, not at all suited to each other, and sure not to come.

'Undoubtedly,' he said, as he twirled and untwirled a note signed Helen Ambrose, 'the gifts needed to make a great commander have been absurdly overrated. About half the intellectual effort which is needed to review a book of modern poetry has enabled me to get together seven or eight people, of opposite sexes, at the same spot at the same hour on the same day. What else is generalship, Hirst? What more did Wellington do on the field of Waterloo?[70] It's like counting the number of pebbles of a path, tedious but not difficult.'

He was sitting in his bedroom, one leg over the arm of the chair, and Hirst was writing a letter opposite. Hirst was quick to point out that all the difficulties remained.

'For instance, here are two women you've never seen. Suppose one of them suffers from mountain-sickness, as my sister does, and the other – '

'Oh, the women are for you,' Hewet interrupted. 'I asked them solely for your benefit. What you want, Hirst, you know, is the society of young women of your own age. You don't know how to get on with women, which is a great defect, considering that half the world consists of women.'

Hirst groaned that he was quite aware of that.

But Hewet's complacency was a little chilled as he walked with Hirst to the place where a general meeting had been appointed. He wondered why on earth he had asked these people, and what one really expected to get from bunching human beings up together.

'Cows,' he reflected, 'draw together in a field; ships in a calm; and we're just the same when we've nothing else to do. But why do we do it? – is it to prevent ourselves from seeing to the bottom of things' (he stopped by a stream and began stirring it with his walking-stick and clouding the water with mud), 'making cities and mountains and whole universes out of nothing, or do we really love each other, or do we, on the other hand, live in a state of perpetual uncertainty, knowing nothing, leaping from moment to moment as from world to world? – which is, on the whole, the view *I* incline to.'

He jumped over the stream; Hirst went round and joined him, remarking that he had long ceased to look for the reason of any human action.

Half a mile farther, they came to a group of plane trees and the salmon-pink farmhouse standing by the stream which had been chosen as meeting-place. It was a shady spot, lying conveniently just where the hill sprung out from the flat. Between the thin stems of the plane trees the young men could see little knots of donkeys pasturing, and a tall woman rubbing the nose of one of them, while another woman was kneeling by the stream lapping water out of her palms.

As they entered the shady place, Helen looked up and then held out her hand.

'I must introduce myself,' she said. 'I am Mrs Ambrose.'

Having shaken hands, she said, 'That's my niece.'

Rachel approached awkwardly. She held out her hand, but withdrew it. 'It's all wet,' she said.

Scarcely had they spoken, when the first carriage drew up.

The donkeys were quickly jerked into attention, and the second carriage arrived. By degrees the grove filled with people – the Elliots, the Thornburys, Mr Venning and Susan, Miss Allan, Evelyn Murgatroyd and Mr Perrott. Mr Hirst acted the part of hoarse energetic sheepdog. By means of a few words of caustic Latin he had the animals marshalled, and by inclining a sharp shoulder he lifted the ladies. 'What Hewet fails to understand,' he remarked, 'is that we must break the back of the ascent before midday.' He was assisting a young lady, by name Evelyn Murgatroyd, as he spoke. She rose light as a bubble to her seat. With a feather drooping from a broad-brimmed hat, in white from top to toe, she looked like a gallant lady of the time of Charles I leading royalist troops into action.

'Ride with me,' she commanded; and, as soon as Hirst had swung himself across a mule, the two started, leading the cavalcade.

'You're not to call me Miss Murgatroyd. I hate it,' she said. 'My name's Evelyn. What's yours?'

'St John,' he said.

'I like that,' said Evelyn. 'And what's your friend's name?'

'His initials being R. S. T., we call him Monk,' said Hirst.

'Oh, you're all too clever,' she said. 'Which way? Pick me a branch. Let's canter.'

She gave her donkey a sharp cut with a switch and started forward. The full and romantic career of Evelyn Murgatroyd is best hit off by her own words, 'Call me Evelyn and I'll call you St John.' She said that on very slight provocation – her surname was enough – but although a great many young men had answered her already with considerable spirit she went on saying it and making choice of none. But her donkey stumbled to a jog-trot, and she had to ride in advance alone, for the path when it began to ascend one of the spines of the hill became narrow and scattered with stones. The cavalcade wound on like a jointed caterpillar, tufted with the white parasols of the ladies, and the panama hats of the gentlemen. At one point where the ground rose sharply, Evelyn M. jumped off, threw her reins to the native boy, and adjured St John Hirst to dismount too. Their example was followed by those who felt the need of stretching.

'I don't see any need to get off,' said Miss Allan to Mrs Elliot just behind her, 'considering the difficulty I had getting on.'

'These little donkeys stand anything, *n'est-ce pas*?' Mrs Elliot addressed the guide, who obligingly bowed his head.

'Flowers,' said Helen, stooping to pick the lovely little bright flowers which grew separately here and there. 'You pinch their leaves and then they smell,' she said, laying one on Miss Allan's knee.

'Haven't we met before?' asked Miss Allan, looking at her.

'I was taking it for granted,' Helen laughed, for in the confusion of meeting they had not been introduced.

'How sensible!' chirped Mrs Elliot. 'That's just what one would always like – only unfortunately it's not possible.'

'Not possible?' said Helen. 'Everything's possible. Who knows what mayn't happen before nightfall?' she continued, mocking the timidity of the poor lady who depended so implicitly upon one thing following another that the mere glimpse of a world where dinner could be disregarded, or the table moved one inch from its accustomed place, filled her with fears for her own stability.

Higher and higher they went, becoming separated from the world. The world, when they turned to look back, flattened itself out, and was marked with squares of thin green and grey.

'Towns are very small,' Rachel remarked, obscuring the whole of Santa Marina and its suburbs with one hand. The sea filled in all the angles of the coast smoothly, breaking in a white frill, and here and there ships were set firmly in the blue. The sea was stained with purple and green blots, and there was a glittering line upon the rim where it met the sky. The air was very clear and silent save for the sharp noise of grasshoppers and the hum of bees, which sounded loud in the ear as they shot past and vanished. The party halted and sat for a time in a quarry on the hillside.

'Amazingly clear,' exclaimed St John, identifying one cleft in the land after another.

Evelyn M. sat beside him, propping her chin on her hand. She surveyed the view with a certain look of triumph.

'D'you think Garibaldi [71] was ever up here?' she asked Mr Hirst. Oh, if she had been his bride! If, instead of a picnic party, this was a party of patriots, and she, red-shirted like the rest, had lain among grim men, flat on the turf, aiming her gun at the white turrets beneath them, screening her eyes to pierce through the smoke! So thinking, her foot stirred restlessly, and she exclaimed: 'I don't call this *life*, do you?'

'What do you call life?' said St John.

'Fighting – revolution,' she said, still gazing at the doomed city. 'You only care for books, I know.'

'You're quite wrong,' said St John.

'Explain,' she urged, for there were no guns to be aimed at bodies, and she turned to another kind of warfare.

'What do I care for? People,' he said.

'Well, I *am* surprised!' she exclaimed. 'You look so awfully serious. Do let's be friends and tell each other what we're like. I hate being cautious, don't you?'

But St John was decidedly cautious, as she could see by the sudden constriction of his lips, and had no intention of revealing his soul to a young lady. 'The ass is eating my hat,' he remarked, and stretched out for it instead of answering her. Evelyn blushed very slightly and then turned with some impetuosity upon Mr Perrott, and when they mounted again it was Mr Perrott who lifted her to her seat.

'When one has laid the eggs one eats the omelette,' said Hughling Elliot, exquisitely in French, a hint to the rest of them that it was time to ride on again.

The midday sun which Hirst had foretold was beginning to beat down hotly. The higher they got the more of the sky appeared, until the mountain was only a small tent of earth against an enormous blue background. The English fell silent; the natives who walked beside the donkeys broke into queer wavering songs and tossed jokes from one to the other. The way grew very steep, and each rider kept his eyes fixed on the hobbling curved form of the rider and donkey directly in front of him.

Rather more strain was being put upon their bodies than is quite legitimate in a party of pleasure, and Hewet overheard one or two slightly grumbling remarks.

'Expeditions in such heat are perhaps a little unwise,' Mrs Elliot murmured to Miss Allan. But Miss Allan returned, 'I always like to get to the top'; and it was true, although she was a big woman, stiff in the joints, and unused to donkey-riding, but as her holidays were few she made the most of them.

The vivacious white figure rode well in front; she had somehow possessed herself of a leafy branch and wore it round her hat like a garland. They went on for a few minutes in silence.

'The view will be wonderful,' Hewet assured them, turning round in his saddle and smiling encouragement. Rachel caught his eye and smiled too. They struggled on for some time longer, nothing being heard but the clatter of hooves striving on the loose stones. Then they saw that Evelyn was off her ass, and that Mr Perrott was standing in the attitude of a statesman in Parliament Square, stretching an arm of stone towards the view. A little to the left of them was a low ruined wall, the stump of an Elizabethan watchtower.

'I couldn't have stood it much longer,' Mrs Elliot confided to Mrs Thornbury, but the excitement of being at the top in another moment and seeing the view prevented anyone from answering her. One after another they came out on the flat space at the top and stood overcome with wonder. Before them they beheld an immense space – grey sands running into forest, and forest merging in mountains, and mountains washed by air, the infinite distances of South America. A river ran across the plain, as flat as the land, and appearing quite as stationary. The effect of so much space was at first rather chilling. They felt themselves very small, and for some time no one said anything. Then Evelyn exclaimed, 'Splendid!' She took hold of the hand that was next her; it chanced to be Miss Allan's hand.

'North – South – East – West,' said Miss Allan, jerking her head slightly towards the points of the compass.

Hewet, who had gone a little in front, looked up at his guests as if to justify himself for having brought them. He observed how strangely the people standing in a row with their figures bent slightly forward and their clothes plastered by the wind to the shape of their bodies resembled naked statues. On their pedestal of earth they looked unfamiliar and noble, but in another moment they had broken their rank, and he had to see to the laying out of food. Hirst came to his help, and they handed packets of chicken and bread from one to another.

As St John gave Helen her packet she looked him full in the face and said: 'Do you remember – two women?'

He looked at her sharply.

'I do,' he answered.

'So you're the two women!' Hewet exclaimed, looking from Helen to Rachel.

'Your lights tempted us,' said Helen. 'We watched you playing cards, but we never knew that we were being watched.'

'It was like a thing in a play,' Rachel added.

'And Hirst couldn't describe you,' said Hewet.

It was certainly odd to have seen Helen and to find nothing to say about her.

Hughling Elliot put up his eyeglass and grasped the situation.

'I don't know of anything more dreadful,' he said, pulling at the joint of a chicken's leg, 'than being seen when one isn't conscious of it. One feels sure one has been caught doing something ridiculous – looking at one's tongue in a hansom, for instance.'

Now the others ceased to look at the view, and drawing together sat down in a circle round the baskets.

'And yet those little looking-glasses in hansoms have a fascination of their own,' said Mrs Thornbury. 'One's features look so different when one can only see a bit of them.'

'There will soon be very few hansom cabs left,' said Mrs Elliot. 'And four-wheeled cabs – I assure you even at Oxford it's almost impossible to get a four-wheeled cab.'

'I wonder what happens to the horses,' said Susan.

'Veal pie,' said Arthur.

'It's high time that horses should become extinct anyhow,' said Hirst. 'They're distressingly ugly, besides being vicious.'

But Susan, who had been brought up to understand that the horse is the noblest of God's creatures, could not agree, and Venning thought Hirst an unspeakable ass, but was too polite not to continue the conversation.

'When they see us falling out of aeroplanes they get some of their own back, I expect,' he remarked.

'You fly?' said old Mr Thornbury, putting on his spectacles to look at him.

'I hope to, some day,' said Arthur.

Here flying was discussed at length, and Mrs Thornbury delivered an opinion which was almost a speech to the effect that it would be quite necessary in time of war, and in England we were terribly behindhand.

'If I were a young fellow,' she concluded, 'I should certainly qualify.' It was odd to look at the little elderly lady, in her grey coat and skirt, with a sandwich in her hand, her eyes lighting up with zeal as she imagined herself a young man in an aeroplane. For some reason, however, the talk did not run easily after this, and all they said was about drink and salt and the view. Suddenly Miss Allan, who was seated with her back to the ruined wall, put down her sandwich, picked something off her neck, and remarked, 'I'm covered with little creatures.' It was true, and the discovery was very welcome. The ants were pouring down a glacier of loose earth heaped between the stones of the ruin – large brown ants with polished bodies. She held out one on the back of her hand for Helen to look at.

'Suppose they sting?' said Helen.

'They will not sting, but they may infest the victuals,' said Miss Allan, and measures were taken at once to divert the ants from their course. At Hewet's suggestion it was decided to adopt the methods of modern warfare against an invading army. The tablecloth represented the invaded country, and round it they built barricades of baskets, set up the wine bottles in a rampart, made fortifications of bread and dug fosses of salt. When an ant got through it was exposed to a fire of bread-crumbs, until Susan pronounced that that was cruel, and rewarded those brave spirits with spoil in the shape of tongue. Playing this game they lost their stiffness, and even became unusually daring, for Mr Perrott, who was very shy, said, 'Permit me,' and removed an ant from Evelyn's neck.

'It would be no laughing matter really,' said Mrs Elliot confidentially to Mrs Thornbury, 'if an ant did get between the vest and the skin.'

The noise grew suddenly more clamorous, for it was discovered that a long line of ants had found their way on to the tablecloth by a back entrance, and if success could be gauged by noise, Hewet had every reason to think his party a success. Nevertheless he became, for no reason at all, profoundly depressed.

'They are not satisfactory; they are ignoble,' he thought, surveying his guests from a little distance, where he was gathering together the plates. He glanced at them all, stooping and swaying and gesticulating round the tablecloth. Amiable and modest, respectable in many ways, lovable even in their contentment and desire to be kind, how mediocre they all were, and capable of what insipid cruelty to one another! There was Mrs Thornbury, sweet but trivial in her maternal egoism; Mrs Elliot, perpetually complaining of her lot; her husband a mere pea in a pod; and Susan – she had no self, and counted neither one way nor the other; Venning was as honest and as brutal as a schoolboy; poor old

Thornbury merely trod his round like a horse in a mill; and the less one examined into Evelyn's character the better, he suspected. Yet these were the people with money, and to them rather than to others was given the management of the world. Put among them someone more vital, who cared for life or for beauty, and what an agony, what a waste would they inflict on him if he tried to share with them and not to scourge!

'There's Hirst,' he concluded, coming to the figure of his friend; with his usual little frown of concentration upon his forehead he was peeling the skin off a banana. 'And he's as ugly as sin.' For the ugliness of St John Hirst, and the limitations that went with it, he made the rest in some way responsible. It was their fault that he had to live alone. Then he came to Helen, attracted to her by the sound of her laugh. She was laughing at Miss Allan. 'You wear combinations in this heat?' she said in a voice which was meant to be private. He liked the look of her immensely, not so much her beauty, but her largeness and simplicity, which made her stand out from the rest like a great stone woman, and he passed on in a gentler mood. His eye fell upon Rachel. She was lying back rather behind the others resting on one elbow; she might have been thinking precisely the same thoughts as Hewet himself. Her eyes were fixed rather sadly but not intently upon the row of people opposite her. Hewet crawled up to her on his knees, with a piece of bread in his hand.

'What are you looking at?' he asked.

She was a little startled, but answered directly, 'Human beings.'

Chapter 11

One after another they rose and stretched themselves, and in a few minutes divided more or less into two separate parties. One of these parties was dominated by Hughling Elliot and Mrs Thornbury, who, having both read the same books and considered the same questions, were now anxious to name the places beneath them and to hang upon them stores of information about navies and armies, political parties, natives and mineral products – all of which combined, they said, to prove that South America was the country of the future.

Evelyn M. listened with her bright blue eyes fixed upon the oracles.

'How it makes one long to be a man!' she exclaimed.

Mr Perrott answered, surveying the plain, that a country with a future was a very fine thing.

'If I were you,' said Evelyn, turning to him and drawing her glove vehemently through her fingers, 'I'd raise a troop and conquer some great territory and make it splendid. You'd want women for that. I'd love to start life from the very beginning as it ought to be – nothing squalid – but great halls and gardens and splendid men and women. But you – you only like Law Courts!'

'And would you really be content without pretty frocks and sweets and all the things young ladies like?' asked Mr Perrott, concealing a certain amount of pain beneath his ironical manner.

'I'm not a young lady,' Evelyn flashed; she bit her underlip. 'Just because I like splendid things you laugh at me. Why are there no men like Garibaldi now?' she demanded.

'Look here,' said Mr Perrott, 'you don't give me a chance. You think we ought to begin things fresh. Good. But I don't see precisely – conquer a territory? They're all conquered already, aren't they?'

'It's not any territory in particular,' Evelyn explained. 'It's the idea, don't you see? We lead such tame lives. And I feel sure you've got splendid things in you.'

Hewet saw the scars and hollows in Mr Perrott's sagacious face relax pathetically. He could imagine the calculations which even then went on within his mind, as to whether he would be justified in asking a woman to marry him, considering that he made no more than five hundred a year at the Bar, owned no private means, and had an invalid sister to support. Mr Perrott again knew that he was not 'quite', as Susan stated in her diary; not quite a gentleman she meant, for he was the son of a grocer in Leeds, had started life with a basket on his back, and now, though practically indistinguishable from a born gentleman, showed his origin to keen eyes in an impeccable neatness of dress, lack of freedom in manner, extreme cleanliness of person, and a certain indescribable timidity and precision with his knife and fork which might be the relic of days when meat was rare, and the way of handling it by no means gingerly.

The two parties who were strolling about and losing their unity now came together, and joined each other in a long stare over the yellow and green patches of the heated landscape below. The hot air danced across it, making it impossible to see the roofs of a village on the plain distinctly. Even on the top of the mountain where a breeze played lightly, it was very hot, and the heat, the food, the immense space, and perhaps some less well-defined cause produced a comfortable drowsiness and a sense of happy relaxation in them. They did not say much, but felt no constraint in being silent.

'Suppose we go and see what's to be seen over there?' said Arthur to Susan, and the pair walked off together, their departure certainly sending some thrill of emotion through the rest.

'An odd lot, aren't they?' said Arthur. 'I thought we should never get 'em all to the top. But I'm glad we came, by Jove! I wouldn't have missed this for something.'

'I don't *like* Mr Hirst,' said Susan inconsequently. 'I suppose he's very clever, but why should clever people be so – I expect he's awfully nice, really,' she added, instinctively qualifying what might have seemed an unkind remark.

'Hirst? Oh, he's one of these learned chaps,' said Arthur indifferently. 'He don't look as if he enjoyed it. You should hear him talking to Elliot. It's as much as I can do to follow 'em at all . . . I was never good at my books.'

With these sentences and the pauses that came between them they reached a little hillock, on the top of which grew several slim trees.

'D'you mind if we sit down here?' said Arthur, looking about him. 'It's jolly in the shade – and the view – ' They sat down, and looked straight ahead of them in silence for some time.

'But I do envy those clever chaps sometimes,' Arthur remarked. 'I don't suppose they ever . . . ' He did not finish his sentence.

'I can't see why you should envy them,' said Susan, with great sincerity.

'Odd things happen to one,' said Arthur. 'One goes along smoothly enough, one thing following another, and it's all very jolly and plain sailing, and you think you know all about it, and suddenly one doesn't know where one is a bit, and everything seems different from what it used to seem. Now today, coming up that path, riding behind you, I seemed to see everything as if – ' he paused and plucked a piece of grass up by the roots. He scattered the little lumps of earth which were sticking to the roots – 'As if it had a kind of meaning. You've made the difference to me,' he jerked out, 'I don't see why I shouldn't tell you. I've felt it ever since I knew you . . . It's because I love you.'

Even while they had been saying commonplace things Susan had been conscious of the excitement of intimacy, which seemed not only to lay bare something in her, but in the trees and the sky, and the progress of his speech which seemed inevitable was positively painful to her, for no human being had ever come so close to her before.

She was struck motionless as his speech went on, and her heart gave great separate leaps at the last words. She sat with her fingers curled round a stone, looking straight in front of her down the mountain over the plain. So then, it had actually happened to her, a proposal of marriage.

Arthur looked round at her; his face was oddly twisted. She was drawing her breath with such difficulty that she could hardly answer.

'You might have known.' He seized her in his arms; again and again and again they clasped each other, murmuring inarticulately.

'Well,' sighed Arthur, sinking back on the ground, 'that's the most wonderful thing that's ever happened to me.' He looked as if he were trying to put things seen in a dream beside real things.

There was a long silence.

'It's the most perfect thing in the world,' Susan stated, very gently and with great conviction. It was no longer merely a proposal of marriage, but of marriage with Arthur, with whom she was in love.

In the silence that followed, holding his hand tightly in hers, she prayed to God that she might make him a good wife.

'And what will Mr Perrott say?' she asked at the end of it.

'Dear old fellow,' said Arthur who, now that the first shock was over, was relaxing into an enormous sense of pleasure and contentment. 'We must be very nice to him, Susan.'

He told her how hard Perrott's life had been, and how absurdly devoted he was to Arthur himself. He went on to tell her about his mother, a widow lady, of strong character. In return Susan sketched the portraits of her own family – Edith in particular, her youngest sister, whom she loved better than anyone else, 'except you, Arthur . . . Arthur,' she continued, 'what was it that you first liked me for?'

'It was a buckle you wore one night at sea,' said Arthur, after due consideration. 'I remember noticing – it's an absurd thing to notice! – that you didn't take peas, because I don't either.'

From this they went on to compare their more serious tastes, or rather Susan ascertained what Arthur cared about, and professed herself very fond of the same thing. They would live in London, perhaps have a cottage in the country near Susan's family, for they would find it strange without her at first. Her mind, stunned to begin with, now flew to the various changes that her engagement would make – how delightful it would be to join the ranks of the married women – no longer to hang on to groups of girls much younger than herself – to escape the long solitude of an old maid's life. Now and then her amazing good fortune overcame her, and she turned to Arthur with an exclamation of love.

They lay in each other's arms and had no notion that they were observed. Yet two figures suddenly appeared among the trees above them. 'Here's shade,' began Hewet, when Rachel suddenly stopped dead. They saw a man and woman lying on the ground beneath them, rolling slightly this way and that as the embrace tightened and slackened. The man then sat upright and the woman, who now appeared to be Susan Warrington, lay back upon the ground, with her eyes shut and an absorbed look upon her face, as though she were not altogether conscious. Nor could you tell from her expression whether she was happy, or had suffered something. When Arthur again turned to her, butting her as a lamb butts a ewe, Hewet and Rachel retreated without a word. Hewet felt uncomfortably shy.

'I don't like that,' said Rachel after a moment.

'I can remember not liking it either,' said Hewet. 'I can remember –' but he changed his mind and continued in an ordinary tone of voice, 'Well, we may take it for granted that they're engaged. D'you think he'll ever fly, or will she put a stop to that?'

But Rachel was still agitated; she could not get away from the sight they had just seen. Instead of answering Hewet she persisted.

'Love's an odd thing, isn't it, making one's heart beat.'

'It's so enormously important, you see,' Hewet replied. 'Their lives are now changed for ever.'

'And it makes one sorry for them too,' Rachel continued, as though she were tracing the course of her feelings. 'I don't know either of them, but I could almost burst into tears. That's silly, isn't it?'

'Just because they're in love,' said Hewet. 'Yes,' he added after a moment's consideration, 'there's something horribly pathetic about it, I agree.'

And now, as they had walked some way from the grove of trees, and had come to a rounded hollow very tempting to the back, they proceeded to sit down, and the impression of the lovers lost some of its force, though a certain intensity of vision, which was probably the result of the sight, remained with them. As a day upon which any emotion has been repressed is different from other days, so this day was now different, merely because they had seen other people at a crisis of their lives.

'A great encampment of tents they might be,' said Hewet, looking in front of him at the mountains. 'Isn't it like a watercolour too – you know the way watercolours dry in ridges all across the paper – I've been wondering what they looked like.'

His eyes became dreamy, as though he were matching things, and reminded Rachel in their colour of the green flesh of a snail. She sat beside him looking at the mountains too. When it became painful to look any longer, the great size of the view seeming to enlarge her eyes beyond their natural limit, she looked at the ground; it pleased her to scrutinise this inch of the soil of South America so minutely that she noticed every grain of earth and made it into a world where she was endowed with the supreme power. She bent a blade of grass, and set an insect on the utmost tassel of it, and wondered if the insect realised his strange adventure, and thought how strange it was that she should have bent that tassel rather than any other of the million tassels.

'You've never told me you name,' said Hewet suddenly. 'Miss Somebody Vinrace . . . I like to know people's Christian names.'

'Rachel,' she replied.

'Rachel,' he repeated. 'I have an aunt called Rachel, who put the life of Father Damien[72] into verse. She is a religious fanatic – the result of the way she was brought up, down in Northamptonshire, never seeing a soul. Have you any aunts?'

'I live with them,' said Rachel.

'And I wonder what they're doing now?' Hewet enquired.

'They are probably buying wool,' Rachel determined. She tried to describe them. 'They are small, rather pale women,' she began, 'very clean. We live in Richmond. They have an old dog, too, who will only eat the marrow out of bones . . . They are always going to church. They tidy their drawers a good deal.' But here she was overcome by the difficulty of describing people.

'It's impossible to believe that it's all going on still!' she exclaimed.

The sun was behind them and two long shadows suddenly lay upon the ground in front of them, one waving because it was made by a skirt, and the other stationary, because thrown by a pair of legs in trousers.

'You look very comfortable!' said Helen's voice above them.

'Hirst,' said Hewet, pointing at the scissorlike shadow; he then rolled round to look up at them.

'There's room for us all here,' he said.

When Hirst had seated himself comfortably, he said: 'Did you congratulate the young couple?'

It appeared that, coming to the same spot a few minutes after Hewet and Rachel, Helen and Hirst had seen precisely the same thing.

'No, we didn't congratulate them,' said Hewet. 'They seemed very happy.'

'Well,' said Hirst, pursing up his lips, 'so long as I needn't marry either of them – '

'We were very much moved,' said Hewet.

'I thought you would be,' said Hirst. 'Which was it, Monk? The thought of the immortal passions, or the thought of new-born males to keep the Roman Catholics out? I assure you,' he said to Helen, 'he's capable of being moved by either.'

Rachel was a good deal stung by his banter, which she felt to be directed equally against them both, but she could think of no repartee.

'Nothing moves Hirst,' Hewet laughed; he did not seem to be stung at all. 'Unless it were a transfinite number falling in love with a finite one – I suppose such things do happen, even in mathematics.'

'On the contrary,' said Hirst with a touch of annoyance, 'I consider myself a person of very strong passions.' It was clear from the way he spoke that he meant it seriously; he spoke of course for the benefit of the ladies.

'By the way, Hirst,' said Hewet, after a pause, 'I have a terrible confession to make. Your book – the poems of Wordsworth, which if you remember I took off your table just as we were starting, and certainly put in my pocket here – '

'Is lost,' Hirst finished for him.

'I consider that there is still a chance,' Hewet urged, slapping himself to right and left, 'that I never did take it after all.'

'No,' said Hirst. 'It is here.' He pointed to his breast.

'Thank God,' Hewet exclaimed. 'I need no longer feel as though I'd murdered a child!'

'I should think you were always losing things,' Helen remarked, looking at him meditatively.

'I don't lose things,' said Hewet. 'I mislay them. That was the reason why Hirst refused to share a cabin with me on the voyage out.'

'You came out together?' Helen enquired.

'I propose that each member of this party now gives a short biographical sketch of himself or herself,' said Hirst, sitting upright. 'Miss Vinrace, you come first; begin.'

Rachel stated that she was twenty-four years of age, the daughter of a ship-owner, that she had never been properly educated; played the piano, had no brothers or sisters, and lived at Richmond with aunts, her mother being dead.

'Next,' said Hirst, having taken in these facts; he pointed at Hewet. 'I am the son of an English gentleman. I am twenty-seven,' Hewet began. 'My father was a fox-hunting squire. He died when I was ten in the hunting field. I can remember his body coming home, on a shutter I suppose, just as I was going down to tea, and noticing that there was jam for tea, and wondering whether I should be allowed – '

'Yes; but keep to the facts,' Hirst put in.

'I was educated at Winchester[73] and Cambridge, which I had to leave after a time. I have done a good many things since – '

'Profession?'

'None – at least – '

'Tastes?'

'Literary. I'm writing a novel.'

'Brothers and sisters?'

'Three sisters, no brother, and a mother.'

'Is that all we're to hear about you?' said Helen. She stated that she was very old – forty last October, and her father had been a solicitor in the city who had gone bankrupt, for which reason she had never had much education – they lived in one place after another – but an elder brother used to lend her books.

'If I were to tell you everything – ' she stopped and smiled. 'It would take too long,' she concluded. 'I married when I was thirty, and I have two children. My husband is a scholar. And now – it's your turn,' she nodded at Hirst.

'You've left out a great deal,' he reproved her. 'My name is St John Alaric Hirst,' he began in a jaunty tone of voice. 'I'm twenty-four years old. I'm the son of the Reverend Sidney Hirst, vicar of Great Wappyng in Norfolk. Oh, I got scholarships everywhere – Westminster – King's.[74] I'm now a fellow of King's. Don't it sound dreary? Parents both alive (alas). Two brothers and one sister. I'm a very distinguished young man,' he added.

'One of the three, or is it five, most distinguished men in England,' Hewet remarked.

'Quite correct,' said Hirst.

'That's all very interesting,' said Helen after a pause. 'But of course we've left out the only questions that matter. For instance, are we Christians?'

'I am not,' 'I am not,' both the young men replied.

'I am,' Rachel stated.

'You believe in a personal God?' Hirst demanded, turning round and fixing her with his eyeglasses.

'I believe – I believe,' Rachel stammered, 'I believe there are things we don't know about, and the world might change in a minute and anything appear.'

At this Helen laughed outright. 'Nonsense,' she said. 'You're not a Christian. You've never thought what you are. – And there are lots of other questions,' she continued, 'though perhaps we can't ask them yet.' Although they had talked so freely they were all uncomfortably conscious that they really knew nothing about each other.

'The important questions,' Hewet pondered, 'the really interesting ones. I doubt that one ever does ask them.'

Rachel, who was slow to accept the fact that only a very few things can be said even by people who know each other well, insisted on knowing what he meant.

'Whether we've ever been in love?' she enquired. 'Is that the kind of question you mean?'

Again Helen laughed at her, benignantly strewing her with handfuls of the long tasselled grass, for she was so brave and so foolish.

'Oh, Rachel,' she cried. 'It's like having a puppy in the house having you with one – a puppy that brings one's underclothes down into the hall.'

But again the sunny earth in front of them was crossed by fantastic wavering figures, the shadows of men and women.

'There they are!' exclaimed Mrs Elliot. There was a touch of peevishness in her voice. 'And we've had *such* a hunt to find you. Do you know what the time is?'

Mrs Elliot and Mr and Mrs Thornbury now confronted them; Mrs Elliot was holding out her watch, and playfully tapping it upon the face. Hewet was recalled to the fact that this was a party for which he was responsible, and he immediately led them back to the watchtower, where they were to have tea before starting home again. A bright crimson scarf fluttered from the top of the wall, which Mr Perrott and

Evelyn were tying to a stone as the others came up. The heat had changed just so far that instead of sitting in the shadow they sat in the sun, which was still hot enough to paint their faces red and yellow, and to colour great sections of the earth beneath them.

'There's nothing half so nice as tea!' said Mrs Thornbury, taking her cup.

'Nothing,' said Helen. 'Can't you remember as a child chopping up hay – ' she spoke much more quickly than usual, and kept her eye fixed upon Mrs Thornbury, 'and pretending it was tea, and getting scolded by the nurses – why I can't imagine, except that nurses are such brutes, won't allow pepper instead of salt though there's no earthly harm in it. Weren't your nurses just the same?'

During this speech Susan came into the group, and sat down by Helen's side. A few minutes later Mr Venning strolled up from the opposite direction. He was a little flushed, and in the mood to answer hilariously whatever was said to him.

'What have you been doing to that old chap's grave?' he asked, pointing to the red flag which floated from the top of the stones.

'We have tried to make him forget his misfortune in having died three hundred years ago,' said Mr Perrott.

'It would be awful – to be dead!' ejaculated Evelyn M.

'To be dead?' said Hewet. 'I don't think it would be awful. It's quite easy to imagine. When you go to bed tonight fold your hands so – breathe slower and slower – ' He lay back with his hands clasped upon his breast, and his eyes shut, 'Now,' he murmured in an even monotonous voice, 'I shall never, never, never move again.' His body, lying flat among them, did for a moment suggest death.

'This is a horrible exhibition, Mr Hewet!' cried Mrs Thornbury.

'More cake for us!' said Arthur.

'I assure you there's nothing horrible about it,' said Hewet, sitting up and laying hands upon the cake.

'It's so natural,' he repeated. 'People with children should make them do that exercise every night . . . Not that I look forward to being dead.'

'And when you allude to a grave,' said Mr Thornbury, who spoke almost for the first time, 'have you any authority for calling that ruin a grave? I am quite with you in refusing to accept the common interpretation which declares it to be the remains of an Elizabethan watchtower – any more than I believe that the circular mounds or barrows which we find on the top of our English downs were camps. The antiquaries call everything a camp. I am always asking them, Well then, where do you think our ancestors kept their cattle? Half the camps in England are merely the ancient pound or barton as we call it in my part of the world. The argument that no one would keep his cattle in such exposed and inaccessible spots has no weight at all, if you reflect that in those days a man's cattle were his capital, his stock-in-trade, his daughter's dowries. Without cattle he was a serf, another man's man . . . ' His eyes slowly lost their intensity, and he muttered a few concluding words under his breath, looking curiously old and forlorn.

Hughling Elliot, who might have been expected to engage the old gentleman in argument, was absent at the moment. He now came up holding out a large square of cotton upon which a fine design was printed in pleasant bright colours that made his hand look pale.

'A bargain,' he announced, laying it down on the cloth. 'I've just bought it from the big man with the ear-rings. Fine, isn't it? It wouldn't suit everyone, of course, but it's just the thing – isn't it, Hilda? – for Mrs Raymond Parry.'

'Mrs Raymond Parry!' cried Helen and Mrs Thornbury at the same moment.

They looked at each other as though a mist hitherto obscuring their faces had been blown away.

'Ah – you have been to those wonderful parties too?' Mrs Elliot asked with interest.

Mrs Parry's drawing-room, though thousands of miles away, behind a vast curve of water on a tiny piece of earth, came before their eyes. They who had had no solidity or anchorage before seemed to be attached to it somehow, and at once grown more substantial. Perhaps they had been in the drawing-room at the same moment; perhaps they had passed each other on the stairs; at any rate they knew some of the same people. They looked one another up and down with new interest. But they could do no more than look at each other, for there was no time to enjoy the fruits of the discovery. The donkeys were advancing, and it was advisable to begin the descent immediately, for the night fell so quickly that it would be dark before they were home again.

Accordingly, remounting in order, they filed off down the hillside. Scraps of talk came floating back from one to another. There were jokes to begin with, and laughter; some walked part of the way, and picked flowers, and sent stones bounding before them.

'Who writes the best Latin verse in your college, Hirst?' Mr Elliot called back incongruously, and Mr Hirst returned that he had no idea.

The dusk fell as suddenly as the natives had warned them, the hollows of the mountain on either side filling up with darkness and the path becoming so dim that it was surprising to hear the donkeys' hooves still striking on hard rock. Silence fell upon one, and then upon another, until they were all silent, their minds spilling out into the deep blue air. The way seemed shorter in the dark than in the day; and soon the lights of the town were seen on the flat far beneath them.

Suddenly someone cried, 'Ah!'

In a moment a slow yellow drop rose again from the plain below; it rose, paused, opened like a flower, and fell in a shower of drops.

'Fireworks,' they cried.

Another went up more quickly; and then another; they could almost hear it twist and roar.

'Some saint's day, I suppose,' said a voice. The rush and embrace of the rockets as they soared up into the air seemed like the fiery way in which lovers suddenly rose and united, leaving the crowd gazing up at them with strained white faces. But Susan and Arthur, riding down the hill, never said a word to each other, and kept accurately apart.

Then the fireworks became erratic, and soon they ceased altogether, and the rest of the journey was made almost in darkness, the mountain being a great shadow behind them, and bushes and trees little shadows which threw darkness across the road. Among the plane trees they separated, bundling into carriages and driving off, without saying good-night, or saying it only in a half-muffled way.

It was so late that there was no time for normal conversation between their arrival at the hotel and their retirement to bed. But Hirst wandered into Hewet's room with a collar in his hand.

'Well, Hewet,' he remarked, on the crest of a gigantic yawn, 'that was a great success, I consider.' He yawned. 'But take care you're not landed with that young woman . . . I don't really like young women . . . '

Hewet was too much drugged by hours in the open air to make any reply. In fact every one of the party was sound asleep within ten minutes or so of each other, with the exception of Susan Warrington. She lay for a considerable time looking blankly at the wall opposite, her hands clasped above her heart, and her light burning by her side. All articulate thought had long ago deserted her; her heart seemed to have grown to the size of a sun, and to illuminate her entire body, shedding like the sun a steady tide of warmth.

'I'm happy, I'm happy, I'm happy,' she repeated. 'I love everyone. I'm happy.'

Chapter 12

When Susan's engagement had been approved at home, and made public to anyone who took an interest in it at the hotel – and by this time the society at the hotel was divided so as to point to invisible chalk-marks such as Mr Hirst had described, the news was felt to justify some celebration – an expedition? That had been done already. A dance then. The advantage of a dance was that it abolished one of those long evenings which were apt to become tedious and lead to absurdly early hours in spite of bridge.

Two or three people standing under the erect body of the stuffed leopard in the hall very soon had the matter decided. Evelyn slid a pace or two this way and that, and pronounced that the floor was excellent. Signor Rodriguez informed them of an old Spaniard who fiddled at weddings – fiddled so as to make a tortoise waltz; and his daughter, although endowed with eyes as black as coal-scuttles, had the same power over the piano. If there were any so sick or so surly as to prefer sedentary occupations on the night in question to spinning and watching others spin, the drawing-room and billiard-room were theirs. Hewet made it his business to conciliate the outsiders as much as possible. To Hirst's theory of the invisible chalk-marks he would pay no attention whatever. He was treated to a snub or two, but, in reward, found obscure lonely gentlemen delighted to have this opportunity of talking to their kind, and the lady of doubtful character showed every symptom of confiding her case to him in the near future. Indeed it was made quite obvious to him that the two or three hours between dinner and bed contained an amount of unhappiness which was really pitiable, so many people had not succeeded in making friends.

It was settled that the dance was to be on Friday, one week after the engagement, and at dinner Hewet declared himself satisfied.

'They're all coming!' he told Hirst. 'Pepper!' he called, seeing William Pepper slip past in the wake of the soup with a pamphlet beneath his arm, 'We're counting on you to open the ball.'

'You will certainly put sleep out of the question,' Pepper returned.

'You are to take the floor with Miss Allan,' Hewet continued, consulting a sheet of pencilled notes.

Pepper stopped and began a discourse upon round dances, country dances, morris dances and quadrilles, all of which are entirely superior to the bastard waltz and spurious polka which have ousted them most unjustly in contemporary popularity – when the waiters gently pushed him on to his table in the corner.

The dining-room at this moment had a certain fantastic resemblance to a farmyard scattered with grain on which bright pigeons kept descending. Almost all the ladies wore dresses which they had not yet displayed, and their hair rose in waves and scrolls so as to appear like carved wood in Gothic churches rather than hair. The dinner was shorter and less formal than usual, even the waiters seeming to be affected with the general excitement. Ten minutes before the clock struck nine the committee made a tour through the ballroom. The hall, when emptied of its furniture, brilliantly lit, adorned with flowers whose scent tinged the air, presented a wonderful appearance of ethereal gaiety.

'It's like a starlit sky on an absolutely cloudless night,' Hewet murmured, looking about him at the airy empty room.

'A heavenly floor, anyhow,' Evelyn added, taking a run and sliding two or three feet along.

'What about those curtains?' asked Hirst. The crimson curtains were drawn across the long windows. 'It's a perfect night outside.'

'Yes, but curtains inspire confidence,' Miss Allan decided. 'When the ball is in full swing it will be time to draw them. We might even open the windows a little . . . If we do it now elderly people will imagine there are draughts.'

Her wisdom had come to be recognised, and held in respect. Meanwhile as they stood talking, the musicians were unwrapping their instruments, and the violin was repeating again and again a note struck upon the piano. Everything was ready to begin.

After a few minutes' pause, the father, the daughter and the son-in-law who played the horn flourished with one accord. Like the rats who followed the piper, heads instantly appeared in the doorway. There was another flourish; and then the trio dashed spontaneously into the triumphant swing of the waltz. It was as though the room were instantly flooded with water. After a moment's hesitation first one couple, then another, leapt into midstream, and went round and round in the eddies. The rhythmic swish of the dancers sounded like a swirling pool. By degrees the room grew perceptibly hotter. The smell of kid gloves mingled with the strong scent of flowers. The eddies seemed to circle faster and faster, until the music wrought itself into a crash, ceased, and the circles were smashed into little separate bits. The couples struck off in different directions, leaving a thin row of elderly people stuck fast to the walls, and here and there a piece of trimming or a handkerchief or a flower lay upon the floor. There was a pause, and then the music started again, the eddies whirled, the couples circled round in them, until there was a crash, and the circles were broken up into separate pieces.

When this had happened about five times, Hirst, who leant against a window-frame, like some singular gargoyle, perceived that Helen Ambrose and Rachel stood in the doorway. The crowd was such that they could not move, but he recognised them by a piece of Helen's shoulder and a glimpse of Rachel's head turning round. He made his way to them; they greeted him with relief.

'We are suffering the tortures of the damned,' said Helen.

'This is my idea of hell,' said Rachel.

Her eyes were bright and she looked bewildered.

Hewet and Miss Allan, who had been waltzing somewhat laboriously, paused and greeted the newcomers.

'This *is* nice,' said Hewet. 'But where is Mr Ambrose?'

'Pindar,' said Helen. 'May a married woman who was forty in October dance? I can't stand still.' She seemed to fade into Hewet, and they both dissolved in the crowd.

'We must follow suit,' said Hirst to Rachel, and he took her resolutely by the elbow. Rachel, without being expert, danced well, because of a good ear for rhythm, but Hirst had no taste for music, and a few dancing lessons at Cambridge had only put him into possession of the anatomy of a waltz, without imparting any of its spirit. A single turn proved to them that their methods were incompatible; instead of fitting into each other their bones seemed to jut out in angles making smooth turning an impossibility, and cutting, moreover, into the circular progress of the other dancers.

'Shall we stop?' said Hirst. Rachel gathered from his expression that he was annoyed.

They staggered to seats in the corner, from which they had a view of the room. It was still surging, in waves of blue and yellow, striped by the black evening-clothes of the gentlemen.

'An amazing spectacle,' Hirst remarked. 'Do you dance much in London?' They were both breathing fast, and both a little excited, though each was determined not to show any excitement at all.

'Scarcely ever. Do you?'

'My people give a dance every Christmas.'

'This isn't half a bad floor,' Rachel said. Hirst did not attempt to answer her platitude. He sat quite silent, staring at the dancers. After three minutes the silence became so intolerable to Rachel that she was goaded to advance another commonplace about the beauty of the night. Hirst interrupted her ruthlessly.

'Was that all nonsense what you said the other day about being a Christian and having no education?' he asked.

'It was practically true,' she replied. 'But I also play the piano very well,' she said, 'better, I expect than anyone in this room. You are the most distinguished man in England, aren't you?' she asked shyly.

'One of the three,' he corrected.

Helen whirling past here tossed a fan into Rachel's lap.

'She is very beautiful,' Hirst remarked.

They were again silent. Rachel was wondering whether he thought her also nice-looking; St John was considering the immense difficulty of talking to girls who had no experience of life. Rachel had obviously never thought or felt or seen anything, and she might be intelligent or she might be just like all the rest. But Hewet's taunt rankled in his mind – 'You don't know how to get on with women' – and he was determined to profit by this opportunity. Her evening-clothes bestowed on her just that degree of unreality and distinction which made it romantic to speak to her, and stirred a desire to talk, which irritated him because he did not know how to begin. He glanced at her, and she seemed to him very remote and inexplicable, very young and chaste. He drew a sigh, and began.

'About books now. What have you read? Just Shakespeare and the Bible?'

'I haven't read many classics,' Rachel stated. She was slightly annoyed by his jaunty and rather unnatural manner, while his masculine acquirements induced her to take a very modest view of her own power.

'D'you mean to tell me you've reached the age of twenty-four without reading Gibbon?' he demanded.

'Yes, I have,' she answered.

'Mon Dieu!' he exclaimed, throwing out his hands. 'You must begin tomorrow. I shall send you my copy. What I want to know is – ' he looked at her critically. 'You see, the problem is, can one really talk to you? Have you got a mind, or are you like the rest of your sex? You seem to me absurdly young compared with men of your age.'

Rachel looked at him but said nothing.

'About Gibbon,' he continued. 'D'you think you'll be able to appreciate him? He's the test, of course. It's awfully difficult to tell about women,' he continued, 'how much, I mean, is due to lack of training, and how much is native incapacity. I don't see myself why you shouldn't understand – only I suppose you've led an absurd life until now – you've just walked in a crocodile, I suppose, with your hair down your back.'

The music was again beginning. Hirst's eye wandered about the room in search of Mrs Ambrose. With the best will in the world he was conscious that they were not getting on well together.

'I'd like awfully to lend you books,' he said, buttoning his gloves, and rising from his seat. 'We shall meet again. I'm going to leave you now.'

He got up and left her.

Rachel looked round. She felt herself surrounded, like a child at a party, by the faces of strangers all hostile to her, with hooked noses and sneering, indifferent eyes. She was by a window, she pushed it open with a jerk. She stepped out into the garden. Her eyes swam with tears of rage.

'Damn that man!' she exclaimed, having acquired some of Helen's words. 'Damn his insolence!'

She stood in the middle of the pale square of light which the window she had opened threw upon the grass. The forms of great black trees rose massively in front of her. She stood still, looking at them, shivering slightly with anger and excitement. She heard the trampling and swinging of the dancers behind her, and the rhythmic sway of the waltz music.

'There are trees,' she said aloud. Would the trees make up for St John Hirst? She would be a Persian princess far from civilisation, riding her horse upon the mountains alone, and making her women sing to her in the evening, far from all this, from the strife and men and women – a form came out of the shadow; a little red light burnt high up in its blackness.

'Miss Vinrace, is it?' said Hewet, peering at her. 'You were dancing with Hirst?'

'He's made me furious!' she cried vehemently. 'No one's any right to be insolent!'

'Insolent?' Hewet repeated, taking his cigar from his mouth in surprise. 'Hirst – insolent?'

'It's insolent to – ' said Rachel, and stopped. She did not know exactly why she had been made so angry. With a great effort she pulled herself together.

'Oh, well,' she added, the vision of Helen and her mockery before her, 'I dare say I'm a fool.' She made as though she were going back into the ballroom, but Hewet stopped her.

'Please explain to me,' he said. 'I feel sure Hirst didn't mean to hurt you.'

When Rachel tried to explain, she found it very difficult. She could not say that she found the vision of herself walking in a crocodile with her hair down her back peculiarly unjust and horrible, nor could she explain why Hirst's assumption of the superiority of his nature and experience had seemed to her not only galling but terrible – as if a gate had clanged in her face. Pacing up and down the terrace beside Hewet she said bitterly: 'It's no good; we should live separate; we cannot understand each other; we only bring out what's worst.'

Hewet brushed aside her generalisation as to the natures of the two sexes, for such generalisations bored him and seemed to him generally untrue. But, knowing Hirst, he guessed fairly accurately what had happened, and, though secretly much amused, was determined that Rachel should not store the incident away in her mind to take its place in the view she had of life.

'Now you'll hate him,' he said, 'which is wrong. Poor old Hirst – he can't help his method. And really, Miss Vinrace, he was doing his best; he was paying you a compliment – he was trying – he was trying – ' he could not finish for the laughter that overcame him.

Rachel veered round suddenly and laughed out too. She saw that there was something ridiculous about Hirst, and perhaps about herself.

'It's his way of making friends, I suppose,' she laughed. 'Well – I shall do my part. I shall begin – "Ugly in body, repulsive in mind as you are, Mr Hirst – " '

'Hear, hear!' cried Hewet. 'That's the way to treat him. You see, Miss Vinrace, you must make allowances for Hirst. He's lived all his life in front of a looking-glass, so to speak, in a beautiful panelled room, hung with Japanese prints and lovely old chairs and tables, just one splash of colour, you know, in the right place – between the windows I think it is – and there he sits hour after hour with his toes on the fender, talking about philosophy and God and his liver and his heart and the hearts of his friends. They're all broken. You can't expect him to be at his best in a ballroom. He wants a cosy, smoky, masculine place, where he can stretch his legs out, and only speak when he's got something to say. For myself, I find it rather dreary. But I do respect it. They're all so much in earnest. They do take the serious things very seriously.'

The description of Hirst's way of life interested Rachel so much that she almost forgot her private grudge against him, and her respect revived.

'They are really very clever then?' she asked.

'Of course they are. So far as brains go I think it's true what he said the other day; they're the cleverest people in England. But – you ought to take him in hand,' he added. 'There's a great deal more in him than's ever been got at. He wants someone to laugh at him . . . The idea of Hirst telling you that you've had no experiences! Poor old Hirst!'

They had been pacing up and down the terrace while they talked, and now one by one the dark windows were uncurtained by an invisible hand, and panes of light fell regularly at equal intervals upon the grass. They stopped to look in at the drawing-room, and perceived Mr Pepper writing alone at a table.

'There's Pepper writing to his aunt,' said Hewet. 'She must be a very remarkable old lady, eighty-five he tells me, and he takes her for walking tours in the New Forest . . . Pepper!' he cried, rapping on the window. 'Go and do your duty. Miss Allan expects you.'

When they came to the windows of the ballroom, the swing of the dancers and the lilt of the music was irresistible.

'Shall we?' said Hewet, and they clasped hands and swept off magnificently into the great swirling pool. Although this was only the second time they had met, the first time they had seen a man and woman kissing each other, and the second time Mr Hewet had found that a young woman angry is very like a child. So that when they joined hands in the dance they felt more at their ease than is usual.

It was midnight and the dance was now at its height. Servants were peeping in at the windows; the garden was sprinkled with the white shapes of couples sitting out. Mrs Thornbury and Mrs Elliot sat side by side under a palm tree, holding fans, handkerchiefs and brooches deposited in their laps by flushed maidens. Occasionally they exchanged comments.

'Miss Warrington *does* look happy,' said Mrs Elliot; they both smiled; they both sighed.

'He has a great deal of character,' said Mrs Thornbury, alluding to Arthur.

'And character is what one wants,' said Mrs Elliot. 'Now that young man is *clever* enough,' she added, nodding at Hirst, who came past with Miss Allan on his arm.

'He does not look strong,' said Mrs Thornbury. 'His complexion is not good. – Shall I tear it off?' she asked, for Rachel had stopped, conscious of a long strip trailing behind her.

'I hope you are enjoying yourselves?' Hewet asked the ladies.

'This is a very familiar position for me!' smiled Mrs Thornbury. 'I have brought out five daughters – and they all loved dancing! You love it too, Miss Vinrace?' she asked, looking at Rachel with maternal eyes. 'I know I did when I was your age. How I used to beg my mother to let me stay – and now I sympathise with the poor mothers – but I sympathise with the daughters too!'

She smiled sympathetically, and at the same time rather keenly, at Rachel.

'They seem to find a great deal to say to each other,' said Mrs Elliot, looking significantly at the backs of the couple as they turned away. 'Did you notice at the picnic? He was the only person who could make her utter.'

'Her father is a very interesting man,' said Mrs Thornbury. 'He has one of the largest shipping businesses in Hull. He made a very able reply, you remember, to Mr Asquith at the last election. It is so interesting to find that a man of his experience is a strong Protectionist.'[75]

She would have liked to discuss politics, which interested her more than personalities, but Mrs Elliot would only talk about the Empire in a less abstract form.

'I hear there are dreadful accounts from England about the rats,' she said. 'A sister-in-law, who lives at Norwich, tells me it has been quite unsafe to order poultry. The plague – you see. It attacks the rats, and through them other creatures.'

'And the local authorities are not taking proper steps?' asked Mrs Thornbury.

'That she does not say. But she describes the attitude of the educated people – who should know better – as callous in the extreme. Of course, my sister-in-law is one of those active modern women who always takes things up, you know – the kind of woman one admires, though one does not feel, at least I do not feel – but then she has a constitution of iron.'

Mrs Elliot, brought back to the consideration of her own delicacy, here sighed.

'A very animated face,' said Mrs Thornbury, looking at Evelyn M. who had stopped near them to pin tight a scarlet flower at her breast. It would not stay, and, with a spirited gesture of impatience, she thrust it into her partner's buttonhole. He was a tall melancholy youth, who received the gift as a knight might receive his lady's token.

'Very trying to the eyes,' was Mrs Elliot's next remark, after watching the yellow whirl, in which so few of the whirlers had either name or character for her, for a few minutes. Bursting out of the crowd, Helen approached them, and took a vacant chair.

'May I sit by you?' she said, smiling and breathing fast. 'I suppose I ought to be ashamed of myself,' she went on, sitting down, 'at my age.'

Her beauty, now that she was flushed and animated, was more

expansive than usual, and both the ladies felt the same desire to touch her.

'I *am* enjoying myself,' she panted. 'Movement – isn't it amazing?'

'I have always heard that nothing comes up to dancing if one is a good dancer,' said Mrs Thornbury, looking at her with a smile.

Helen swayed slightly as if she sat on wires.

'I could dance for ever!' she said. 'They ought to let themselves go more!' she exclaimed. 'They ought to leap and swing. Look! How they mince!'

'Have you seen those wonderful Russian dancers?' began Mrs Elliot. But Helen saw her partner coming and rose as the moon rises. She was half round the room before they took their eyes off her, for they could not help admiring her, although they thought it a little odd that a woman of her age should enjoy dancing.

Directly Helen was left alone for a minute she was joined by St John Hirst, who had been watching for an opportunity.

'Should you mind sitting out with me?' he asked. 'I'm quite incapable of dancing.' He piloted Helen to a corner which was supplied with two armchairs, and thus enjoyed the advantage of semi-privacy. They sat down, and for a few minutes Helen was too much under the influence of dancing to speak.

'Astonishing!' she exclaimed at last. 'What sort of shape can she think her body is?' This remark was called forth by a lady who came past them, waddling rather than walking, and leaning on the arm of a stout man with globular green eyes set in a fat white face. Some support was necessary, for she was very stout, and so compressed that the upper part of her body hung considerably in advance of her feet, which could only trip in tiny steps, owing to the tightness of the skirt round her ankles. The dress itself consisted of a small piece of shiny yellow satin, adorned here and there indiscriminately with round shields of blue and green beads made to imitate hues of a peacock's breast. On the summit of a frothy castle of hair a purple plume stood erect, while her short neck was encircled by a black velvet ribbon knobbed with gems, and golden bracelets were tightly wedged into the flesh of her fat gloved arms. She had the face of an impertinent but jolly little pig, mottled red under a dusting of powder.

St John could not join in Helen's laughter.

'It makes me sick,' he declared. 'The whole thing makes me sick . . . Consider the minds of those people – their feelings. Don't you agree?'

'I always make a vow never to go to another party of any description,' Helen replied, 'and I always break it.'

She leant back in her chair and looked laughingly at the young man. She could see that he was genuinely cross, if at the same time slightly excited.

'However,' he said, resuming his jaunty tone, 'I suppose one must just make up one's mind to it.'

'To what?'

'There never will be more than five people in the world worth talking to.'

Slowly the flush and sparkle in Helen's face died away, and she looked as quiet and as observant as usual.

'Five people?' she remarked. 'I should say there were more than five.'

'You've been very fortunate, then,' said Hirst. 'Or perhaps I've been very unfortunate.' He became silent. 'Should you say I was a difficult kind of person to get on with?' he asked sharply.

'Most clever people are when they're young,' Helen replied.

'And of course I am – immensely clever,' said Hirst. 'I'm infinitely cleverer than Hewet. It's quite possible,' he continued in his curiously impersonal manner, 'that I'm going to be one of the people who really matter. That's utterly different from being clever, though one can't expect one's family to see it,' he added bitterly.

Helen thought herself justified in asking, 'Do you find your family difficult to get on with?'

'Intolerable . . . They want me to be a peer and a privy councillor. I've come out here partly in order to settle the matter. It's got to be settled. Either I must go to the Bar, or I must stay on in Cambridge. Of course, there are obvious drawbacks to each, but the arguments certainly do seem to me in favour of Cambridge. This kind of thing!' he waved his hand at the crowded ballroom. 'Repulsive. I'm conscious of great powers of affection too. I'm not susceptible, of course, in the way Hewet is. I'm very fond of a few people. I think, for example, that there's something to be said for my mother, though she is in many ways so deplorable . . . At Cambridge, of course, I should inevitably become the most important man in the place, but there are other reasons why I dread Cambridge – ' he ceased. 'Are you finding me a dreadful bore?' he asked. He changed curiously from a friend confiding in a friend to a conventional young man at a party.

'Not in the least,' said Helen. 'I like it very much.'

'You can't think,' he exclaimed, speaking almost with emotion, 'what a difference it makes finding someone to talk to! Directly I saw you I felt you might possibly understand me. I'm very fond of Hewet, but he hasn't the remotest idea what I'm like. You're the only woman I've ever met who seems to have the faintest conception of what I mean when I say a thing.'

The next dance was beginning; it was the Barcarolle out of Hoffman,[76] which made Helen beat her toe in time to it; but she felt that after such a compliment it was impossible to get up and go, and, besides being amused, she was really flattered, and the honesty of his conceit attracted her. She suspected that he was not happy, and was sufficiently feminine to wish to receive confidences.

'I'm very old,' she sighed.

'The odd thing is that I don't find you old at all,' he replied. 'I feel as though we were exactly the same age. Moreover – ' here he hesitated, but took courage from a glance at her face, 'I feel as if I could talk quite plainly to you as one does to a man – about the relations between the sexes, about . . . and . . . '

In spite of his certainty a slight redness came into his face as he spoke the last two words.

She reassured him at once by the laugh with which she exclaimed, 'I should hope so!'

He looked at her with real cordiality, and the lines which were drawn about his nose and lips slackened for the first time.

'Thank God!' he exclaimed. 'Now we can behave like civilised human beings.'

Certainly a barrier which usually stands fast had fallen, and it was possible to speak of matters which are generally only alluded to between men and women when doctors are present, or the shadow of death. In five minutes he was telling her the history of his life. It was long, for it was full of extremely elaborate incidents, which led on to a discussion of the principles on which morality is founded, and thus to several very interesting matters, which even in this ballroom had to be discussed in a whisper, lest one of the pouter pigeon ladies or resplendent merchants should overhear them, and proceed to demand that they should leave the place. When they had come to an end, or, to speak more accurately, when Helen intimated by a slight slackening of her attention that they had sat there long enough, Hirst rose, exclaiming, 'So there's no reason whatever for all this mystery!'

'None, except that we are English people,' she answered. She took his arm and they crossed the ballroom, making their way with difficulty between the spinning couples, who were now perceptibly dishevelled, and certainly to a critical eye by no means lovely in their shapes. The excitement of undertaking a friendship and the length of their talk made them hungry, and they went in search of food to the dining-room, which was now full of people eating at little separate tables. In the doorway they met Rachel, going up to dance again with Arthur Venning. She was flushed and looked very happy, and Helen was struck by the fact that in this mood she was certainly more attractive than the generality of young women. She had never noticed it so clearly before.

'Enjoying yourself?' she asked, as they stopped for a second.

'Miss Vinrace,' Arthur answered for her, 'has just made a confession: she'd no idea that dances could be so delightful.'

'Yes!' Rachel exclaimed. 'I've changed my view of life completely!'

'You don't say so!' Helen mocked. They passed on.

'That's typical of Rachel,' she said. 'She changes her view of life about every other day. D'you know, I believe you're just the person I want,' she said, as they sat down, 'to help me complete her education? She's been brought up practically in a nunnery. Her father's too absurd. I've been doing what I can – but I'm too old, and I'm a woman. Why shouldn't you talk to her – explain things to her – talk to her, I mean, as you talk to me?'

'I have made one attempt already this evening,' said St John. 'I rather doubt that it was successful. She seems to me so very young and inexperienced. I have promised to lend her Gibbon.'

'It's not Gibbon exactly,' Helen pondered. 'It's the facts of life, I think – d'you see what I mean? What really goes on, what people feel, although they generally try to hide it? There's nothing to be frightened of. It's so much more beautiful than the pretences – always more interesting – always better, I should say, than *that* kind of thing.'

She nodded her head at a table near them, where two girls and two young men were chaffing each other very loudly, and carrying on an arch insinuating dialogue, sprinkled with endearments, about, it seemed, a pair of stockings or a pair of legs. One of the girls was flirting a fan and pretending to be shocked, and the sight was very unpleasant, partly because it was obvious that the girls were secretly hostile to each other.

'In my old age, however,' Helen sighed, 'I'm coming to think that it doesn't much matter in the long run what one does: people always go their own way – nothing will ever influence them.' She nodded her head at the supper party.

But St John did not agree. He said that he thought one could really make a great deal of difference by one's point of view, books and so on, and added that few things at the present time mattered more than the enlightenment of women. He sometimes thought that almost everything was due to education.

In the ballroom, meanwhile, the dancers were being formed into squares for the lancers. Arthur and Rachel, Susan and Hewet, Miss Allan and Hughling Elliot found themselves together.

Miss Allan looked at her watch.

'Half-past one,' she stated. 'And I have to despatch Alexander Pope[77] tomorrow.'

'Pope!' snorted Mr Elliot. 'Who reads Pope, I should like to know? And as for reading about him – No, no, Miss Allan; be persuaded you will benefit the world much more by dancing than by writing.' It was one of Mr Elliot's affectations that nothing in the world could compare with the delights of dancing – nothing in the world was so tedious as literature. Thus he sought pathetically enough to ingratiate himself with the young, and to prove to them beyond a doubt that though married to a ninny of a wife, and rather pale and bent and careworn by his weight of learning, he was as much alive as the youngest of them all.

'It's a question of bread and butter,' said Miss Allan calmly. 'However, they seem to expect me.' She took up her position and pointed a square black toe.

'Mr Hewet, you bow to me.' It was evident at once that Miss Allan was the only one of them who had a thoroughly sound knowledge of the figures of the dance.

After the lancers there was a waltz; after the waltz a polka; and then a terrible thing happened: the music, which had been sounding regularly with five-minute pauses, stopped suddenly. The lady with the great dark eyes began to swathe her violin in silk, and the gentleman placed his horn carefully in its case. They were surrounded by couples imploring them in English, in French, in Spanish, for one more dance, one only; it was still early. But the old man at the piano merely exhibited his watch and shook his head. He turned up the collar of his coat and produced a red silk muffler, which completely dashed his festive appearance. Strange as it seemed, the musicians were pale and heavy-eyed; they looked bored and prosaic, as if the summit of their desire was cold meat and beer, succeeded immediately by bed.

Rachel was one of those who had begged them to continue. When they refused she began turning over the sheets of dance music which lay upon the piano. The pieces were generally bound in coloured covers, with pictures on them of romantic scenes – gondoliers astride on the crescent of the moon, nuns peering through the bars of a convent window, or young women with their hair down pointing a gun at the stars. She remembered that the general effect of the music to which they had danced so gaily was one of passionate regret for dead love and the innocent years of youth; dreadful sorrows had always separated the dancers from their past happiness.

'No wonder they get sick of playing stuff like this,' she remarked reading a bar or two; 'they're really hymn tunes, played very fast, with bits out of Wagner and Beethoven.'

'Do you play? Would you play? Anything, so long as we can dance to it!' From all sides her gift for playing the piano was insisted upon, and she had to consent. As very soon she had played the only pieces of dance music she could remember, she went on to play an air from a sonata by Mozart.

'But that's not a dance,' said someone pausing by the piano.

'It is,' she replied, emphatically nodding her head. 'Invent the steps.' Sure of her melody she marked the rhythm boldly so as to simplify the way. Helen caught the idea; seized Miss Allan by the arm, and whirled round the room, now curtseying, now spinning round, now tripping this way and that like a child skipping through a meadow.

'This is the dance for people who don't know how to dance!' she cried. The tune changed to a minuet; St John hopped with incredible swiftness first on his left leg, then on his right; the tune flowed melodiously; Hewet, swaying his arms and holding out the tails of his coat, swam down the room in imitation of the voluptuous dreamy dance of an Indian maiden dancing before her Rajah. The tune marched; and Miss Allen advanced with skirts extended and bowed profoundly to the engaged pair. Once their feet fell in with the rhythm they showed a complete lack of self-consciousness. From Mozart Rachel passed without stopping to old English hunting songs, carols and hymn tunes, for, as she had observed, any good tune, with a little management, became a tune one could dance to. By degrees every person in the room was tripping and turning in pairs or alone. Mr Pepper executed an ingenious pointed step derived from figure-skating, for which he once held some local championship; while Mrs Thornbury tried to recall an old country dance which she had seen danced by her father's tenants in Dorsetshire in the old days. As for Mr and Mrs Elliot, they galloped round and round the room with such impetuosity that the other dancers shivered at their approach. Some people were heard to criticise the performance as a romp; to others it was the most enjoyable part of the evening.

'Now for the great round dance!' Hewet shouted. Instantly a gigantic circle was formed, the dancers holding hands and shouting out, 'D'you ken John Peel,' as they swung faster and faster and faster, until the strain was too great, and one link of the chain – Mrs Thornbury – gave way, and the rest went flying across the room in all directions, to land upon the floor or the chairs or in each other's arms as seemed most convenient.

Rising from these positions, breathless and unkempt, it struck them for the first time that the electric lights pricked the air very vainly, and instinctively a great many eyes turned to the windows. Yes – there was the dawn. While they had been dancing the night had passed, and it had come. Outside, the mountains showed very pure and remote; the dew was sparkling on the grass, and the sky was flushed with blue, save for the pale yellows and pinks in the East. The dancers came crowding to the windows, pushed them open, and here and there ventured a foot upon the grass.

'How silly the poor old lights look!' said Evelyn M. in a curiously subdued tone of voice. 'And ourselves; it isn't becoming.' It was true; the untidy hair, and the green and yellow gems which had seemed so festive half an hour ago, now looked cheap and slovenly. The complexions of the elder ladies suffered terribly, and, as if conscious that a cold eye had been turned upon them, they began to say good-night and to make their way up to bed.

Rachel, though robbed of her audience, had gone on playing to herself. From John Peel she passed to Bach, who was at this time the subject of her intense enthusiasm, and one by one some of the younger dancers came in from the garden and sat upon the deserted gilt chairs round the piano, the room being now so clear that they turned out the lights. As they sat and listened, their nerves were quieted; the heat and soreness of their lips, the result of incessant talking and laughing, was smoothed away. They sat very still as if they saw a building with spaces and columns succeeding each other rising in the empty space. Then they began to see themselves and their lives, and the whole of human life advancing very nobly under the direction of the music. They felt themselves ennobled, and when Rachel stopped playing they desired nothing but sleep.

Susan rose. 'I think this has been the happiest night of my life!' she exclaimed. 'I do adore music,' she said, as she thanked Rachel. 'It just seems to say all the things one can't say oneself.' She gave a nervous little laugh and looked from one to another with great benignity, as though she would like to say something but could not find the words in which to express it. 'Everyone's been so kind – so very kind,' she said. Then she too went to bed.

The party having ended in the very abrupt way in which parties do end, Helen and Rachel stood by the door with their cloaks on, looking for a carriage.

'I suppose you realise that there are no carriages left?' said St John, who had been out to look. 'You must sleep here.'

'Oh, no,' said Helen; 'we shall walk.'

'May we come too?' Hewet asked. 'We can't go to bed. Imagine lying among bolsters and looking at one's washstand on a morning like this – Is that where you live?' They had begun to walk down the avenue, and he turned and pointed at the white and green villa on the hillside, which seemed to have its eyes shut.

'That's not a light burning, is it?' Helen asked anxiously.

'It's the sun,' said St John. The upper windows had each a spot of gold on them.

'I was afraid it was my husband, still reading Greek,' she said. 'All this time he's been editing *Pindar*.'

They passed through the town and turned up the steep road, which was perfectly clear, though still unbordered by shadows. Partly because they were tired, and partly because the early light subdued them, they scarcely spoke, but breathed in the delicious fresh air, which seemed to belong to a different state of life from the air at midday. When they came to the high yellow wall, where the lane turned off from the road, Helen was for dismissing the two young men.

'You've come far enough,' she said. 'Go back to bed.'

But they seemed unwilling to move.

'Let's sit down a moment,' said Hewet. He spread his coat on the ground. 'Let's sit down and consider.' They sat down and looked out over the bay; it was very still, the sea was rippling faintly, and lines of green and blue were beginning to stripe it. There were no sailing boats as yet, but a steamer was anchored in the bay, looking very ghostly in the mist; it gave one unearthly cry, and then all was silent.

Rachel occupied herself in collecting one grey stone after another and building them into a little cairn; she did it very quietly and carefully.

'And so you've changed your view of life, Rachel?' said Helen.

Rachel added another stone and yawned. 'I don't remember,' she said, 'I feel like a fish at the bottom of the sea.' She yawned again. None of these people possessed any power to frighten her out here in the dawn, and she felt perfectly familiar even with Mr Hirst.

'My brain, on the contrary,' said Hirst, 'is in a condition of abnormal activity.' He sat in his favourite position with his arms binding his legs together and his chin resting on the top of his knees. 'I see through everything – absolutely everything. Life has no more mysteries for me.' He spoke with conviction, but did not appear to wish for an answer.

Near though they sat, and familiar though they felt, they seemed mere shadows to each other.

'And all those people down there going to sleep,' Hewet began dreamily, 'thinking such different things: Miss Warrington, I suppose, is now on her knees; the Elliots are a little startled, it's not often *they* get out of breath, and they want to get to sleep as quickly as possible; then there's the poor lean young man who danced all night with Evelyn; he's putting his flower in water and asking himself, "Is this love?" – and poor old Perrott, I dare say, can't get to sleep at all, and is reading his favourite Greek book to console himself – and the others – no, Hirst,' he wound up, 'I don't find it simple at all.'

'I have a key,' said Hirst cryptically. His chin was still upon his knees and his eyes fixed in front of him.

A silence followed. Then Helen rose and bade them good-night. 'But,' she said, 'remember that you've got to come and see us.'

They waved good-night and parted, but the two young men did not go back to the hotel; they went for a walk, during which they scarcely spoke, and never mentioned the names of the two women, who were, to a considerable extent, the subject of their thoughts. They did not wish to share their impressions. They returned to the hotel in time for breakfast.

Chapter 13

There were many rooms in the villa, but one room which possessed a character of its own because the door was always shut, and no sound of music or laughter issued from it. Everyone in the house was vaguely conscious that something went on behind that door, and without in the least knowing what it was, were influenced in their own thoughts by the knowledge that if they passed it the door would be shut, and if they made a noise Mr Ambrose inside would be disturbed. Certain acts therefore possessed merit, and others were bad, so that life became more harmonious and less disconnected than it would have been had Mr Ambrose given up editing *Pindar*, and taken to a nomad existence, in and out of every room in the house. As it was, everyone was conscious that by observing certain rules, such as punctuality and quiet, by cooking well, and performing other small duties, one ode after another was satisfactorily restored to the world, and they shared the continuity of the scholar's life. Unfortunately, as age puts one barrier between human beings, and learning another, and sex a third, Mr Ambrose in his study was some thousand miles distant from the nearest human being, who in this household was inevitably a woman. He sat hour after hour among white-leaved books, alone like an idol in an empty church, still except for the passage of his hand from one side of the sheet to another, silent save for an occasional choke, which drove him to extend his pipe a moment in the air. As he worked his way further and further into the heart of the poet, his chair became more and more deeply encircled by books, which lay open on the floor, and could only be crossed by a careful process of stepping, so delicate that his visitors generally stopped and addressed him from the outskirts.

On the morning after the dance, however, Rachel came into her uncle's room and hailed him twice, 'Uncle Ridley,' before he paid her any attention.

At length he looked over his spectacles.

'Well?' he asked.

'I want a book,' she replied. 'Gibbon's *History of the Roman Empire*. May I have it?'

She watched the lines on her uncle's face gradually rearrange themselves at her question. It had been smooth as a mask before she spoke.

'Please say that again,' said her uncle, either because he had not heard or because he had not understood.

She repeated the same words and reddened slightly as she did so.

'Gibbon! What on earth d'you want him for?' he enquired.

'Somebody advised me to read it,' Rachel stammered.

'But I don't travel about with a miscellaneous collection of eighteenth-century historians!' her uncle exclaimed. 'Gibbon! Ten big volumes at least.'

Rachel said that she was sorry to interrupt, and was turning to go.

'Stop!' cried her uncle. He put down his pipe, placed his book on one side, and rose and led her slowly round the room, holding her by the arm. 'Plato,' he said, laying one finger on the first of a row of small dark books, 'and Jorrocks[78] next door, which is wrong. Sophocles,[79] Swift.[80] You don't care for German commentators, I presume. French, then. You read French? You should read Balzac.[81] Then we come to Wordsworth and Coleridge,[82] Pope, Johnson, Addison,[83] Wordsworth, Shelley, Keats. One thing leads to another. Why is Marlowe[84] here? Mrs Chailey, I presume. But what's the use of reading if you don't read Greek? After all, if you read Greek, you need never read anything else, pure waste of time – pure waste of time,' thus speaking half to himself, with quick movements of his hands; they had come round again to the circle of books on the floor, and their progress was stopped.

'Well,' he demanded, 'which shall it be?'

'Balzac,' said Rachel, 'or have you the *Speech on the American Revolution*, Uncle Ridley?'

'*The Speech on the American Revolution*?' he asked. He looked at her very keenly again. 'Another young man at the dance?'

'No. That was Mr Dalloway,' she confessed.

'Good Lord!' he flung back his head in recollection of Mr Dalloway.

She chose for herself a volume at random, submitted it to her uncle, who, seeing that it was *La Cousine Bette*,[85] bade her throw it away if she found it too horrible, and was about to leave him when he demanded whether she had enjoyed her dance?

He then wanted to know what people did at dances, seeing that he had only been to one thirty-five years ago, when nothing had seemed to him more meaningless and idiotic. Did they enjoy turning round and round to the screech of a fiddle? Did they talk, and say pretty things, and if so, why didn't they do it under reasonable conditions? As for himself – he sighed and pointed at the signs of industry lying all about him, which, in spite of his sigh, filled his face with such satisfaction that his niece thought it good to leave. On bestowing a kiss she was allowed to go, but not until she had bound herself to learn at any rate the Greek alphabet, and to return her French novel when done with, upon which something more suitable would be found for her.

As the rooms in which people live are apt to give off something of the same shock as their faces when seen for the first time, Rachel walked very slowly downstairs, lost in wonder at her uncle, and his books, and his neglect of dances, and his queer, utterly inexplicable, but apparently satisfactory view of life, when her eye was caught by a note with her name on it lying in the hall. The address was written in a small strong hand unknown to her, and the note, which had no beginning, ran:

I send the first volume of Gibbon as I promised. Personally I find little to be said for the moderns, but I'm going to send you Wedekind[86] when I've done him. Donne? Have you read Webster[87] and all that set? I envy you reading them for the first time. Completely exhausted after last night. And you?

The flourish of initials which she took to be St J. A. H., wound up the letter. She was very much flattered that Mr Hirst should have remembered her, and fulfilled his promise so quickly.

There was still an hour to luncheon, and with Gibbon in one hand and Balzac in the other she strolled out of the gate and down the little path of beaten mud between the olive trees on the slope of the hill. It was too hot for climbing hills, but along the valley there were trees and a grass path running by the river bed. In this land where the population was centred in the towns it was possible to lose sight of civilisation in a very short time, passing only an occasional farmhouse, where the women were handling red roots in the courtyard, or a little boy lying on his elbows on the hillside surrounded by a flock of black strong-smelling goats. Save for a thread of water at the bottom, the river was merely a deep channel of dry yellow stones. On the bank grew those trees which Helen had said it was worth the voyage out merely to see. April had burst their buds, and they bore large blossoms among their glossy green leaves with petals of a thick waxlike substance coloured an exquisite cream or pink or deep crimson. But, filled with one of those unreasonable exultations which start generally from an unknown cause and sweep whole countries and skies into their embrace, she walked without seeing. The night was encroaching upon the day. Her ears hummed with the tunes she had played the night before; she sang, and the singing made her walk faster and faster. She did not see distinctly where she was going, the trees and the landscape appearing only as masses of green and blue, with an occasional space of differently

coloured sky. Faces of people she had seen last night came before her;
she heard their voices; she stopped singing, and began saying things
over again or saying things differently, or inventing things that might
have been said. The constraint of being among strangers in a long silk
dress made it unusually exciting to stride thus alone. Hewet, Hirst, Mr
Venning, Miss Allan, the music, the light, the dark trees in the garden,
the dawn – as she walked they went surging round in her head, a
tumultuous background from which the present moment, with its
opportunity of doing exactly as she liked, sprang more wonderfully
vivid even than the night before.

So she might have walked until she had lost all knowledge of her way,
had it not been for the interruption of a tree, which, although it did not
grow across her path, stopped her as effectively as if the branches had
struck her in the face. It was an ordinary tree, but to her it appeared so
strange that it might have been the only tree in the world. Dark was the
trunk in the middle, and the branches sprang here and there, leaving
jagged intervals of light between them as distinctly as if it had but that
second risen from the ground. Having presented a sight that would last
her for a lifetime, and for a lifetime would preserve that second, the tree
once more sank into the ordinary ranks of trees, and she was able to seat
herself in its shade and to pick the red flowers with the thin green leaves
which were growing beneath it. She laid them side by side, flower to
flower and stalk to stalk, caressing them for walking alone. Flowers and
even pebbles in the earth had their own life and disposition, and brought
back the feelings of a child to whom they were companions. Looking up,
her eye was caught by the line of the mountains flying out energetically
across the sky like the lash of a curling whip. She looked at the pale
distant sky, and the high bare places on the mountain-tops lying exposed
to the sun. When she sat down she had dropped her books on to the
earth at her feet, and now she looked down on them lying there, so
square in the grass, a tall stem bending over and tickling the smooth
brown cover of Gibbon, while the mottled blue Balzac lay naked in the
sun. With a feeling that to open and read would certainly be a surprising
experience, she turned the historian's page and read that –

His generals, in the early part of his reign, attempted the reduction of
Aethiopia and Arabia Felix. They marched near a thousand miles to
the south of the tropic; but the heat of the climate soon repelled the
invaders and protected the unwarlike natives of those sequestered
regions . . . The northern countries of Europe scarcely deserved the
expense and labour of conquest. The forests and morasses of Germany

were filled with a hardy race of barbarians, who despised life when it was separated from freedom.

Never had any words been so vivid and so beautiful – Arabia Felix – Aethiopia. But those were not more noble than the others: hardy barbarians, forests and morasses. They seemed to drive roads back to the very beginning of the world, on either side of which the populations of all times and countries stood in avenues, and by passing down them all knowledge would be hers, and the book of the world turned back to the very first page. Such was her excitement at the possibilities of knowledge now opening before her that she ceased to read, and a breeze turning the page, the covers of Gibbon gently ruffled and closed together. She then rose again and walked on. Slowly her mind became less confused and sought the origins of her exaltation, which were twofold and could be limited by an effort to the persons of Mr Hirst and Mr Hewet. Any clear analysis of them was impossible owing to the haze of wonder in which they were enveloped. She could not reason about them as about people whose feelings went by the same rule as her own did, and her mind dwelt on them with a kind of physical pleasure such as is caused by the contemplation of bright things hanging in the sun. From them all life seemed to radiate; the very words of books were steeped in radiance. She then became haunted by a suspicion which she was so reluctant to face that she welcomed a trip and stumble over the grass because thus her attention was dispersed, but in a second it had collected itself again. Unconsciously she had been walking faster and faster, her body trying to outrun her mind; but she was now on the summit of a little hillock of earth which rose above the river and displayed the valley. She was no longer able to juggle with several ideas, but must deal with the most persistent, and a kind of melancholy replaced her excitement. She sank down on to the earth clasping her knees together, and looking blankly in front of her. For some time she observed a great yellow butterfly, which was opening and closing its wings very slowly on a little flat stone.

'What is it to be in love?' she demanded, after a long silence; each word as it came into being seemed to shove itself out into an unknown sea. Hypnotised by the wings of the butterfly, and awed by the discovery of a terrible possibility in life, she sat for some time longer. When the butterfly flew away, she rose, and with her two books beneath her arm returned home again, much as a soldier prepared for battle.

Chapter 14

The sun of that same day going down, dusk was saluted as usual at the hotel by an instantaneous sparkle of electric lights. The hours between dinner and bedtime were always difficult enough to kill, and the night after the dance they were further tarnished by the peevishness of dissipation. Certainly, in the opinion of Hirst and Hewet, who lay back in long armchairs in the middle of the hall, with their coffee-cups beside them, and their cigarettes in their hands, the evening was unusually dull, the women unusually badly dressed, the men unusually fatuous. Moreover, when the mail had been distributed half an hour ago there were no letters for either of the two young men. As every other person, practically, had received two or three plump letters from England, which they were now engaged in reading, this seemed hard, and prompted Hirst to make the caustic remark that the animals had been fed. Their silence, he said, reminded him of the silence in the lion-house when each beast holds a lump of raw meat in its paws. He went on, stimulated by this comparison, to liken some to hippopotamuses, some to canary birds, some to swine, some to parrots, and some to loathsome reptiles curled round the half-decayed bodies of sheep. The intermittent sounds – now a cough, now a horrible wheezing or throat-clearing, now a little patter of conversation – were just, he declared, what you hear if you stand in the lion-house when the bones are being mauled. But these comparisons did not rouse Hewet, who, after a careless glance round the room, fixed his eyes upon a thicket of native spears which were so ingeniously arranged as to run their points at you whichever way you approached them. He was clearly oblivious of his surroundings; whereupon Hirst, perceiving that Hewet's mind was a complete blank, fixed his attention more closely upon his fellow-creatures. He was too far from them, however, to hear what they were saying, but it pleased him to construct little theories about them from their gestures and appearance.

Mrs Thornbury had received a great many letters. She was completely engrossed in them. When she had finished a page she handed it to her husband, or gave him the sense of what she was reading in a series of short quotations linked together by a sound at the back of her throat. 'Evie writes that George has gone to Glasgow. "He finds Mr

Chadbourne so nice to work with, and we hope to spend Christmas together, but I should not like to move Betty and Alfred any great distance [no, quite right], though it is difficult to imagine cold weather in this heat . . . Eleanor and Roger drove over in the new trap . . . Eleanor certainly looked more like herself than I've seen her since the winter. She has put Baby on three bottles now, which I'm sure is wise [I'm sure it is too], and so gets better nights . . . My hair still falls out. I find it on the pillow! But I am cheered by hearing from Tottie Hall Green . . . Muriel is in Torquay enjoying herself greatly at dances. She *is* going to show her black pug after all." . . . A line from Herbert – so busy, poor fellow! Ah! Margaret says, "Poor old Mrs Fairbank died on the eighth, quite suddenly in the conservatory, only a maid in the house, who hadn't the presence of mind to lift her up, which they think might have saved her, but the doctor says it might have come at any moment, and one can only feel thankful that it was in the house and not in the street [I should think so!]. The pigeons have increased terribly, just as the rabbits did five years ago . . ." ' While she read her husband kept nodding his head very slightly, but very steadily in sign of approval.

Near by, Miss Allan was reading her letters too. They were not altogether pleasant, as could be seen from the slight rigidity which came over her large fine face as she finished reading them and replaced them neatly in their envelopes. The lines of care and responsibility on her face made her resemble an elderly man rather than a woman. The letters brought her news of the failure of last year's fruit crop in New Zealand, which was a serious matter, for Hubert, her only brother, made his living on a fruit farm, and if it failed again, of course, he would throw up his place, come back to England, and what were they to do with him this time? The journey out here, which meant the loss of a term's work, became an extravagance and not the just and wonderful holiday due to her after fifteen years of punctual lecturing and correcting essays upon English literature. Emily, her sister, who was a teacher also, wrote: 'We ought to be prepared, though I have no doubt Hubert will be more reasonable this time.' And then went on in her sensible way to say that she was enjoying a very jolly time in the Lakes. 'They are looking exceedingly pretty just now. I have seldom seen the trees so forward at this time of year. We have taken our lunch out several days. Old Alice is as young as ever, and asks after everyone affectionately. The days pass very quickly, and term will soon be here. Political prospects *not* good, I think privately, but do not like to damp Ellen's enthusiasm. Lloyd George[88] has taken the Bill up, but so have many before now, and we are where we are; but trust to find myself mistaken. Anyhow, we have our work cut out for us . . . Surely Meredith lacks the *human* note one likes in W. W.?' she concluded, and went on to discuss some questions of English literature which Miss Allan had raised in her last letter.

At a little distance from Miss Allan, on a seat shaded and made semi-private by a thick clump of palm trees, Arthur and Susan were reading each other's letters. The big slashing manuscripts of hockey-playing young women in Wiltshire lay on Arthur's knee, while Susan deciphered tight little legal hands which rarely filled more than a page, and always conveyed the same impression of jocular and breezy goodwill.

'I do hope Mr Hutchinson will like me, Arthur,' she said, looking up.

'Who's your loving Flo?' asked Arthur.

'Flo Graves – the girl I told you about, who was engaged to that dreadful Mr Vincent,' said Susan. 'Is Mr Hutchinson married?' she asked.

Already her mind was busy with benevolent plans for her friends, or rather with one magnificent plan – which was simple too – they were all to get married – at once – directly she got back. Marriage, marriage that was the right thing, the only thing, the solution required by every one she knew, and a great part of her meditations was spent in tracing every instance of discomfort, loneliness, ill-health, unsatisfied ambition, restlessness, eccentricity, taking things up and dropping them again, public speaking and philanthropic activity on the part of men and particularly on the part of women to the fact that they wanted to marry, were trying to marry, and had not succeeded in getting married. If, as she was bound to own, these symptoms sometimes persisted after marriage, she could only ascribe them to the unhappy law of nature which decreed that there was only one Arthur Venning, and only one Susan who could marry him. Her theory, of course, had the merit of being fully supported by her own case. She had been vaguely uncomfortable at home for two or three years now, and a voyage like this with her selfish old aunt, who paid her fare but treated her as servant and companion in one, was typical of the kind of thing people expected of her. Directly she became engaged, Mrs Paley behaved with instinctive respect, positively protested when Susan as usual knelt down to lace her shoes, and appeared really grateful for an hour of Susan's company where she had been used to exact two or three as her right. She therefore foresaw a life of far greater comfort than she had been used to, and the change had already produced a great increase of warmth in her feelings towards other people.

It was close on twenty years now since Mrs Paley had been able to lace her own shoes or even to see them, the disappearance of her feet having coincided more or less accurately with the death of her husband, a man of business, soon after which event Mrs Paley began to grow stout. She was a selfish, independent old woman, possessed of a considerable income, which she spent upon the upkeep of a house that needed seven servants and a charwoman in Lancaster Gate, and another with a garden and carriage-horses in Surrey. Susan's engagement relieved her of the one great anxiety of her life – that her son Christopher should 'entangle himself' with his cousin. Now that this familiar source of interest was removed, she felt a little low and inclined to see more in Susan than she used to. She had decided to give her a very handsome wedding present, a cheque for two hundred, two hundred and fifty, or possibly, conceivably – it depended upon the under-gardener and Huths' bill for doing up the drawing-room – three hundred pounds sterling.

She was thinking of this very question, revolving the figures, as she sat in her wheeled chair with a table spread with cards by her side. The Patience had somehow got into a muddle, and she did not like to call for Susan to help her, as Susan seemed to be busy with Arthur.

'She's every right to expect a handsome present from me, of course,' she thought, looking vaguely at the leopard on its hind legs, 'and I've no doubt she does! Money goes a long way with everyone. The young are very selfish. If I were to die, nobody would miss me but Dakyns, and she'll be consoled by the will! However, I've got no reason to complain . . . I can still enjoy myself. I'm not a burden to anyone . . . I like a great many things a good deal, in spite of my legs.'

Being slightly depressed, however, she went on to think of the only people she had known who had not seemed to her at all selfish or fond of money, who had seemed to her somehow rather finer than the general run; people she willingly acknowledged, who were finer than she was. There were only two of them. One was her brother, who had been drowned before her eyes, the other was a girl, her greatest friend, who had died in giving birth to her first child. These things had happened some fifty years ago.

'They ought not to have died,' she thought. 'However, they did – and we selfish old creatures go on.' The tears came to her eyes; she felt a genuine regret for them, a kind of respect for their youth and beauty, and a kind of shame for herself; but the tears did not fall; and she opened one of those innumerable novels which she used to pronounce good or bad, or pretty middling, or really wonderful. 'I can't think how people come to imagine such things,' she would say, taking off her spectacles and looking up with the old faded eyes, that were becoming ringed with white.

Just behind the stuffed leopard Mr Elliot was playing chess with Mr Pepper. He was being defeated, naturally, for Mr Pepper scarcely took his eyes off the board, and Mr Elliot kept leaning back in his chair and throwing out remarks to a gentleman who had only arrived the night before, a tall handsome man, with a head resembling the head of an intellectual ram. After a few remarks of a general nature had passed, they were discovering that they knew some of the same people, as indeed had been obvious from their appearance directly they saw each other.

'Ah yes, old Truefit,' said Mr Elliot. 'He has a son at Oxford. I've often stayed with them. It's a lovely old Jacobean house. Some exquisite Greuzes[89] – one or two Dutch pictures which the old boy kept in the cellars. Then there were stacks upon stacks of prints. Oh, the dirt in that house! He was a miser, you know. The boy married a daughter of Lord Pinwells. I know them too. The collecting mania tends to run in families. This chap collects buckles – men's shoe-buckles they must be, in use between the years 1580 and 1660; the dates mayn't be right, but fact's as I say. Your true collector always has some unaccountable fad of that kind. On other points he's as level-headed as a breeder of shorthorns, which is what he happens to be. Then the Pinwells, as you probably know, have their share of eccentricity too. Lady Maud, for instance – ' he was interrupted here by the necessity of considering his move – 'Lady Maud has a horror of cats and clergymen, and people with big front teeth. I've heard her shout across a table, "Keep your mouth shut, Miss Smith; they're as yellow as carrots!" – across a table, mind you. To me she's always been civility itself. She dabbles in literature, likes to collect a few of us in her drawing-room, but mention a clergyman, a bishop even, nay, the Archbishop himself, and she gobbles like a turkey-cock. I've been told it's a family feud – something to do with an ancestor in the reign of Charles I. Yes,' he continued, suffering check after check, 'I always like to know something of the grandmothers of our fashionable young men. In my opinion they preserve all that we admire in the eighteenth century, with the advantage, in the majority of cases, that they are personally clean. Not that one would insult old Lady Barborough by calling her clean. How often d'you think, Hilda,' he called out to his wife, 'her ladyship takes a bath?'

'I should hardly like to say, Hugh,' Mrs Elliot tittered, 'but wearing puce velvet, as she does even on the hottest August day, it somehow doesn't show.'

'Pepper, you have me,' said Mr Elliot. 'My chess is even worse than I remembered.' He accepted his defeat with great equanimity, because he really wished to talk.

He drew his chair beside Mr Wilfrid Flushing, the newcomer.

'Are these at all in your line?' he asked, pointing at a case in front of them, where highly polished crosses, jewels and bits of embroidery, the work of the natives, were displayed to tempt visitors.

'Shams, all of them,' said Mr Flushing briefly. 'This rug, now, isn't at all bad.' He stopped and picked up a piece of the rug at their feet. 'Not old, of course, but the design is quite in the right tradition. Alice, lend me your brooch. See the difference between the old work and the new.'

A lady, who was reading with great concentration, unfastened her brooch and gave it to her husband without looking at him or acknowledging the tentative bow which Mr Elliot was desirous of giving her. If she had listened, she might have been amused by the reference to old Lady Barborough, her great-aunt, but, oblivious of her surroundings, she went on reading.

The clock, which had been wheezing for some minutes like an old man preparing to cough, now struck nine. The sound slightly disturbed certain somnolent merchants, government officials, and men of independent means who were lying back in their chairs, chatting, smoking, ruminating about their affairs, with their eyes half shut; they raised their lids for an instant at the sound and then closed them again. They had the appearance of crocodiles so fully gorged by their last meal that the future of the world gives them no anxiety whatever. The only disturbance in the placid bright room was caused by a large moth which shot from light to light, whizzing over elaborate heads of hair, and causing several young women to raise their hands nervously and exclaim, 'Someone ought to kill it!'

Absorbed in their own thoughts, Hewet and Hirst had not spoken for a long time.

When the clock struck, Hirst said: 'Ah, the creatures begin to stir . . . ' He watched them raise themselves, look about them, and settle down again. 'What I abhor most of all,' he concluded, 'is the female breast. Imagine being Venning and having to get into bed with Susan! But the really repulsive thing is that they feel nothing at all – about what I do when I have a hot bath. They're gross, they're absurd, they're utterly intolerable!'

So saying, and drawing no reply from Hewet, he proceeded to think about himself, about science, about Cambridge, about the Bar, about Helen and what she thought of him, until, being very tired, he was nodding off to sleep.

Suddenly Hewet woke him up.

'How d'you know what you feel, Hirst?'

'Are you in love?' asked Hirst. He put in his eyeglass.

'Don't be a fool,' said Hewet.

'Well, I'll sit down and think about it,' said Hirst. 'One really ought to. If these people would only think about things, the world would be a far better place for us all to live in. Are you trying to think?'

That was exactly what Hewet had been doing for the last half-hour, but he did not find Hirst sympathetic at the moment.

'I shall go for a walk,' he said.

'Remember we weren't in bed last night,' said Hirst with a prodigious yawn.

Hewet rose and stretched himself.

'I want to go and get a breath of air,' he said.

An unusual feeling had been bothering him all the evening and forbidding him to settle into any one train of thought. It was precisely as if he had been in the middle of a talk which interested him profoundly when someone came up and interrupted him. He could not finish the talk, and the longer he sat there the more he wanted to finish it. As the talk that had been interrupted was a talk with Rachel, he had to ask himself why he felt this, and why he wanted to go on talking to her. Hirst would merely say that he was in love with her. But he was not in love with her. Did love begin in that way, with the wish to go on talking? No. It always began in his case with definite physical sensations, and these were now absent, he did not even find her physically attractive. There was something, of course, unusual about her – she was young, inexperienced and inquisitive, they had been more open with each other than was usually possible. He always found girls interesting to talk to, and surely these were good reasons why he should wish to go on talking to her; and last night, what with the crowd and the confusion, he had only been able to begin to talk to her. What was she doing now? Lying on a sofa and looking at the ceiling, perhaps. He could imagine her doing that, and Helen in an armchair, with her hands on the arm of it, so – looking ahead of her, with her great big eyes – oh no, they'd be talking, of course, about the dance. But suppose Rachel was going away in a day or two, suppose this was the end of her visit, and her father had arrived in one of the steamers anchored in the bay – it was intolerable to know so little. Therefore he exclaimed, 'How d'you know what you feel, Hirst?' to stop himself from thinking.

But Hirst did not help him, and the other people with their aimless movements and their unknown lives were disturbing, so that he longed for the empty darkness. The first thing he looked for when he stepped out of the hall door was the light of the Ambroses' villa. When he had definitely decided that a certain light apart from the others higher up the hill was their light, he was considerably reassured. There seemed to be at once a little stability in all this incoherence. Without any definite plan in his head, he took the turning to the right and walked through the town and came to the wall by the meeting of the roads, where he stopped. The booming of the sea was audible. The dark-blue mass of the mountains rose against the paler blue of the sky. There was no moon, but myriads of stars, and lights were anchored up and down in the dark waves of earth all round him. He had meant to go back, but the single light of the Ambroses' villa had now become three separate lights, and he was tempted to go on. He might as well make sure that Rachel was still there. Walking fast, he soon stood by the iron gate of their garden, and pushed it open; the outline of the house suddenly appeared sharply before his eyes, and the thin column of the verandah cutting across the palely lit gravel of the terrace. He hesitated. At the back of the house someone was rattling cans. He approached the front; the light on the terrace showed him that the sitting-rooms were on that side. He stood as near the light as he could by the corner of the house, the leaves of a creeper brushing his face. After a moment he could hear a voice. The voice went on steadily; it was not talking, but from the continuity of the sound it was a voice reading aloud. He crept a little closer; he crumpled the leaves together so as to stop their rustling about his ears. It might be Rachel's voice. He left the shadow and stepped into the radius of the light, and then heard a sentence spoken quite distinctly.

'And there we lived from the year 1860 to 1895, the happiest years of my parents' lives, and there in 1862 my brother Maurice was born, to the delight of his parents, as he was destined to be the delight of all who knew him.'

The voice quickened, and the tone became conclusive, rising slightly in pitch, as if these words were at the end of the chapter. Hewet drew back again into the shadow. There was a long silence. He could just hear chairs being moved inside. He had almost decided to go back, when suddenly two figures appeared at the window, not six feet from him.

'It was Maurice Fielding, of course, that your mother was engaged to,' said Helen's voice. She spoke reflectively, looking out into the dark garden, and thinking evidently as much of the look of the night as of what she was saying.

'Mother?' said Rachel. Hewet's heart leapt, and he noticed the fact. Her voice, though low, was full of surprise.

'You didn't know that?' said Helen.

'I never knew there'd been anyone else,' said Rachel. She was clearly surprised, but all they said was said low and inexpressively, because they were speaking out into the cool dark night.

'More people were in love with her than with anyone I've ever known,' Helen stated. 'She had that power – she enjoyed things. She wasn't beautiful, but – I was thinking of her last night at the dance. She got on with every kind of person, and then she made it all so amazingly – funny.'

It appeared that Helen was going back into the past, choosing her words deliberately, comparing Theresa with the people she had known since Theresa died.

'I don't know how she did it,' she continued, and ceased, and there was a long pause, in which a little owl called first here, then there, as it moved from tree to tree in the garden.

'That's so like Aunt Lucy and Aunt Katie,' said Rachel at last. 'They always make out that she was very sad and very good.'

'Then why, for goodness' sake, did they do nothing but criticise her when she was alive?' said Helen. Very gentle their voices sounded, as if they fell through the waves of the sea.

'If I were to die tomorrow . . . ' she began.

The broken sentences had an extraordinary beauty and detachment in Hewet's ears, and a kind of mystery too, as though they were spoken by people in their sleep.

'No, Rachel,' Helen's voice continued, 'I'm not going to walk in the garden; it's damp – it's sure to be damp; besides, I see at least a dozen toads.'

'Toads? Those are stones, Helen. Come out. It's nicer out. The flowers smell,' Rachel replied.

Hewet drew still farther back. His heart was beating very quickly. Apparently Rachel tried to pull Helen out on to the terrace, and Helen resisted. There was a certain amount of scuffling, entreating, resisting, and laughter from both of them. Then a man's form appeared. Hewet could not hear what they were all saying. In a minute they had gone in; he could hear bolts grating then; there was dead silence, and all the lights went out.

He turned away, still crumpling and uncrumpling a handful of leaves which he had torn from the wall. An exquisite sense of pleasure and relief possessed him; it was all so solid and peaceful after the ball at the hotel, whether he was in love with them or not, and he was not in love with them; no, but it was good that they should be alive.

After standing still for a minute or two he turned and began to walk towards the gate. With the movement of his body, the excitement, the romance and the richness of life crowded into his brain. He shouted out a line of poetry, but the words escaped him, and he stumbled among lines and fragments of lines which had no meaning at all except for the beauty of the words. He shut the gate, and ran swinging from side to side down the hill, shouting any nonsense that came into his head. 'Here am I,' he cried rhythmically, as his feet pounded to the left and to the right, 'plunging along, like an elephant in the jungle, stripping the branches as I go' (he snatched at the twigs of a bush at the roadside), roaring innumerable words, lovely words about innumerable things, running downhill and talking nonsense aloud to myself about roads and leaves and lights and women coming out into the darkness – about women – about Rachel, about Rachel.' He stopped and drew a deep breath. The night seemed immense and hospitable, and although so dark there seemed to be things moving down there in the harbour and movement out at sea. He gazed until the darkness numbed him, and then he walked on quickly, still murmuring to himself. 'And I ought to be in bed, snoring and dreaming, dreaming, dreaming. Dreams and realities, dreams and realities, dreams and realities,' he repeated all the way up the avenue, scarcely knowing what he said, until he reached the front door. Here he paused for a second, and collected himself before he opened the door.

His eyes were dazed, his hands very cold, and his brain excited and yet half asleep. Inside the door everything was as he had left it except that the hall was now empty. There were the chairs turning in towards each other where people had sat talking, and the empty glasses on little tables, and the newspapers scattered on the floor. As he shut the door he felt as if he were enclosed in a square box, and instantly shrivelled up. It was all very bright and very small. He stopped for a minute by the long table to find a paper which he had meant to read, but he was still too much under the influence of the dark and the fresh air to consider carefully which paper it was or where he had seen it.

As he fumbled vaguely among the papers he saw a figure cross the tail of his eye, coming downstairs. He heard the swishing sound of skirts, and to his great surprise, Evelyn M. came up to him, laid her hand on the table as if to prevent him from taking up a paper, and said: 'You're just the person I wanted to talk to.' Her voice was a little unpleasant and metallic, her eyes were very bright, and she kept them fixed upon him.

'To talk to me?' he repeated. 'But I'm half asleep.'

'But I think you understand better than most people,' she answered, and sat down on a little chair placed beside a big leather chair so that Hewet had to sit down beside her.

'Well?' he said. He yawned openly, and lit a cigarette. He could not believe that this was really happening to him. 'What is it?'

'Are you really sympathetic, or is it just a pose?' she demanded.

'It's for you to say,' he replied. 'I'm interested, I think.' He still felt numb all over and as if she was much too close to him.

'Anyone can be interested!' she cried impatiently. 'Your friend Mr Hirst's interested, I dare say. However, I do believe in you. You look as if you'd got a nice sister, somehow.' She paused, picking at some sequins on her knees, and then, as if she had made up her mind, she started off, 'Anyhow, I'm going to ask your advice. D'you ever get into a state where you don't know your own mind? That's the state I'm in now. You see, last night at the dance, Raymond Oliver – he's the tall dark boy who looks as if he had Indian blood in him, but he says he's not really – well, we were sitting out together, and he told me all about himself, how unhappy he is at home, and how he hates being out here. They've put him into some beastly mining business. He says it's beastly – I should like it, I know, but that's neither here nor there. And I felt awfully sorry for him, one couldn't help being sorry for him, and when he asked me to let him kiss me, I did. I don't see any harm in that, do you? And then this morning he said he'd thought I meant something more, and I wasn't the sort to let anyone kiss me. And we talked and talked. I dare say I was very silly, but one can't help liking people when one's sorry for them. I do like him most awfully – ' She paused. 'So I gave him half a promise, and then, you see, there's Alfred Perrott.'

'Oh, Perrott,' said Hewet.

'We got to know each other on that picnic the other day,' she continued. 'He seemed so lonely, especially as Arthur had gone off with Susan, and one couldn't help guessing what was in his mind. So we had quite a long talk when you were looking at the ruins, and he told me all about his life, and his struggles, and how fearfully hard it had been. D'you know, he was a boy in a grocer's shop and took parcels to people's houses in a basket? That interested me awfully, because I always say it doesn't matter how you're born if you've got the right stuff in you. And he told me about his sister who's paralysed, poor girl, and one can see she's a great trial, though he's evidently very devoted to her. I must say I do admire people like that! I don't expect you do because you're so clever. Well, last night we sat out in the garden together, and I couldn't help seeing what he wanted to say, and comforting him a

little, and telling him I did care – I really do – only, then, there's
Raymond Oliver. What I want you to tell me is, can one be in love with
two people at once, or can't one?'

She became silent, and sat with her chin on her hands, looking very
intent, as if she were facing a real problem which had to be discussed
between them.

'I think it depends what sort of person you are,' said Hewet. He
looked at her. She was small and pretty, aged perhaps twenty-eight or
twenty-nine, but though dashing and sharply cut, her features expressed
nothing very clearly, except a great deal of spirit and good health.

'Who are you, what are you; you see, I know nothing about you,' he
continued.

'Well, I was coming to that,' said Evelyn M. She continued to rest
her chin on her hands and to look intently ahead of her. 'I'm the
daughter of a mother and no father, if that interests you,' she said. 'It's
not a very nice thing to be. It's what often happens in the country. She
was a farmer's daughter, and he was rather a swell – the young man up
at the great house. He never made things straight – never married her –
though he allowed us quite a lot of money. His people wouldn't let him.
Poor father! I can't help liking him. Mother wasn't the sort of woman
who could keep him straight, anyhow. He was killed in the war. I
believe his men worshipped him. They say great big troopers broke
down and cried over his body on the battlefield. I wish I'd known him.
Mother had all the life crushed out of her. The world – ' She clenched
her fist. 'Oh, people can be horrid to a woman like that!'

She turned upon Hewet. 'Well,' she said, 'd'you want to know any
more about me?'

'But you?' he asked. 'Who looked after you?'

'I've looked after myself mostly,' she laughed. 'I've had splendid
friends. I do like people! That's the trouble. What would you do if you
liked two people, both of them tremendously, and you couldn't tell
which most?'

'I should go on liking them – I should wait and see. Why not?'

'But one has to make up one's mind,' said Evelyn. 'Or are you one of
the people who doesn't believe in marriages and all that? Look here –
this isn't fair, I do all the telling, and you tell nothing. Perhaps you're
the same as your friend' – she looked at him suspiciously; 'perhaps you
don't like me?'

'I don't know you,' said Hewet.

'I know when I like a person directly I see them! I knew I liked you
the very first night at dinner. Oh dear,' she continued impatiently,

'what a lot of bother would be saved if only people would say the things they think straight out! I'm made like that. I can't help it.'

'But don't you find it leads to difficulties?' Hewet asked.

'That's men's fault,' she answered. 'They always drag it in – love, I mean.'

'And so you've gone on having one proposal after another,' said Hewet.

'I don't suppose I've had more proposals than most women,' said Evelyn, but she spoke without conviction.

'Five, six, ten?' Hewet ventured.

Evelyn seemed to intimate that perhaps ten was the right figure, but that it really was not a high one.

'I believe you're thinking me a heartless flirt,' she protested. 'But I don't care if you are. I don't care what anyone thinks of me. Just because one's interested and likes to be friends with men, and talk to them as one talks to women, one's called a flirt.'

'But Miss Murgatroyd – '

'I wish you'd call me Evelyn,' she interrupted.

'After ten proposals do you honestly think that men are the same as women?'

'Honestly, honestly – how I hate that word! It's always used by prigs,' cried Evelyn. 'Honestly I think they ought to be. That's what's so disappointing. Every time one thinks it's not going to happen, and every time it does.'

'The Pursuit of Friendship,' said Hewet. 'The title of a comedy.'

'You're horrid,' she cried. 'You don't care a bit really. You might be Mr Hirst.'

'Well,' said Hewet, 'let's consider. Let us consider – ' He paused, because for the moment he could not remember what it was that they had to consider. He was far more interested in her than in her story, for as she went on speaking his numbness had disappeared, and he was conscious of a mixture of liking, pity and distrust. 'You've promised to marry both Oliver and Perrott?' he concluded.

'Not exactly promised,' said Evelyn. 'I can't make up my mind which I really like best. Oh how I detest modern life!' she flung off. 'It must have been so much easier for the Elizabethans! I thought the other day on that mountain how I'd have liked to be one of those colonists, to cut down trees and make laws and all that, instead of fooling about with all these people who think one's just a pretty young lady. Though I'm not. I really might *do* something.' She reflected in silence for a minute. Then she said: 'I'm afraid right down in my heart that Alfred Perrot *won't* do. He's not strong, is he?'

'Perhaps he couldn't cut down a tree,' said Hewet. 'Have you never cared for anybody?' he asked.

'I've cared for heaps of people, but not to marry them,' she said. 'I suppose I'm too fastidious. All my life I've wanted somebody I could look up to, somebody great and big and splendid. Most men are so small.'

'What d'you mean by splendid?' Hewet asked. 'People are – nothing more.'

Evelyn was puzzled.

'We don't care for people because of their qualities,' he tried to explain. 'It's just them that we care for' – he struck a match – 'just that,' he said, pointing to the flames.

'I see what you mean,' she said, 'but I don't agree. I do know why I care for people, and I think I'm hardly ever wrong. I see at once what they've got in them. Now I think you must be rather splendid; but not Mr Hirst.'

Hewet shook his head.

'He's not nearly so unselfish, or so sympathetic, or so big, or so understanding,' Evelyn continued.

Hewet sat silent, smoking his cigarette.

'I should hate cutting down trees,' he remarked.

'I'm not trying to flirt with you, though I suppose you think I am!' Evelyn shot out. 'I'd never have come to you if I'd thought you'd merely think odious things of me!' The tears came into her eyes.

'Do you never flirt?' he asked.

'Of course I don't,' she protested. 'Haven't I told you? I want friendship; I want to care for someone greater and nobler than I am, and if they fall in love with me it isn't my fault; I don't want it; I positively hate it.'

Hewet could see that there was very little use in going on with the conversation, for it was obvious that Evelyn did not wish to say anything in particular, but to impress upon him an image of herself, being, for some reason which she would not reveal, unhappy, or insecure. He was very tired, and a pale waiter kept walking ostentatiously into the middle of the room and looking at them meaningly.

'They want to shut up,' he said. 'My advice is that you should tell Oliver and Perrott tomorrow that you've made up your mind that you don't mean to marry either of them. I'm certain you don't. If you change your mind you can always tell them so. They're both sensible men; they'll understand. And then all this bother will be over.' He got up.

But Evelyn did not move. She sat looking up at him with her bright eager eyes, in the depths of which he thought he detected some disappointment, or dissatisfaction.

'Good-night,' he said.

'There are heaps of things I want to say to you still,' she said. 'And I'm going to, some time. I suppose you must go to bed now?'

'Yes,' said Hewet. 'I'm half asleep.' He left her still sitting by herself in the empty hall.

'Why is it that they *won't* be honest?' he muttered to himself as he went upstairs. Why was it that relations between different people were so unsatisfactory, so fragmentary, so hazardous, and words so dangerous that the instinct to sympathise with another human being was an instinct to be examined carefully and probably crushed? What had Evelyn really wished to say to him? What was she feeling left alone in the empty hall? The mystery of life and the unreality even of one's own sensations overcame him as he walked down the corridor which led to his room. It was dimly lighted, but sufficiently for him to see a figure in a bright dressing-gown pass swiftly in front of him, the figure of a woman crossing from one room to another.

Chapter 15

Whether too slight or too vague the ties that bind people casually meeting in a hotel at midnight, they possess one advantage at least over the bonds which unite the elderly, who have lived together once and so must live for ever. Slight they may be, but vivid and genuine, merely because the power to break them is within the grasp of each, and there is no reason for continuance except a true desire that continue they shall. When two people have been married for years they seem to become unconscious of each other's bodily presence so that they move as if alone, speak aloud things which they do not expect to be answered, and in general seem to experience all the comfort of solitude without its loneliness. The joint lives of Ridley and Helen had arrived at this stage of community, and it was often necessary for one or the other to recall with an effort whether a thing had been said or only thought, shared or dreamt in private. At four o'clock in the afternoon two or three days later Mrs Ambrose was standing brushing her hair, while her husband was in the dressing-room which opened out of her room, and occasionally, through the cascade of water – he was washing his face – she caught exclamations, 'So it goes on year after year; I wish, I wish, I wish I could make an end of it,' to which she paid no attention.

'It's white? Or only brown?' Thus she herself murmured, examining a hair which gleamed suspiciously among the brown. She pulled it out and laid it on the dressing-table. She was criticising her own appearance, or rather approving of it, standing a little way back from the glass and looking at her own face with superb pride and melancholy, when her husband appeared in the doorway in his shirt sleeves, his face half obscured by a towel.

'You often tell me I don't notice things,' he remarked.

'Tell me if this is a white hair, then?' she replied. She laid the hair on his hand.

'There's not a white hair on your head,' he exclaimed.

'Ah, Ridley, I begin to doubt,' she sighed; and bowed her head under his eyes so that he might judge, but the inspection produced only a kiss where the line of parting ran, and husband and wife then proceeded to move about the room, casually murmuring.

'What was that you were saying?' Helen remarked, after an interval of conversation which no third person could have understood.

'Rachel – you ought to keep an eye upon Rachel,' he observed significantly, and Helen, though she went on brushing her hair, looked at him. His observations were apt to be true.

'Young gentlemen don't interest themselves in young women's education without a motive,' he remarked.

'Oh, Hirst,' said Helen.

'Hirst and Hewet, they're all the same to me – all covered with spots,' he replied. 'He advises her to read Gibbon. Did you know that?'

Helen did not know that, but she would not allow herself inferior to her husband in powers of observation. She merely said: 'Nothing would surprise me. Even that dreadful flying man we met at the dance – even Mr Dalloway – even – '

'I advise you to be circumspect,' said Ridley. 'There's Willoughby, remember – Willoughby;' he pointed at a letter.

Helen looked with a sigh at an envelope which lay upon her dressing-table. Yes, there lay Willoughby, curt, inexpressive, perpetually jocular, robbing a whole continent of mystery, enquiring after his daughter's manners and morals – hoping she wasn't a bore, and bidding them pack her off to him on board the very next ship if she were – and then grateful and affectionate with suppressed emotion, and then half a page about his own triumphs over wretched little natives who went on strike and refused to load his ships until he roared English oaths at them, 'popping my head out of the window just as I was, in my shirt sleeves. The beggars had the sense to scatter.'

'If Theresa married Willoughby,' she remarked, turning the page with a hairpin, 'one doesn't see what's to prevent Rachel – '

But Ridley was now off on grievances of his own connected with the washing of his shirts, which somehow led to the frequent visits of Hughling Elliot, who was a bore, a pedant, a dry stick of a man, and yet Ridley couldn't simply point at the door and tell him to go. The truth of it was, they saw too many people. And so on and so on, more conjugal talk pattering softly and unintelligibly, until they were both ready to go down to tea.

The first thing that caught Helen's eye as she came downstairs was a carriage at the door, filled with skirts and feathers nodding on the tops of hats. She had only time to gain the drawing-room before two names were oddly mispronounced by the Spanish maid, and Mrs Thornbury came in slightly in advance of Mrs Wilfrid Flushing.

'Mrs Wilfrid Flushing,' said Mrs Thornbury, with a wave of her hand. 'A friend of our common friend Mrs Raymond Parry.'

Mrs Flushing shook hands energetically. She was a woman of forty perhaps, very well set up and erect, splendidly robust, though not as tall as the upright carriage of her body made her appear.

She looked Helen straight in the face and said, 'You have a charmin' house.'

She had a strongly marked face, her eyes looked straight at you, and though naturally she was imperious in her manner she was nervous at the same time. Mrs Thornbury acted as interpreter, making things smooth all round by a series of charming commonplace remarks.

'I've taken it upon myself, Mr Ambrose,' she said, 'to promise that you will be so kind as to give Mrs Flushing the benefit of your experience. I'm sure no one here knows the country as well as you do. No one takes such wonderful long walks. No one, I'm sure, has your encyclopaedic knowledge upon every subject. Mr Wilfrid Flushing is a collector. He has discovered really beautiful things already. I had no notion that the peasants were so artistic – though of course in the past – '

'Not old things – new things,' interrupted Mrs Flushing curtly. 'That is, if he takes my advice.'

The Ambroses had not lived for many years in London without knowing something of a good many people, by name at least, and Helen remembered hearing of the Flushings. Mr Flushing was a man who kept an old furniture shop; he had always said he would not marry because most women have red cheeks, and would not take a house because most houses have narrow staircases, and would not eat meat because most animals bleed when they are killed; and then he had married an eccentric aristocratic lady, who certainly was not pale, who looked as if she ate meat, who had forced him to do all the things he most disliked – and this then was the lady. Helen looked at her with interest. They had moved out into the garden, where the tea was laid under a tree, and Mrs Flushing was helping herself to cherry jam. She had a peculiar jerking movement of the body when she spoke, which caused the canary-coloured plume on her hat to jerk too. Her small but finely-cut and vigorous features, together with the deep red of lips and cheeks, pointed to many generations of well-trained and well-nourished ancestors behind her.

'Nothin' that's more than twenty years old interests me,' she continued. 'Mouldy old pictures, dirty old books, they stick 'em in museums when they're only fit for burnin'.'

'I quite agree,' Helen laughed. 'But my husband spends his life in digging up manuscripts which nobody wants.' She was amused by Ridley's expression of startled disapproval.

'There's a clever man in London called John [90] who paints ever so much better than the old masters,' Mrs Flushing continued. 'His pictures excite me – nothin' that's old excites me.'

'But even his pictures will become old,' Mrs Thornbury intervened.

'Then I'll have 'em burnt, or I'll put it in my will,' said Mrs Flushing.

'And Mrs Flushing lived in one of the most beautiful old houses in England – Chillingley,' Mrs Thornbury explained to the rest of them.

'If I'd my way I'd burn that tomorrow,' Mrs Flushing laughed. She had a laugh like the cry of a jay, at once startling and joyless.

'What does any sane person want with those great big houses?' she demanded. 'If you go downstairs after dark you're covered with black beetles, and the electric lights always goin' out. What would you do if spiders came out of the tap when you turned on the hot water?' she demanded, fixing her eye on Helen.

Mrs Ambrose shrugged her shoulders with a smile.

'This is what I like,' said Mrs Flushing. She jerked her head at the villa. 'A little house in a garden. I had one once in Ireland. One could lie in bed in the mornin' and pick roses outside the window with one's toes.'

'And the gardeners, weren't they surprised?' Mrs Thornbury enquired.

'There were no gardeners,' Mrs Flushing chuckled. 'Nobody but me and an old woman without any teeth. You know the poor in Ireland lose their teeth after they're twenty. But you wouldn't expect a politician to understand that – Arthur Balfour [91] wouldn't understand that.'

Ridley sighed that he never expected anyone to understand anything, least of all politicians.

'However,' he concluded, 'there's one advantage I find in extreme old age – nothing matters a hang except one's food and one's digestion. All I ask is to be left alone to moulder away in solitude. It's obvious that the world's going as fast as it can to – to the Nethermost Pit, and all I can do is to sit still and consume as much of my own smoke as possible.' He groaned, and with a melancholy glance laid the jam on his bread, for he felt the atmosphere of this abrupt lady distinctly unsympathetic.

'I always contradict my husband when he says that,' said Mrs Thornbury sweetly. 'You men! Where would you be if it weren't for the women!'

'Read the *Symposium*,'[92] said Ridley grimly.

'*Symposium*?' cried Mrs Flushing. 'That's Latin or Greek? Tell me, is there a good translation?'

'No,' said Ridley. 'You will have to learn Greek.'

Mrs Flushing cried, 'Ah, ah, ah! I'd rather break stones in the road. I always envy the men who break stones and sit on those nice little heaps all day wearin' spectacles. I'd infinitely rather break stones than clean out poultry runs, or feed the cows, or – '

Here Rachel came up from the lower garden with a book in her hand.

'What's that book?' said Ridley, when she had shaken hands.

'It's Gibbon,' said Rachel as she sat down.

'*The Decline and Fall of the Roman Empire*?' said Mrs Thornbury. 'A very wonderful book, I know. My dear father was always quoting it at us, with the result that we resolved never to read a line.'

'Gibbon the historian?' enquired Mrs Flushing. 'I connect him with some of the happiest hours of my life. We used to lie in bed and read Gibbon – about the massacres of the Christians, I remember – when we were supposed to be asleep. It's no joke, I can tell you, readin' a great big book, in double columns, by a night-light, and the light that comes through a chink in the door. Then there were the moths – tiger moths, yellow moths and horrid cockchafers. Louisa, my sister, would have the window open. I wanted it shut. We fought every night of our lives over that window. Have you ever seen a moth dyin' in a night-light?' she enquired.

Again there was an interruption. Hewet and Hirst appeared at the drawing-room window and came up to the tea-table.

Rachel's heart beat hard. She was conscious of an extraordinary intensity in everything, as though their presence stripped some cover off the surface of things; but the greetings were remarkably commonplace.

'Excuse me,' said Hirst, rising from his chair directly he had sat down. He went into the drawing-room, and returned with a cushion which he placed carefully upon his seat.

'Rheumatism,' he remarked, as he sat down for the second time.

'The result of the dance?' Helen enquired.

'Whenever I get at all run down I tend to be rheumatic,' Hirst stated. He bent his wrist back sharply. 'I hear little pieces of chalk grinding together!'

Rachel looked at him. She was amused, and yet she was respectful; if such a thing could be, the upper part of her face seemed to laugh, and the lower part to check its laughter.

Hewet picked up the book that lay on the ground.

'You like this?' he asked in an undertone.

'No, I don't like it,' she replied. She had indeed been trying all the afternoon to read it, and for some reason the glory which she had perceived at first had faded, and, read as she would, she could not grasp the meaning with her mind.

'It goes round, round, round, like a roll of oilcloth,' she hazarded. Evidently she meant Hewet alone to hear her words, but Hirst demanded, 'What d'you mean?'

She was instantly ashamed of her figure of speech, for she could not explain it in words of sober criticism.

'Surely it's the most perfect style, so far as style goes, that's ever been invented,' he continued. 'Every sentence is practically perfect, and the wit – '

'Ugly in body, repulsive in mind,' she thought, instead of thinking about Gibbon's style. 'Yes, but strong, searching, unyielding in mind.' She looked at his big head, a disproportionate part of which was occupied by the forehead, and at the direct, severe eyes.

'I give you up in despair,' he said. He meant it lightly, but she took it seriously, and believed that her value as a human being was lessened because she did not happen to admire the style of Gibbon. The others were talking now in a group about the native villages which Mrs Flushing ought to visit.

'I despair too,' she said impetuously. 'How are you going to judge people merely by their minds?'

'You agree with my spinster aunt, I expect,' said St John in his jaunty manner, which was always irritating because it made the person he talked to appear unduly clumsy and in earnest. ' "Be good, sweet maid" [93] – I thought Mr Kingsley and my aunt were now obsolete.'

'One can be very nice without having read a book,' she asserted. Very silly and simple her words sounded, and laid her open to derision.

'Did I ever deny it?' Hirst enquired, raising his eyebrows.

Most unexpectedly Mrs Thornbury here intervened, either because it was her mission to keep things smooth or because she had long wished to speak to Mr Hirst, feeling as she did that young men were her sons.

'I have lived all my life with people like your aunt, Mr Hirst,' she said, leaning forward in her chair. Her brown squirrel-like eyes became even brighter than usual. 'They have never heard of Gibbon. They only care for their pheasants and their peasants. They are great big men who look so fine on horseback, as people must have done, I think, in the days of the great wars. Say what you like against them – they are animal, they are unintellectual; they don't read themselves, and they don't want others to read, but they are some of the finest and the kindest human beings on the face of the earth! You would be surprised at some of the stories I could tell. You have never guessed, perhaps, at all the romances that go on in the heart of the country. There are the people, I feel, among whom Shakespeare will be born if he is ever born again. In those old houses, up among the Downs – '

'My aunt,' Hirst interrupted, 'spends her life in East Lambeth among the degraded poor. I only quoted my aunt because she is inclined to persecute people she calls "intellectual", which is what I suspect Miss Vinrace of doing. It's all the fashion now. If you're clever it's always taken for granted that you're completely without sympathy, understanding, affection – all the things that really matter. Oh, you Christians! You're the most conceited, patronising, hypocritical set of old humbugs in the kingdom! Of course,' he continued, 'I'm the first to allow your country gentlemen great merits. For one thing, they're probably quite frank about their passions, which we are not. My father, who is a clergyman in Norfolk, says that there is hardly a squire in the country who does not – '

'But about Gibbon?' Hewet interrupted. The look of nervous tension which had come over every face was relaxed by the interruption. 'You find him monotonous, I suppose. But you know – ' He opened the book, and began searching for passages to read aloud, and in a little time he found a good one which he considered suitable. But there was nothing in the world that bored Ridley more than being read aloud to, and he was besides scrupulously fastidious as to the dress and behaviour of ladies. In the space of fifteen minutes he had decided against Mrs Flushing on the ground that her orange plume did not suit her complexion, that she spoke too loud, that she crossed her legs, and finally, when he saw her accept a cigarette that Hewet offered her, he jumped up, exclaiming something about 'bar parlours', and left them. Mrs Flushing was evidently relieved by his departure. She puffed her cigarette, stuck her legs out, and examined Helen closely as to the character and reputation of their common friend Mrs Raymond Parry. By a series of little strategems she drove her to define Mrs Parry as somewhat elderly, by no means beautiful, very much made up – an insolent old harridan, in short, whose parties were amusing because one met odd people; but Helen herself always pitied poor Mr Parry, who was understood to be shut up downstairs with cases full of gems, while his wife enjoyed herself in the drawing-room. 'Not that I believe what people say against her – although she hints, of course – ' Upon which Mrs Flushing cried out with delight: 'She's my first cousin! Go on – go on!'

When Mrs Flushing rose to go she was obviously delighted with her new acquaintances. She made three or four different plans for meeting or going on an expedition, or showing Helen the things they had bought, on her way to the carriage. She included them all in a vague but magnificent invitation.

As Helen returned to the garden again, Ridley's words of warning came into her head, and she hesitated a moment and looked at Rachel sitting between Hirst and Hewet. But she could draw no conclusions, for Hewet was still reading Gibbon aloud, and Rachel, for all the expression she had, might have been a shell, and his words water rubbing against her ears, as water rubs a shell on the edge of a rock.

Hewet's voice was very pleasant. When he reached the end of the period Hewet stopped, and no one volunteered any criticism.

'I do adore the aristocracy!' Hirst exclaimed after a moment's pause. 'They're so amazingly unscrupulous. None of us would dare to behave as that woman behaves.'

'What I like about them,' said Helen as she sat down, 'is that they're so well put together. Naked, Mrs Flushing would be superb. Dressed as she dresses, it's absurd, of course.'

'Yes,' said Hirst. A shade of depression crossed his face. 'I've never weighed more than ten stone in my life,' he said, 'which is ridiculous, considering my height, and I've actually gone down in weight since we came here. I dare say that accounts for the rheumatism.' Again he jerked his wrist back sharply, so that Helen might hear the grinding of the chalk stones. She could not help smiling.

'It's no laughing matter for me, I assure you,' he protested. 'My mother's a chronic invalid, and I'm always expecting to be told that I've got heart disease myself. Rheumatism always goes to the heart in the end.'

'For goodness' sake, Hirst,' Hewet protested; 'one might think you were an old cripple of eighty. If it comes to that, I had an aunt who died of cancer myself, but I put a bold face on it – ' He rose and began tilting his chair backwards and forwards on its hind legs. 'Is anyone here inclined for a walk?' he said. 'There's a magnificent walk, up behind the house. You come out on to a cliff and look right down into the sea. The rocks are all red; you can see them through the water. The other day I saw a sight that fairly took my breath away – about twenty jellyfish, semi-transparent, pink, with long streamers, floating on the top of the waves.'

'Sure they weren't mermaids?' said Hirst. 'It's much too hot to climb uphill.' He looked at Helen, who showed no signs of moving.

'Yes, it's too hot,' Helen decided.

There was a short silence.

'I'd like to come,' said Rachel.

'But she might have said that anyhow,' Helen thought to herself as Hewet and Rachel went away together, and Helen was left alone with St John, to St John's obvious satisfaction.

He may have been satisfied, but his usual difficulty in deciding that one subject was more deserving of notice than another prevented him from speaking for some time. He sat staring intently at the head of a dead match, while Helen considered – so it seemed from the expression of her eyes – something not closely connected with the present moment.

At last St John exclaimed, 'Damn! Damn everything! Damn everybody!' he added. 'At Cambridge there are people to talk to.'

'At Cambridge there are people to talk to,' Helen echoed him, rhythmically and absent-mindedly. Then she woke up. 'By the way, have you settled what you're going to do – is it to be Cambridge or the Bar?'

He pursed his lips, but made no immediate answer, for Helen was still slightly inattentive. She had been thinking about Rachel and which of the two young men she was likely to fall in love with, and now sitting opposite to Hirst she thought, 'He's ugly. It's a pity they're so ugly.'

She did not include Hewet in this criticism; she was thinking of the clever, honest, interesting young men she knew, of whom Hirst was a good example, and wondering whether it was necessary that thought and scholarship should thus maltreat their bodies, and should thus elevate their minds to a very high tower from which the human race appeared to them like rats and mice squirming on the flat.

'And the future?' she reflected, vaguely envisaging a race of men becoming more and more like Hirst, and a race of women becoming more and more like Rachel. 'Oh no,' she concluded, glancing at him, 'one wouldn't marry you. Well, then, the future of the race is in the hands of Susan and Arthur; no – that's dreadful. Of farm labourers; no – not of the English at all, but of Russians and Chinese.' This train of thought did not satisfy her, and was interrupted by St John, who began again: 'I wish you knew Bennett. He's the greatest man in the world.'

'Bennett?' she enquired.

Becoming more at ease, St John dropped the concentrated abruptness of his manner, and explained that Bennett was a man who lived in an old windmill six miles out of Cambridge. He lived the perfect life, according to St John, very lonely, very simple, caring only for the truth of things, always ready to talk, and extraordinarily modest, though his mind was of the greatest.

'Don't you think,' said St John, when he had done describing him, 'that kind of thing makes this kind of thing rather flimsy? Did you notice at tea how poor old Hewet had to change the conversation? How they were all ready to pounce upon me because they thought I was going to say something improper? It wasn't anything, really. If Bennett had been there he'd have said exactly what he meant to say, or he'd have got up and gone. But there's something rather bad for the character in that – I mean if one hasn't got Bennett's character. It's inclined to make one bitter. Should you say that I was bitter?'

Helen did not answer, and he continued: 'Of course I am, disgustingly bitter, and it's a beastly thing to be. But the worst of me is that I'm so envious. I envy everyone. I can't endure people who do things better than I do – perfectly absurd things too – waiters balancing piles of plates – even Arthur, because Susan's in love with him. I want people to like me, and they don't. It's partly my appearance, I expect,' he continued, 'though it's an absolute lie to say I've Jewish blood in me – as a matter of fact we've been in Norfolk, Hirst of Hirstbourne Hall, for three centuries at least. It must be awfully soothing to be like you – everyone liking one at once.'

'I assure you they don't,' Helen laughed.

'They do,' said Hirst with conviction. 'In the first place, you're the most beautiful woman I've ever seen; in the second, you have an exceptionally nice nature.'

If Hirst had looked at her instead of looking intently at his teacup he would have seen Helen blush, partly with pleasure, partly with an impulse of affection towards the young man who had seemed, and would seem again, so ugly and so limited. She pitied him, for she suspected that he suffered, and she was interested in him, for many of the things he said seemed to her true; she admired the morality of youth, and yet she felt imprisoned. As if her instinct were to escape to something brightly coloured and impersonal, which she could hold in her hands, she went into the house and returned with her embroidery. But he was not interested in her embroidery; he did not even look at it.

'About Miss Vinrace,' he began – 'oh, look here, do let's be St John and Helen, and Rachel and Terence – what's she like? Does she reason, does she feel, or is she merely a kind of footstool?'

'Oh no,' said Helen, with great decision. From her observations at tea she was inclined to doubt whether Hirst was the person to educate Rachel. She had gradually come to be interested in her niece, and fond of her; she disliked some things about her very much, she was amused by others; but she felt her, on the whole, a live if unformed human being, experimental, and not always fortunate in her experiments, but with powers of some kind, and a capacity for feeling. Somewhere in the depths of her, too, she was bound to Rachel by the indestructible if inexplicable ties of sex. 'She seems vague, but she's a will of her own,' she said, as if in the interval she had run through her qualities.

The embroidery, which was a matter for thought, the design being difficult and the colours wanting consideration, brought lapses into the dialogue when she seemed to be engrossed in her skeins of silk, or, with head a little drawn back and eyes narrowed, considered the effect of the whole. Thus she merely said, 'Um-m-m,' to St John's next remark, 'I shall ask her to go for a walk with me.'

Perhaps he resented this division of attention. He sat silent watching Helen closely.

'You're absolutely happy,' he proclaimed at last.

'Yes?' Helen enquired, sticking in her needle.

'Marriage, I suppose,' said St John.

'Yes,' said Helen, gently drawing her needle out.

'Children?' St John enquired.

'Yes,' said Helen, sticking her needle in again. 'I don't know why I'm happy,' she suddenly laughed, looking him full in the face. There was a considerable pause.

'There's an abyss between us,' said St John. His voice sounded as if it issued from the depths of a cavern in the rocks. 'You're infinitely simpler than I am. Women always are, of course. That's the difficulty. One never knows how a woman gets there. Supposing all the time you're thinking, "Oh, what a morbid young man!" '

Helen sat and looked at him with her needle in her hand. From her position she saw his head in front of the dark pyramid of a magnolia tree. With one foot raised on the rung of a chair, and her elbow out in the attitude for sewing, her own figure possessed the sublimity of a woman's of the early world, spinning the thread of fate – the sublimity possessed by many women of the present day who fall into the attitude required by scrubbing or sewing. St John looked at her.

'I suppose you've never paid anyone a compliment in the course of your life,' he said irrelevantly.

'I spoil Ridley rather,' Helen considered.

'I'm going to ask you point blank – do you like me?'

After a certain pause, she replied, 'Yes, certainly.'

'Thank God!' he exclaimed. 'That's one mercy. You see,' he continued with emotion, 'I'd rather you liked me than anyone I've ever met.'

'What about the five philosophers?' said Helen, with a laugh, stitching firmly and swiftly at her canvas. 'I wish you'd describe them.'

Hirst had no particular wish to describe them, but when he began to consider them he found himself soothed and strengthened. Far away on the other side of the world as they were, in smoky rooms, and grey medieval courts, they appeared remarkable figures, free-spoken men with whom one could be at ease; incomparably more subtle in emotion than the people here. They gave him, certainly, what no woman could give him, not Helen even. Warming at the thought of them, he went on to lay his case before Mrs Ambrose. Should he stay on at Cambridge or should he go to the Bar? One day he thought one thing, another day another. Helen listened attentively. At last, without any preface, she pronounced her decision.

'Leave Cambridge and go to the Bar,' she said.

He pressed her for her reasons.

'I think you'd enjoy London more,' she said. It did not seem a very subtle reason, but she appeared to think it sufficient. She looked at him against the background of flowering magnolia. There was something curious in the sight. Perhaps it was that the heavy waxlike flowers were so smooth and inarticulate, and his face – he had thrown his hat away, his hair was rumpled, he held his eyeglasses in his hand, so that a red mark appeared on either side of his nose – was so worried and garrulous. It was a beautiful bush, spreading very widely, and all the time she had sat there talking she had been noticing the patches of shade and the shape of the leaves, and the way the great white flowers sat in the midst of the green. She had noticed it half-consciously, nevertheless the pattern had become part of their talk. She laid down her sewing, and began to walk up and down the garden, and Hirst rose too and paced by her side. He was rather disturbed, uncomfortable, and full of thought. Neither of them spoke.

The sun was beginning to go down, and a change had come over the mountains, as if they were robbed of their earthly substance, and composed merely of intense blue mist. Long thin clouds of flamingo red, with edges like the edges of curled ostrich feathers, lay up and down the sky at different altitudes. The roofs of the town seemed to have sunk lower than usual; the cypresses appeared very black between the roofs, and the roofs themselves were brown and white. As usual in the evening, single cries and single bells became audible rising from beneath.

St John stopped suddenly.

'Well, you must take the responsibility,' he said. 'I've made up my mind; I shall go to the Bar.'

His words were very serious, almost emotional; they recalled Helen after a second's hesitation.

'I'm sure you're right,' she said warmly, and shook the hand he held out. 'You'll be a great man, I'm certain.'

Then, as if to make him look at the scene, she swept her hand round the immense circumference of the view. From the sea, over the roofs of the town, across the crests of the mountains, over the river and the plain, and again across the crests of the mountains it swept until it reached the villa, the garden, the magnolia tree, and the figures of Hirst and herself standing together, when it dropped to her side.

Chapter 16

Hewet and Rachel had long ago reached the particular place on the edge of the cliff where, looking down into the sea, you might chance on jellyfish and dolphins. Looking the other way, the vast expanse of land gave them a sensation which is given by no view, however extended, in England, the villages and the hills there having names, and the farthest horizon of hills as often as not dipping and showing a line of mist which is the sea; here the view was one of infinite sun-dried earth, earth pointed in pinnacles, heaped in vast barriers, earth widening and spreading away and away like the immense floor of the sea, earth chequered by day and by night, and partitioned into different lands, where famous cities were founded, and the races of men changed from dark savages to white civilised men, and back to dark savages again. Perhaps their English blood made this prospect uncomfortably impersonal and hostile to them, for having once turned their faces that way they next turned them to the sea, and for the rest of the time sat looking at the sea. The sea, though it was a thin and sparkling water here, which seemed incapable of surge or anger, eventually narrowed itself, clouded its pure tint with grey, and swirled through narrow channels and dashed in a shiver of broken waters against massive granite rocks. It was this sea that flowed up to the mouth of the Thames; and the Thames washed the roots of the city of London.

Hewet's thoughts had followed some such course as this, for the first thing he said as they stood on the edge of the cliff was –

'I'd like to be in England!'

Rachel lay down on her elbow, and parted the tall grasses which grew on the edge, so that she might have a clear view. The water was very calm; rocking up and down at the base of the cliff, and so clear that one could see the red of the stones at the bottom of it. So it had been at the birth of the world, and so it had remained ever since. Probably no human being had ever broken that water with boat or with body. Obeying some impulse, she determined to mar that eternity of peace, and threw the largest pebble she could find. It struck the water, and the ripples spread out and out.

Hewet looked down too. 'It's wonderful,' he said, as they widened and ceased. The freshness and the newness seemed to him wonderful. He threw a pebble next. There was scarcely any sound.

'But England,' Rachel murmured in the absorbed tone of one whose eyes are concentrated upon some sight. 'What d'you want with England?'

'My friends chiefly,' he said, 'and all the things one does.'

He could look at Rachel without her noticing it. She was still absorbed in the water and the exquisitely pleasant sensations which a little depth of the sea washing over rocks suggests. He noticed that she was wearing a dress of deep blue colour, made of a soft thin cotton stuff, which clung to the shape of her body. It was a body with the angles and hollows of a young woman's body not yet developed, but in no way distorted, and thus interesting and even lovable. Raising his eyes Hewet observed her head; she had taken her hat off, and the face rested on her hand. As she looked down into the sea, her lips were slightly parted. The expression was one of childlike intentness, as if she were watching for a fish to swim past over the clear red rocks. Nevertheless her twenty-four years of life had given her a look of reserve. Her hand, which lay on the ground, the fingers curling slightly in, was well shaped and competent; the square-tipped and nervous fingers were the fingers of a musician. With something like anguish Hewet realised that, far from being unattractive, her body was very attractive to him. She looked up suddenly. Her eyes were full of eagerness and interest.

'You write novels?' she asked.

For the moment he could not think what he was saying. He was overcome with the desire to hold her in his arms.

'Oh yes,' he said. 'That is, I want to write them.'

She would not take her large grey eyes off his face.

'Novels,' she repeated. 'Why do you write novels? You ought to write music. Music, you see' – she shifted her eyes, and became less desirable as her brain began to work, inflicting a certain change upon her face – 'music goes straight for things. It says all there is to say at once. With writing it seems to me there's so much' – she paused for an expression, and rubbed her fingers in the earth – 'scratching on the matchbox. Most of the time when I was reading Gibbon this afternoon I was horribly, oh infernally, damnably bored!' She gave a shake of laughter, looking at Hewet, who laughed too.

'*I* shan't lend you books,' he remarked.

'Why is it,' Rachel continued, 'that I can laugh at Mr Hirst to you, but not to his face? At tea I was completely overwhelmed, not by his ugliness – by his mind.' She enclosed a circle in the air with her hands. She realised with a great sense of comfort how easily she could talk to

Hewet, those thorns or ragged corners which tear the surface of some relationships being smoothed away.

'So I observed,' said Hewet. 'That's a thing that never ceases to amaze me.' He had recovered his composure to such an extent that he could light and smoke a cigarette, and feeling her ease, became happy and easy himself.

'The respect that women, even well-educated, very able women, have for men,' he went on. 'I believe we must have the sort of power over you that we're said to have over horses. They see us three times as big as we are or they'd never obey us. For that very reason, I'm inclined to doubt that you'll ever do anything even when you have the vote.' He looked at her reflectively. She appeared very smooth and sensitive and young. 'It'll take at least six generations before you're sufficiently thick-skinned to go into law courts and business offices. Consider what a bully the ordinary man is,' he continued, 'the ordinary hard-working, rather ambitious solicitor or man of business with a family to bring up and a certain position to maintain. And then, of course, the daughters have to give way to the sons; the sons have to be educated; they have to bully and shove for their wives and families, and so it all comes over again. And meanwhile there are the women in the background . . . Do you really think that the vote will do you any good?'

'The vote?' Rachel repeated. She had to visualise it as a little bit of paper which she dropped into a box before she understood his question, and looking at each other they smiled at something absurd in the question.

'Not to me,' she said. 'But I play the piano . . . Are men really like that?' she asked, returning to the question that interested her. 'I'm not afraid of you.' She looked at him easily.

'Oh, I'm different,' Hewet replied. 'I've got between six and seven hundred a year of my own. And then no one takes a novelist seriously, thank heavens. There's no doubt it helps to make up for the drudgery of a profession if a man's taken very, very seriously by everyone – if he gets appointments, and has offices and a title, and lots of letters after his name, and bits of ribbon and degrees. I don't grudge it 'em, though sometimes it comes over me – what an amazing concoction! What a miracle the masculine conception of life is – judges, civil servants, army, navy, Houses of Parliament, lord mayors – what a world we've made of it! Look at Hirst now. I assure you,' he said, 'not a day's passed since we came here without a discussion as to whether he's to stay on at Cambridge or to go to the Bar. It's his career – his sacred career. And if I've heard it twenty times, I'm sure his mother and sister have heard it five hundred times. Can't you imagine the family conclaves, and the sister told to run out and feed the rabbits because St John must have the schoolroom to himself – "St John's working," "St John wants his tea brought to him." Don't you know the kind of thing? No wonder that St John thinks it a matter of considerable importance. It is too. He has to earn his living. But St John's sister – ' Hewet puffed in silence. 'No one takes her seriously, poor dear. She feeds the rabbits.'

'Yes,' said Rachel. 'I've fed rabbits for twenty-four years; it seems odd now.' She looked meditative, and Hewet, who had been talking much at random and instinctively adopting the feminine point of view, saw that she would now talk about herself, which was what he wanted, for so they might come to know each other.

She looked back meditatively upon her past life.

'How do you spend your day?' he asked.

She meditated still. When she thought of their day it seemed to her it was cut into four pieces by their meals. These divisions were absolutely rigid, the contents of the day having to accommodate themselves within the four rigid bars. Looking back at her life, that was what she saw.

'Breakfast nine; luncheon one; tea five; dinner eight,' she said.

'Well,' said Hewet, 'what d'you do in the morning?'

'I need to play the piano for hours and hours.'

'And after luncheon?'

'Then I went shopping with one of my aunts. Or we went to see someone, or we took a message; or we did something that had to be done – the taps might be leaking. They visit the poor a good deal – old charwomen with bad legs, women who want tickets for hospitals. Or I used to walk in the park by myself. And after tea people sometimes called; or in summer we sat in the garden or played croquet; in winter I read aloud, while they worked; after dinner I played the piano and they wrote letters. If father was at home we had friends of his to dinner, and about once a month we went up to the play. Every now and then we dined out; sometimes I went to a dance in London, but that was difficult because of getting back. The people we saw were old family friends, and relations, but we didn't see many people. There was the clergyman, Mr Pepper and the Hunts. Father generally wanted to be quiet when he came home, because he works very hard at Hull. Also my aunts aren't very strong. A house takes up a lot of time if you do it properly. Our servants were always bad, and so Aunt Lucy used to do a good deal in the kitchen, and Aunt Clara, I think, spent most of the morning dusting the drawing-room and going through the linen and silver. Then there were the dogs. They had to be exercised, besides being washed and brushed. Now Sandy's dead, but Aunt Clara has a very old cockatoo that came from India. Everything in our house,' she exclaimed, 'comes from somewhere! It's full of old furniture, not really old, Victorian, things mother's family had or father's family had, which they didn't like to get rid of, I suppose, though we've really no room for them. It's rather a nice house,' she continued, 'except that it's a little dingy – dull I should say.' She called up before her eyes a vision of the drawing-room at home; it was a large oblong room, with a square window opening on the garden. Green plush chairs stood against the wall; there was a heavy carved bookcase, with glass doors, and a general impression of faded sofa covers, large spaces of pale green, and baskets with pieces of wool-work dropping out of them. Photographs of old Italian master-pieces hung on the walls, and views of Venetian bridges and Swedish waterfalls which members of the family had seen years ago. There were also one or two portraits of fathers and grandmothers, and an engraving of John Stuart Mill,[94] after the picture by Watts. It was a room without definite character, being neither typically and openly hideous, nor strenuously artistic, nor really comfortable. Rachel roused herself from the contemplation of this familiar picture.

'But this isn't very interesting for you,' she said, looking up.

'Good Lord!' Hewet exclaimed. 'I've never been so much interested in my life.' She then realised that while she had been thinking of Richmond, his eyes had never left her face. The knowledge of this excited her.

'Go on, please go on,' he urged. 'Let's imagine it's a Wednesday. You're all at luncheon. You sit there, and Aunt Lucy there, and Aunt Clara here;' he arranged three pebbles on the grass between them.

'Aunt Clara carves the neck of lamb,' Rachel continued. She fixed her gaze upon the pebbles. 'There's a very ugly yellow china stand in front of me, called a dumb waiter, on which are three dishes, one for biscuits, one for butter and one for cheese. There's a pot of ferns. Then there's Blanche the maid, who snuffles because of her nose. We talk – oh yes, it's Aunt Lucy's afternoon at Walworth, so we're rather quick over luncheon. She goes off. She has a purple bag, and a black notebook. Aunt Clara has what they call a G.F.S.[95] meeting in the drawing-room on Wednesday, so I take the dogs out. I go up Richmond Hill, along the terrace, into the park. It's the 18th of April – the same day as it is here. It's spring in England. The ground is rather damp. However, I cross the road and get on to the grass and we walk along, and I sing as I always do when I'm alone, until we come to the open place where you can see the whole of London beneath you on a clear day. Hampstead

Church spire there, Westminster Cathedral over there, and factory chimneys about here. There's generally a haze over the low parts of London; but it's often blue over the park when London's in a mist. It's the open place that the balloons cross going over to Hurlingham. They're pale yellow. Well, then, it smells very good, particularly if they happen to be burning wood in the keeper's lodge which is there. I could tell you now how to get from place to place, and exactly what trees you'd pass, and where you'd cross the roads. You see, I played there when I was small. Spring is good, but it's best in the autumn when the deer are barking; then it gets dusky, and I go back through the streets, and you can't see people properly; they come past very quick, you just see their faces and then they're gone – that's what I like – and no one knows in the least what you're doing – '

'But you have to be back for tea, I suppose?' Hewet checked her.

'Tea? Oh yes. Five o'clock. Then I say what I've done, and my aunts say what they've done, and perhaps someone comes in: Mrs Hunt, let's suppose. She's an old lady with a lame leg. She has or she once had eight children; so we ask after them. They're all over the world; so we ask where they are, and sometimes they're ill, or they're stationed in a cholera district, or in some place where it only rains once in five months. Mrs Hunt,' she said with a smile, 'had a son who was hugged to death by a bear.'

Here she stopped and looked at Hewet to see whether he was amused by the same things that amused her. She was reassured. But she thought it necessary to apologise again; she had been talking too much.

'You can't conceive how it interests me,' he said. Indeed, his cigarette had gone out, and he had to light another.

'Why does it interest you?' she asked.

'Partly because you're a woman,' he replied. When he said this, Rachel, who had become oblivious of anything, and had reverted to a childlike state of interest and pleasure, lost her freedom and became self-conscious. She felt herself at once singular and under observation, as she felt with St John Hirst. She was about to launch into an argument which would have made them both feel bitterly against each other, and to define sensations which had no such importance as words were bound to give them when Hewet led her thoughts in a different direction.

'I've often walked along the streets where people live all in a row, and one house is exactly like another house, and wondered what on earth the women were doing inside,' he said. 'Just consider: it's the beginning of the twentieth century, and until a few years ago no woman had ever come out by herself and said things at all. There it was going on in the background, for all those thousands of years, this curious silent unrepresented life. Of course we're always writing about women – abusing them, or jeering at them, or worshipping them; but it's never come from women themselves. I believe we still don't know in the least how they live, or what they feel, or what they do precisely. If one's a man, the only confidences one gets are from young women about their love affairs. But the lives of women of forty, of unmarried women, of working women, of women who keep shops and bring up children, of women like your aunts or Mrs Thornbury or Miss Allan – one knows nothing whatever about them. They won't tell you. Either they're afraid, or they've got a way of treating men. It's the man's view that's represented, you see. Think of a railway train: fifteen carriages for men who want to smoke. Doesn't it make your blood boil? If I were a woman I'd blow someone's brains out. Don't you laugh at us a great deal? Don't you think it all a great humbug? You, I mean – how does it all strike you?'

His determination to know, while it gave meaning to their talk, hampered her; he seemed to press further and further, and made it appear so important. She took some time to answer, and during that time she went over and over the course of her twenty-four years, lighting now on one point, now on another – on her aunts, her mother, her father, and at last her mind fixed upon her aunts and her father, and she tried to describe them as at this distance they appeared to her.

They were very much afraid of her father. He was a great dim force in the house, by means of which they held on to the great world which is represented every morning in *The Times*. But the real life of the house was something quite different from this. It went on independently of Mr Vinrace, and tended to hide itself from him. He was good-humoured towards them, but contemptuous. She had always taken it for granted that his point of view was just, and founded upon an ideal scale of things where the life of one person was absolutely more important than the life of another, and that in that scale they were of much less importance than he was. But did she really believe that? Hewet's words made her think. She always submitted to her father, just as they did, but it was her aunts who influenced her really; her aunts who built up the fine, closely woven substance of their life at home. They were less splendid but more natural than her father was. All her rages had been against them; it was their world with its four meals, its punctuality, and servants on the stairs at half-past ten, that she examined so closely and wanted so vehemently to smash to atoms. Following these thoughts she looked up and said: 'And there's a sort of beauty in it – there they are at Richmond at this very moment building things up. They're all wrong, perhaps, but there's a sort of beauty in it,' she repeated. 'It's so unconscious, so modest. And yet they feel things. They do mind if people die. Old spinsters are always doing things. I don't quite know what they do. Only that was what I felt when I lived with them. It was very real.'

She reviewed their little journeys to and fro, to Walworth, to charwomen with bad legs, to meetings for this and that, their minute acts of charity and unselfishness which flowered punctually from a definite view of what they ought to do, their friendships, their tastes and habits; she saw all these things like grains of sand falling, falling through innumerable days, making an atmosphere and building up a solid mass, a background. Hewet observed her as she considered this.

'Were you happy?' he demanded.

Again she had become absorbed in something else, and he called her back to an unusually vivid consciousness of herself.

'I was both,' she replied. 'I was happy and I was miserable. You've no conception what it's like – to be a young woman.' She looked straight at him. 'There are terrors and agonies,' she said, keeping her eye on him as if to detect the slightest hint of laughter.

'I can believe it,' he said. He returned her look with perfect sincerity.

'Women one sees in the streets,' she said.

'Prostitutes?'

'Men kissing one.'

He nodded his head.

'You were never told?'

She shook her head.

'And then,' she began and stopped. Here came in the great space of life into which no one had ever penetrated. All that she had been saying about her father and her aunts and walks in Richmond Park, and what they did from hour to hour, was merely on the surface. Hewet was watching her. Did he demand that she should describe that also? Why did he sit so near and keep his eye on her? Why did they not have done with this searching and agony? Why did they not kiss each other simply? She wished to kiss him. But all the time she went on spinning out words.

'A girl is more lonely than a boy. No one cares in the least what she does. Nothing's expected of her. Unless one's very pretty people don't listen to what you say ... And that is what I like,' she added energetically, as if the memory were very happy. 'I like walking in Richmond Park and singing to myself and knowing it doesn't matter a damn to anybody. I like seeing things go on – as we saw you that night when you didn't see us – I love the freedom of it – it's like being the wind or the sea.' She turned with a curious fling of her hands and looked at the sea. It was still very blue, dancing away as far as the eye could reach, but the light on it was yellower, and the clouds were turning flamingo red.

A feeling of intense depression crossed Hewet's mind as she spoke. It seemed plain that she would never care for one person rather than another; she was evidently quite indifferent to him; they seemed to come very near, and then they were as far apart as ever again; and her gesture as she turned away had been oddly beautiful.

'Nonsense,' he said abruptly. 'You like people. You like admiration. Your real grudge against Hirst is that he doesn't admire you.'

She made no answer for some time. Then she said: 'That's probably true. Of course I like people – I like almost everyone I've ever met.'

She turned her back on the sea and regarded Hewet with friendly if critical eyes. He was good-looking in the sense that he had always had a sufficiency of beef to eat and fresh air to breathe. His head was big; the eyes were also large; though generally vague they could be forcible; and the lips were sensitive. One might account him a man of considerable passion and fitful energy, likely to be at the mercy of moods which had little relation to facts; at once tolerant and fastidious. The breadth of his forehead showed capacity for thought. The interest with which Rachel looked at him was heard in her voice.

'What novels do you write?' she asked.

'I want to write a novel about Silence,' he said; 'the things people don't say. But the difficulty is immense.' He sighed. 'However, you don't care,' he continued. He looked at her almost severely. 'Nobody cares. All you read a novel for is to see what sort of person the writer is, and, if you know him, which of his friends he's put in. As for the novel itself, the whole conception, the way one's seen the thing, felt about it, made it stand in relation to other things, not one in a million cares for that. And yet I sometimes wonder whether there's anything else in the whole world worth doing. These other people,' he indicated the hotel, 'are always wanting something they can't get. But there's an extra-ordinary satisfaction in writing, even in the attempt to write. What you said just now is true: one doesn't want to be things; one wants merely to be allowed to see them.'

Some of the satisfaction of which he spoke came into his face as he gazed out to sea.

It was Rachel's turn now to feel depressed. As he talked of writing he had become suddenly impersonal. He might never care for anyone; all that desire to know her and get at her, which she had felt pressing on her almost painfully, had completely vanished.

'Are you a good writer?' she asked.

'Yes,' he said. 'I'm not first-rate, of course; I'm good second-rate; about as good as Thackeray,[96] I should say.'

Rachel was amazed. For one thing it amazed her to hear Thackeray called second-rate; and then she could not widen her point of view to believe that there could be great writers in existence at the present day, or if there were, that anyone she knew could be a great writer, and his self-confidence astounded her, and he became more and more remote.

'My other novel,' Hewet continued, 'is about a young man who is obsessed by an idea – the idea of being a gentleman. He manages to exist at Cambridge on a hundred pounds a year. He has a coat; it was once a very good coat. But the trousers – they're not so good. Well, he goes up to London, gets into good society, owing to an early-morning adventure on the banks of the Serpentine. He is led into telling lies – my idea, you see, is to show the gradual corruption of the soul – calls himself the son of some great landed proprietor in Devonshire. Meanwhile the coat becomes older and older, and he hardly dares to wear the trousers. Can't you imagine the wretched man, after some splendid evening of debauchery, contemplating these garments – hanging them over the end of the bed, arranging them now in full light, now in shade, and wondering whether they will survive him, or he will survive them? Thoughts of suicide cross his mind. He has a friend, too, a man who somehow subsists upon selling small birds, for which he sets traps in the fields near Uxbridge. They're scholars, both of them. I know one or two wretched starving creatures like that who quote Aristotle[97] at you over a fried herring and a pint of porter. Fashionable life, too, I have to represent at some length, in order to show my hero under all circumstances. Lady Theo Bingham Bingley, whose bay mare he had the good fortune to stop, is the daughter of a very fine old Tory peer. I'm going to describe the kind of parties I once went to – the fashionable intellectuals, you know, who like to have the latest book on their tables. They give parties, river parties, parties where you play games. There's no difficulty in conceiving incidents; the difficulty is to put them into shape – not to get run away with, as Lady Theo was. It ended disastrously for her, poor woman, for the book, as I planned it, was going to end in profound and sordid respectability. Disowned by her father, she marries my hero, and they live in a snug little villa outside Croydon, in which town he is set up as a house agent. He never succeeds in becoming a real gentleman after all. That's the interesting part of it. Does it seem to you the kind of book you'd like to read?' he enquired; 'or perhaps you'd like my Stuart tragedy better,' he continued, without waiting for her to answer him. 'My idea is that there's a certain quality of beauty in the past, which the ordinary historical novelist completely ruins by his absurd conventions. The moon becomes the Regent of the Skies. People clap spurs to their horses, and so on. I'm going to treat people as though they were exactly the same as we are. The advantage is that, detached from modern conditions, one can make them more intense and more abstract then people who live as we do.'

Rachel had listened to all this with attention, but with a certain amount of bewilderment. They both sat thinking their own thoughts.

'I'm not like Hirst,' said Hewet, after a pause; he spoke meditatively; 'I don't see circles of chalk between people's feet. I sometimes wish I did. It seems to me so tremendously complicated and confused. One can't come to any decision at all; one's less and less capable of making judgements. D'you find that? And then one never knows what anyone feels. We're all in the dark. We try to find out, but can you imagine anything more ludicrous than one person's opinion of another person? One goes along thinking one knows; but one really doesn't know.'

As he said this he was leaning on his elbow arranging and rearranging in the grass the stones which had represented Rachel and her aunts at luncheon. He was speaking as much to himself as to Rachel. He was reasoning against the desire, which had returned with intensity, to take her in his arms; to have done with indirectness; to explain exactly what he felt. What he said was against his belief; all the things that were important about her he knew; he felt them in the air around them; but he said nothing; he went on arranging the stones.

'I like you; d'you like me?' Rachel suddenly observed.

'I like you immensely,' Hewet replied, speaking with the relief of a person who is unexpectedly given an opportunity of saying what he wants to say. He stopped moving the pebbles.

'Mightn't we call each other Rachel and Terence?' he asked.

'Terence,' Rachel repeated. 'Terence – that's like the cry of an owl.'

She looked up with a sudden rush of delight, and in looking at Terence with eyes widened by pleasure she was struck by the change that had come over the sky behind them. The substantial blue day had faded to a paler and more ethereal blue; the clouds were pink, far away and closely packed together; and the peace of evening had replaced the heat of the southern afternoon, in which they had started on their walk.

'It must be late!' she exclaimed.

It was nearly eight o'clock.

'But eight o'clock doesn't count here, does it?' Terence asked, as they got up and turned inland again. They began to walk rather quickly down the hill on a little path between the olive trees.

They felt more intimate because they shared the knowledge of what eight o'clock in Richmond meant. Terence walked in front, for there was not room for them side by side.

'What I want to do in writing novels is very much what you want to do when you play the piano, I expect,' he began, turning and speaking over his shoulder. 'We want to find out what's behind things, don't we? – Look at the lights down there,' he continued, 'scattered about anyhow. Things I feel come to me like lights . . . I want to combine them . . . Have you ever seen fireworks that make figures? . . . I want to make figures . . . Is that what you want to do?'

Now they were out on the road and could walk side by side.

'When I play the piano? Music is different . . . But I see what you mean.' They tried to invent theories and to make their theories agree. As Hewet had no knowledge of music, Rachel took his stick and drew figures in the thin white dust to explain how Bach wrote his fugues.

'My musical gift was ruined,' he explained, as they walked on after one of these demonstrations, 'by the village organist at home, who had invented a system of notation which he tried to teach me, with the result that I never got to the tune-playing at all. My mother thought music wasn't manly for boys; she wanted me to kill rats and birds – that's the worst of living in the country. We live in Devonshire. It's the loveliest place in the world. Only – it's always difficult at home when one's grown up. I'd like you to know one of my sisters . . . Oh, here's your gate – ' He pushed it open. They paused for a moment. She could not ask him to come in. She could not say that she hoped they would meet again; there was nothing to be said, and so without a word she went through the gate, and was soon invisible. Directly Hewet lost sight of her, he felt the old discomfort return, even more strongly than before. Their talk had been interrupted in the middle, just as he was beginning to say the things he wanted to say. After all, what had they been able to say? He ran his mind over the things they had said, the random, unnecessary things which had eddied round and round and used up all the time, and drawn them so close together and flung them so far apart, and left him in the end unsatisfied, ignorant still of what she felt and of what she was like. What was the use of talking, talking, merely talking?

Chapter 17

It was now the height of the season, and every ship that came from England left a few people on the shores of Santa Marina who drove up to the hotel. The fact that the Ambroses had a house where one could escape momentarily from the slightly inhuman atmosphere of an hotel was a source of genuine pleasure not only to Hirst and Hewet, but to the Elliots, the Thornburys, the Flushings, Miss Allan, Evelyn M., together with other people whose identity was so little developed that the Ambroses did not discover that they possessed names. By degrees there was established a kind of correspondence between the two houses, the big and the small, so that at most hours of the day one house could guess what was going on in the other, and the words 'the villa' and 'the hotel' called up the idea of two separate systems of life. Acquaintances showed signs of developing into friends, for that one tie to Mrs Parry's drawing-room had inevitably split into many other ties attached to different parts of England, and sometimes these alliances seemed cynically fragile, and sometimes painfully acute, lacking as they did the supporting background of organised English life. One night when the moon was round between the trees, Evelyn M. told Helen the story of her life, and claimed her everlasting friendship; or another occasion, merely because of a sigh, or a pause, or a word thoughtlessly dropped, poor Mrs Elliot left the villa half in tears, vowing never again to meet the cold and scornful woman who had insulted her, and in truth, meet again they never did. It did not seem worth while to piece together so slight a friendship.

Hewet, indeed, might have found excellent material at this time up at the villa for some chapters in the novel which was to be called 'Silence, or the Things People Don't Say'. Helen and Rachel had become very silent. Having detected, as she thought, a secret, and judging that Rachel meant to keep it from her, Mrs Ambrose respected it carefully, but from that cause, though unintentionally, a curious atmosphere of reserve grew up between them. Instead of sharing their views upon all subjects, and plunging after an idea wherever it might lead, they spoke chiefly in comment upon the people they saw, and the secret between them made itself felt in what they said even of Thornburys and Elliots. Always calm and unemotional in her judgements, Mrs Ambrose was now inclined to be definitely pessimistic. She was not severe upon individuals so much as incredulous of the kindness of destiny, fate, what happens in the long run, and apt to insist that this was generally adverse to people in proportion as they deserved well. Even this theory she was ready to discard in favour of one which made chaos triumphant, things happening for no reason at all, and everyone groping about in illusion and ignorance. With a certain pleasure she developed these views to her niece, taking a letter from home as her test: which gave good news, but might just as well have given bad. How did she know that at this very moment both her children were not lying dead, crushed by motor omnibuses? 'It's happening to somebody: why shouldn't it happen to me?' she would argue, her face taking on the stoical expression of anticipated sorrow. However sincere these views may have been, they were undoubtedly called forth by the irrational state of her niece's mind. It was so fluctuating, and went so quickly from joy to despair, that it seemed necessary to confront it with some stable opinion which naturally became dark as well as stable. Perhaps Mrs Ambrose had some idea that in leading the talk into these quarters she might discover what was in Rachel's mind, but it was difficult to judge, for sometimes she would agree with the gloomiest thing that was said, at other times she refused to listen, and rammed Helen's theories down her throat with laughter, chatter, ridicule of the wildest, and fierce bursts of anger even at what she called the 'croaking of a raven in the mud'.

'It's hard enough without that,' she asserted.

'What's hard?' Helen demanded.

'Life,' she replied, and then they both became silent.

Helen might draw her own conclusions as to why life was hard, as to why an hour later, perhaps, life was something so wonderful and vivid that the eyes of Rachel beholding it were positively exhilarating to a spectator. True to her creed, she did not attempt to interfere, although there were enough of those weak moments of depression to make it perfectly easy for a less scrupulous person to press through and know all, and perhaps Rachel was sorry that she did not choose. All these moods ran themselves into one general effect, which Helen compared to the sliding of a river, quick, quicker, quicker still, as it races to a waterfall. Her instinct was to cry out Stop! but even had there been any use in crying Stop! she would have refrained, thinking it best that things should take their way, the water racing because the earth was shaped to make it race.

It seemed that Rachel herself had no suspicion that she was watched, or that there was anything in her manner likely to draw attention to her. What had happened to her she did not know. Her mind was very much in the condition of the racing water to which Helen compared it. She wanted to see Terence; she was perpetually wishing to see him when he was not there; it was an agony to miss seeing him; agonies were strewn all about her day on account of him, but she never asked herself what this force driving through her life arose from. She thought of no result any more than a tree perpetually pressed downwards by the wind considers the result of being pressed downwards by the wind.

During the two or three weeks which had passed since their walk, half a dozen notes from him had accumulated in her drawer. She would read them, and spend the whole morning in a daze of happiness; the sunny land outside the window being no less capable of analysing its own colour and heat than she was of analysing hers. In these moods she found it impossible to read or play the piano, even to move being beyond her inclination. The time passed without her noticing it. When it was dark she was drawn to the window by the lights of the hotel. A light that went in and out was the light in Terence's window: there he sat, reading perhaps, or now he was walking up and down pulling out one book after another; and now he was seated in his chair again, and she tried to imagine what he was thinking about. The steady lights marked the rooms where Terence sat with people moving round him. Everyone who stayed in the hotel had a peculiar romance and interest about them. They were not ordinary people. She would attribute wisdom to Mrs Elliot, beauty to Susan Warrington, a splendid vitality to Evelyn M., because Terence spoke to them. As unreflecting and pervasive were the moods of depression. Her mind was as the landscape outside when dark beneath clouds and straitly lashed by wind and hail. Again she would sit passive in her chair exposed to pain, and Helen's fantastical or gloomy words were like so many darts goading her to cry out against the hardness of life. Best of all were the moods when for no reason again this stress of feeling slackened, and life went on as usual, only with a joy and colour in its events that was unknown before; they had a significance like that which she had seen in the tree: the nights were black bars separating her from the days; she would have liked to run all the days into one long continuity of sensation. Although these moods were directly or indirectly caused by the presence of Terence or the thought of him, she never said to herself that she was in love with him, or considered what was to happen if she continued to feel such things, so that Helen's image of the river sliding on to the waterfall had a great likeness to the facts, and the alarm which Helen sometimes felt was justified.

In her curious condition of unanalysed sensations she was incapable of making a plan which should have any effect upon her state of mind. She abandoned herself to the mercy of accidents, missing Terence one day, meeting him the next, receiving his letters always with a start of surprise. Any woman experienced in the progress of courtship would have come by certain opinions from all this which would have given her at least a theory to go upon; but no one had ever been in love with Rachel, and she had never been in love with anyone. Moreover, none of the books she read, from *Wuthering Heights* to *Man and Superman*,[98] and the plays of Ibsen, suggested from their analysis of love that what their heroines felt was what she was feeling now. It seemed to her that her sensations had no name.

She met Terence frequently. When they did not meet, he was apt to send a note with a book or about a book, for he had not been able after all to neglect that approach to intimacy. But sometimes he did not come or did not write for several days at a time. Again when they met their meeting might be one of inspiriting joy or of harassing despair. Over all their partings hung the sense of interruption, leaving them both unsatisfied, though ignorant that the other shared the feeling.

If Rachel was ignorant of her own feelings, she was even more completely ignorant of his. At first he moved as a god; as she came to know him better he was still the centre of light, but combined with this beauty a wonderful power of making her daring and confident of herself. She was conscious of emotions and powers which she had never suspected in herself, and of a depth in the world hitherto unknown. When she thought of their relationship she saw rather than reasoned, representing her view of what Terence felt by a picture of him drawn across the room to stand by her side. This passage across the room amounted to a physical sensation, but what it meant she did not know.

Thus the time went on, wearing a calm, bright look upon its surface. Letters came from England, letters came from Willoughby, and the days accumulated their small events which shaped the year. Superficially, three odes of Pindar were mended, Helen covered about five inches of her embroidery, and St John completed the first two acts of a play. He and Rachel being now very good friends, he read them aloud to her, and she was so genuinely impressed by the skill of his rhythms and the variety of his adjectives, as well as by the fact that he was Terence's friend, that he began to wonder whether he was not intended for literature rather than for law. It was a time of profound thought and sudden revelations for more than one couple, and several single people.

A Sunday came, which no one in the villa with the exception of Rachel and the Spanish maid proposed to recognise. Rachel still went to church, because she had never, according to Helen, taken the trouble to think about it. Since they had celebrated the service at the hotel she went there expecting to get some pleasure from her passage across the garden and through the hall of the hotel, although it was very doubtful whether she would see Terence, or at any rate have the chance of speaking to him.

As the greater number of visitors at the hotel were English, there was almost as much difference between Sunday and Wednesday as there is in England, and Sunday appeared here as there, the mute black ghost or penitent spirit of the busy weekday. The English could not pale the sunshine, but they could in some miraculous way slow down the hours, dull the incidents, lengthen the meals and make even the servants and pageboys wear a look of boredom and propriety. The best clothes which everyone put on helped the general effect; it seemed that no lady could sit down without bending a clean starched petticoat, and no gentleman could breathe without a sudden crackle from a stiff shirt-front.

As the hands of the clock neared eleven, on this particular Sunday, various people tended to draw together in the hall, clasping little red-leaved books in their hands. The clock marked a few minutes to the hour when a stout black figure passed through the hall with a preoccupied expression, as though he would rather not recognise salutations, although aware of them, and disappeared down the corridor which led from it.

'Mr Bax,' Mrs Thornbury whispered.

The little group of people then began to move off in the same direction as the stout black figure. Looked at in an odd way by people who made no effort to join them, they moved with one exception slowly and consciously towards the stairs. Mrs Flushing was the exception. She came running downstairs, strode across the hall, joined the procession much out of breath, demanding of Mrs Thornbury in an agitated whisper, 'Where, where?'

'We are all going,' said Mrs Thornbury gently, and soon they were descending the stairs two by two. Rachel was among the first to descend. She did not see that Terence and Hirst came in at the rear possessed of no black volume, but of one thin book bound in light-blue cloth, which St John carried under his arm.

The chapel was the old chapel of the monks. It was a profound cool place where they had said Mass for hundreds of years, and done penance in the cold moonlight, and worshipped old brown pictures and carved saints which stood with upraised hands of blessing in the hollows in the walls. The transition from Catholic to Protestant worship had been bridged by a time of disuse, when there were no services, and the place was used for storing jars of oil, liqueur and deckchairs; the hotel flourishing, some religious body had taken the place in hand, and it was now fitted out with a number of glazed yellow benches, claret-coloured footstools; it had a small pulpit, and a brass eagle carrying the Bible on its back, while the piety of different women had supplied ugly squares of carpet, and long strips of embroidery heavily wrought with monograms in gold.

As the congregation entered they were met by mild sweet chords issuing from a harmonium, where Miss Willett, concealed from view by a baize curtain, struck emphatic chords with uncertain fingers. The sound spread through the chapel as the rings of water spread from a fallen stone. The twenty or twenty-five people who composed the congregation first bowed their heads and then sat up and looked about them. It was very quiet, and the light down here seemed paler than the light above. The usual bows and smiles were dispensed with, but they recognised each other. The Lord's Prayer was read over them. As the childlike battle of voices rose, the congregation, many of whom had only met on the staircase, felt themselves pathetically united and well-disposed towards each other. As if the prayer were a torch applied to fuel, a smoke seemed to rise automatically and fill the place with the ghosts of innumerable services on innumerable Sunday mornings at home. Susan Warrington in particular was conscious of the sweetest sense of sisterhood, as she covered her face with her hands and saw slips of bent backs through the chinks between her fingers. Her emotions rose calmly and evenly, approving of herself and of life at the same time. It was all so quiet and so good. But having created this peaceful atmosphere Mr Bax suddenly turned the page and read a psalm. Though he read it with no change of voice the mood was broken.

'Be merciful unto me, O God,' he read, 'for man goeth about to devour me: he is daily fighting and troubling me . . . They daily mistake my words: all that they imagine is to do me evil. They hold all together and keep themselves close . . . Break their teeth, O God, in their mouths; smite the jawbones of the lions, O Lord: let them fall away like water that runneth apace; and when they shoot their arrows let them be rooted out.'[99]

Nothing in Susan's experience at all corresponded with this, and as she had no love of language she had long ceased to attend to such remarks, although she followed them with the same kind of mechanical respect with which she heard many of Lear's speeches read aloud. Her mind was still serene and really occupied with praise of her own nature and praise of God, that is of the solemn and satisfactory order of the world.

But it could be seen from a glance at their faces that most of the others, the men in particular, felt the inconvenience of the sudden intrusion of this old savage. They looked more secular and critical as they listened to the ravings of the old black man with a cloth round his loins cursing with vehement gesture by a camp-fire in the desert. After that there was a general sound of pages being turned as if they were in class, and then they read a little bit of the Old Testament about making a well, very much as schoolboys translate an easy passage from the *Anabasis* [100] when they have shut up their French grammar. Then they returned to the New Testament and the sad and beautiful figure of Christ. While Christ spoke they made another effort to fit his interpretation of life upon the lives they lived, but as they were all very different, some practical, some ambitious, some stupid, some wild and experimental, some in love and others long past any feeling except a feeling of comfort, they did very different things with the words of Christ.

From their faces it seemed that for the most part they made no effort at all, and, recumbent as it were, accepted the ideas the words gave as representing goodness, in the same way, no doubt, as one of those industrious needlewomen had accepted the bright ugly pattern on her mat as beauty.

Whatever the reason might be, for the first time in her life, instead of slipping at once into some curious pleasant cloud of emotion, too familiar to be considered, Rachel listened critically to what was being said. By the time they had swung in an irregular way from prayer to psalm, from psalm to history, from history to poetry, and Mr Bax was giving out his text, she was in a state of acute discomfort. Such was the discomfort she felt when forced to sit through an unsatisfactory piece of music badly played. Tantalised, enraged by the clumsy insensitiveness of the conductor, who put the stress on the wrong places, and annoyed by the vast flock of the audience tamely praising and acquiescing without knowing or caring, so she was now tantalised and enraged, only here, with eyes half-shut and lips pursed together, the atmosphere of forced solemnity increased her anger. All round her were people pretending to feel what they did not feel, while somewhere above her floated the idea which they could none of them grasp, which they pretended to grasp, always escaping out of reach, a beautiful idea, an idea like a butterfly. One after another, vast and hard and cold, appeared to her the churches all over the world where this blundering effort and misunderstanding

were perpetually going on, great buildings, filled with innumerable
men and women not seeing clearly, who finally gave up the effort to
see, and relapsed tamely into praise and acquiescence, half-shutting
their eyes and pursing up their lips. The thought had the same sort of
physical discomfort as is caused by a film of mist always coming between
the eyes and the printed page. She did her best to brush away the film
and to conceive something to be worshipped as the service went on, but
failed, always misled by the voice of Mr Bax saying things which mis-
represented the idea, and by the patter of baaing inexpressive human
voices falling round her like damp leaves. The effort was tiring and
dispiriting. She ceased to listen, and fixed her eyes on the face of a
woman near her, a hospital nurse, whose expression of devout attention
seemed to prove that she was at any rate receiving satisfaction. But
looking at her carefully she came to the conclusion that the hospital
nurse was only slavishly acquiescent, and that the look of satisfaction
was produced by no splendid conception of God within her. How,
indeed, could she conceive anything far outside her own experience, a
woman with a commonplace face like hers, a little round red face, upon
which trivial duties and trivial spites had drawn lines, whose weak blue
eyes saw without intensity or individuality, whose features were blurred,
insensitive and callous? She was adoring something shallow and smug,
clinging to it, so the obstinate mouth witnessed, with the assiduity of a
limpet; nothing would tear her from her demure belief in her own
virtue and the virtues of her religion. She was a limpet, with the
sensitive side of her stuck to a rock, forever dead to the rush of fresh
and beautiful things past her. The face of this single worshipper became
printed on Rachel's mind with an impression of keen horror, and she
had it suddenly revealed to her what Helen meant and St John meant
when they proclaimed their hatred of Christianity. With the violence
that now marked her feelings, she rejected all that she had implicitly
believed.

Meanwhile Mr Bax was halfway through the second lesson. She looked
at him. He was a man of the world with supple lips and an agreeable
manner, he was indeed a man of much kindliness and simplicity, though
by no means clever, but she was not in the mood to give anyone credit
for such qualities, and examined him as though he were an epitome of all
the vices of his service.

Right at the back of the chapel Mrs Flushing, Hirst and Hewet sat in
a row in a very different frame of mind. Hewet was staring at the roof
with his legs stuck out in front of him, for as he had never tried to make
the service fit any feeling or idea of his, he was able to enjoy the beauty

of the language without hindrance. His mind was occupied first with accidental things, such as the women's hair in front of him, the light on the faces, then with the words which seemed to him magnificent, and then more vaguely with the characters of the other worshippers. But when he suddenly perceived Rachel, all these thoughts were driven out of his head, and he thought only of her. The psalms, the prayers, the Litany, and the sermon were all reduced to one chanting sound which paused, and then renewed itself, a little higher or a little lower. He stared alternately at Rachel and at the ceiling, but his expression was now produced not by what he saw but by something in his mind. He was almost as painfully disturbed by his thoughts as she was by hers.

Early in the service Mrs Flushing had discovered that she had taken up a Bible instead of a prayer-book, and, as she was sitting next to Hirst, she stole a glance over his shoulder. He was reading steadily in the thin pale-blue volume. Unable to understand, she peered closer, upon which Hirst politely laid the book before her, pointing to the first line of a Greek poem and then to the translation opposite.

'What's that?' she whispered inquisitively.

'Sappho,'[101] he replied. 'The one Swinburne did – the best thing that's ever been written.'

Mrs Flushing could not resist such an opportunity. She gulped down the 'Ode to Aphrodite' during the Litany, keeping herself with difficulty from asking when Sappho lived, and what else she wrote worth reading, and contriving to come in punctually at the end with 'the forgiveness of sins, the resurrection of the body, and the life everlastin'. Amen.'

Meanwhile Hirst took out an envelope and began scribbling on the back of it. When Mr Bax mounted the pulpit he shut up Sappho with his envelope between the pages, settled his spectacles, and fixed his gaze intently upon the clergyman. Standing in the pulpit he looked very large and fat; the light coming through the greenish unstained window-glass made his face appear smooth and white like a very large egg.

He looked round at all the faces looking mildly up at him, although some of them were the faces of men and women old enough to be his grandparents, and gave out his text with weighty significance. The argument of the sermon was that visitors to this beautiful land, although they were on a holiday, owed a duty to the natives. It did not, in truth, differ very much from a leading article upon topics of general interest in the weekly newspapers. It rambled with a kind of amiable verbosity from one heading to another, suggesting that all human beings are very much the same under their skins, illustrating this by the resemblance of the games which little Spanish boys play to the games little boys in

London streets play, observing that very small things do influence people, particularly natives; in fact, a very dear friend of Mr Bax's had told him that the success of our rule in India, that vast country, largely depended upon the strict code of politeness which the English adopted towards the natives, which led to the remark that small things were not necessarily small, and that led somehow to the virtue of sympathy, which was a virtue never more needed than today, when we lived in a time of experiment and upheaval – witness the aeroplane and wireless telegraph, and there were other problems which hardly presented themselves to our fathers, but which no man who called himself a man could leave unsettled. Here Mr Bax became more definitely clerical, if it were possible; he seemed to speak with a certain innocent craftiness, as he pointed out that all this laid a special duty upon earnest Christians. What men were inclined to say now was, 'Oh, that fellow – he's a parson.' What we want them to say is, 'He's a good fellow' – in other words, 'He is my brother.' He exhorted them to keep in touch with men of the modern type; they must sympathise with their multifarious interests in order to keep before their eyes that whatever discoveries were made there was one discovery which could not be superseded, which was indeed as much of a necessity to the most successful and most brilliant of them all as it had been to their fathers. The humblest could help; the least important things had an influence (here his manner became definitely priestly and his remarks seemed to be directed to women, for indeed Mr Bax's congregations were mainly composed of women, and he was used to assigning them their duties in his innocent clerical campaigns). Leaving more definite instruction, he passed on, and his theme broadened into a peroration for which he drew a long breath and stood very upright. 'As a drop of water, detached, alone, separate from others, falling from the cloud and entering the great ocean, alters, so scientists tell us, not only the immediate spot in the ocean where it falls, but all the myriad drops which together compose the great universe of waters, and by this means alters the configuration of the globe and the lives of millions of sea creatures, and finally the lives of the men and women who seek their living upon the shores – as all this is within the compass of a single drop of water, such as any rain shower sends in millions to lose themselves in the earth, to lose themselves we say, but we know very well that the fruits of the earth could not flourish without them – so is a marvel comparable to this within the reach of each one of us, who dropping a little word or a little deed into the great universe alters it; yea, it is a solemn thought, *alters* it, for good or for evil, not for one instant, or in one vicinity, but throughout the entire race, and for all eternity.' Whipping round as though to avoid applause, he continued with the same breath, but in a different tone of voice – 'And now to God the Father . . . '

He gave his blessing, and then, while the solemn chords again issued from the harmonium behind the curtain, the different people began scraping and fumbling and moving very awkwardly and consciously towards the door. Halfway upstairs, at a point where the light and sounds of the upper world conflicted with the dimness and the dying hymn-tune of the under, Rachel felt a hand drop upon her shoulder.

'Miss Vinrace,' Mrs Flushing whispered peremptorily, 'stay to luncheon. It's such a dismal day. They don't even give one beef for luncheon. Please stay.'

Here they came out into the hall, where once more the little band was greeted with curious respectful glances by the people who had not gone to church, although their clothing made it clear that they approved of Sunday to the very verge of going to church. Rachel felt unable to stand any more of this particular atmosphere, and was about to say she must go back, when Terence passed them, drawn along in talk with Evelyn M. Rachel thereupon contented herself with saying that the people looked very respectable, which negative remark Mrs Flushing interpreted to mean that she would stay.

'English people abroad!' she returned with a vivid flash of malice. 'Ain't they awful! But we won't stay here,' she continued, plucking at Rachel's arm. 'Come up to my room.'

She bore her past Hewet and Evelyn and the Thornburys and the Elliots. Hewet stepped forward.

'Luncheon – ' he began.

'Miss Vinrace has promised to lunch with me,' said Mrs Flushing, and began to pound energetically up the staircase, as though the middle classes of England were in pursuit. She did not stop until she had slammed her bedroom door behind them.

'Well, what did you think of it?' she demanded, panting slightly.

All the disgust and horror which Rachel had been accumulating burst forth beyond her control.

'I thought it the most loathsome exhibition I'd ever seen!' she broke out. 'How can they – how dare they – what do they mean by it – Mr Bax, hospital nurses, old men, prostitutes, disgusting – '

She hit off the points she remembered as fast as she could, but she was too indignant to stop to analyse her feelings. Mrs Flushing watched her with keen gusto as she stood ejaculating with emphatic movements of her head and hands in the middle of the room.

'Go on, go on, do go on,' she laughed, clapping her hands. 'It's delightful to hear you!'

'But why do you go?' Rachel demanded.

'I've been every Sunday of my life ever since I can remember,' Mrs Flushing chuckled, as though that were a reason by itself.

Rachel turned abruptly to the window. She did not know what it was that had put her into such a passion; the sight of Terence in the hall had confused her thoughts, leaving her merely indignant. She looked straight at their own villa, halfway up the side of the mountain. The most familiar view seen framed through glass has a certain unfamiliar distinction, and she grew calm as she gazed. Then she remembered that she was in the presence of someone she did not know well, and she turned and looked at Mrs Flushing. Mrs Flushing was still sitting on the edge of the bed, looking up, with her lips parted, so that her strong white teeth showed in two rows.

'Tell me,' she said, 'which d'you like best, Mr Hewet or Mr Hirst?'

'Mr Hewet,' Rachel replied, but her voice did not sound natural.

'Which is the one who reads Greek in church?' Mrs Flushing demanded.

It might have been either of them and while Mrs Flushing proceeded to describe them both, and to say that both frightened her, but one frightened her more than the other, Rachel looked for a chair. The room, of course, was one of the largest and most luxurious in the hotel. There were a great many armchairs and settees covered in brown holland, but each of these was occupied by a large square piece of yellow cardboard, and all the pieces of cardboard were dotted or lined with spots or dashes of bright oil paint.

'But you're not to look at those,' said Mrs Flushing as she saw Rachel's eye wander. She jumped up, and turned as many as she could, face downwards, upon the floor. Rachel, however, managed to possess herself of one of them, and, with the vanity of an artist, Mrs Flushing demanded anxiously, 'Well, well?'

'It's a hill,' Rachel replied. There could be no doubt that Mrs Flushing had represented the vigorous and abrupt fling of the earth up into the air; you could almost see the clods flying as it whirled.

Rachel passed from one to another. They were all marked by something of the jerk and decision of their maker; they were all perfectly untrained onslaughts of the brush upon some half-realised idea suggested by hill or tree; and they were all in some way characteristic of Mrs Flushing.

'I see things movin',' Mrs Flushing explained. 'So' – she swept her hand through a yard of the air. She then took up one of the cardboards which Rachel had laid aside, seated herself on a stool, and began to flourish a stump of charcoal. While she occupied herself in strokes which seemed to serve her as speech serves others, Rachel, who was very restless, looked about her.

'Open the wardrobe,' said Mrs Flushing after a pause, speaking indistinctly because of a paintbrush in her mouth, 'and look at the things.'

As Rachel hesitated, Mrs Flushing came forward, still with a paint-brush in her mouth, flung open the wings of her wardrobe, and tossed a quantity of shawls, stuffs, cloaks, embroideries, on to the bed. Rachel began to finger them. Mrs Flushing came up once more, and dropped a quantity of beads, brooches, earrings, bracelets, tassels and combs among the draperies. Then she went back to her stool and began to paint in silence. The stuffs were coloured and dark and pale; they made a curious swarm of lines and colours upon the counterpane, with the reddish lumps of stone and peacocks' feathers and clear pale tortoiseshell combs lying among them.

'The women wore them hundreds of years ago, they wear 'em still,' Mrs Flushing remarked. 'My husband rides about and finds 'em; they don't know what they're worth, so we get 'em cheap. And we shall sell 'em to smart women in London,' she chuckled, as though the thought of these ladies and their absurd appearance amused her. After painting for some minutes, she suddenly laid down her brush and fixed her eyes upon Rachel.

'I tell you what I want to do,' she said. 'I want to go up there and see things for myself. It's silly stayin' here with a pack of old maids as though we were at the seaside in England. I want to go up the river and see the natives in their camps. It's only a matter of ten days under canvas. My husband's done it. One would lie out under the trees at night and be towed down the river by day, and if we saw anythin' nice we'd shout out and tell 'em to stop.' She rose and began piercing the bed again and again with a long golden pin, as she watched to see what effect her suggestion had upon Rachel.

'We must make up a party,' she went on. 'Ten people could hire a launch. Now you'll come, and Mrs Ambrose'll come, and will Mr Hirst and t'other gentleman come? Where's a pencil?'

She became more and more determined and excited as she evolved her plan. She sat on the edge of the bed and wrote down a list of surnames, which she invariably spelt wrong. Rachel was enthusiastic, for indeed the idea was immeasurably delightful to her. She had always had a great desire to see the river, and the name of Terence threw a lustre over the prospect, which made it almost too good to come true. She did what she could to help Mrs Flushing by suggesting names, helping her to spell them, and counting up the days of the week upon her fingers. As Mrs Flushing wanted to know all she could tell her about the birth and pursuits of every person she suggested, and threw in wild stories of her own as to the temperaments and habits of artists, and people of the same name who used to come to Chillingley in the old days, but were doubtless not the same, though they too were very clever men interested in Egyptology, the business took some time.

At last Mrs Flushing sought her diary for help, the method of reckoning dates on the fingers proving unsatisfactory. She opened and shut every drawer in her writing-table, and then cried furiously, 'Yarmouth! Yarmouth! Drat the woman! She's always out of the way when she's wanted!'

At this moment the luncheon gong began to work itself into its midday frenzy. Mrs Flushing rang her bell violently. The door was opened by a handsome maid who was almost as upright as her mistress.

'Oh, Yarmouth,' said Mrs Flushing, 'just find my diary and see where ten days from now would bring us to, and ask the hall porter how many men 'ud be wanted to row eight people up the river for a week, and what it 'ud cost, and put it on a slip of paper and leave it on my dressing-table. Now – ' she pointed at the door with a superb forefinger so that Rachel had to lead the way.

'Oh, and Yarmouth,' Mrs Flushing called back over her shoulder. 'Put those things away and hang 'em in their right places, there's a good girl, or it fusses Mr Flushin'.'

To all of which Yarmouth merely replied, 'Yes, ma'am.'

As they entered the long dining-room it was obvious that the day was still Sunday, although the mood was slightly abating. The Flushings' table was set by the side in the window, so that Mrs Flushing could scrutinise each figure as it entered, and her curiosity seemed to be intense.

'Old Mrs Paley,' she whispered as the wheeled chair slowly made its way through the door, Arthur pushing behind. 'Thornburys' came next. 'That nice woman,' she nudged Rachel to look at Miss Allan. 'What's her name?' The painted lady who always came in late, tripping into the room with a prepared smile as though she came out upon a stage, might well have quailed before Mrs Flushing's stare, which expressed her steely hostility to the whole tribe of painted ladies. Next came the two young men whom Mrs Flushing called collectively the Hirsts. They sat down opposite, across the gangway.

Mr Flushing treated his wife with a mixture of admiration and indulgence, making up by the suavity and fluency of his speech for the abruptness of hers. While she darted and ejaculated he gave Rachel a sketch of the history of South American art. He would deal with one of his wife's exclamations, and then return as smoothly as ever to his theme. He knew very well how to make a luncheon pass agreeably, without being dull or intimate. He had formed the opinion, so he told Rachel, that wonderful treasures lay hid in the depths of the land; the things Rachel had seen were merely trifles picked up in the course of one short journey. He thought there might be giant gods hewn out of stone in the mountainside; and colossal figures standing by themselves in the middle of vast green pasture lands, where none but natives had ever trod. Before the dawn of European art he believed that the primitive huntsmen and priests had built temples of massive stone slabs, had formed out of the dark rocks and the great cedar trees majestic figures of gods and of beasts, and symbols of the great forces, water, air and forest, among which they lived. There might be prehistoric towns, like those in Greece and Asia, standing in open places among the trees, filled with the works of this early race. Nobody had been there; scarcely anything was known. Thus talking and displaying the most picturesque of his theories, Rachel's attention was fixed upon him.

She did not see that Hewet kept looking at her across the gangway, between the figures of waiters hurrying past with plates. He was inattentive, and Hirst was finding him also very cross and disagreeable. They had touched upon all the usual topics – upon politics and literature, gossip and Christianity. They had quarrelled over the service, which was every bit as fine as Sappho, according to Hewet; so that Hirst's paganism was mere ostentation. Why go to church, he demanded, merely in order to read Sappho? Hirst observed that he had listened to every word of the sermon, as he could prove if Hewet would like a repetition of it; and he went to church in order to realise the nature of his Creator, which he had done very vividly that morning, thanks to Mr Bax, who had inspired him to write three of the most superb lines in English literature, an invocation to the Deity.

'I wrote 'em on the back of the envelope of my aunt's last letter,' he said, and pulled it from between the pages of Sappho.

'Well, let's hear them,' said Hewet, slightly mollified by the prospect of a literary discussion.

'My dear Hewet, do you wish us both to be flung out of the hotel by an enraged mob of Thornburys and Elliots?' Hirst enquired. 'The merest whisper would be sufficient to incriminate me for ever. God!' he broke out, 'what's the use of attempting to write when the world's peopled by such damned fools? Seriously, Hewet, I advise you to give up literature. What's the good of it? There's your audience.'

He nodded his head at the tables where a very miscellaneous collection of Europeans was now engaged in eating, in some cases in gnawing, the stringy foreign fowls. Hewet looked, and grew more out of temper than ever. Hirst looked too. His eyes fell upon Rachel, and he bowed to her.

'I rather think Rachel's in love with me,' he remarked, as his eyes returned to his plate. 'That's the worst of friendships with young women – they tend to fall in love with one.'

To that Hewet made no answer whatever, and sat singularly still. Hirst did not seem to mind getting no answer, for he returned to Mr Bax again, quoting the peroration about the drop of water; and when Hewet scarcely replied to these remarks either, he merely pursed his lips, chose a fig, and relapsed quite contentedly into his own thoughts, of which he always had a very large supply. When luncheon was over they separated, taking their cups of coffee to different parts of the hall.

From his chair beneath the palm tree Hewet saw Rachel come out of the dining-room with the Flushings; he saw them look round for chairs, and choose three in a corner where they could go on talking in private. Mr Flushing was now in the full tide of his discourse. He produced a sheet of paper upon which he made drawings as he went on with his talk. He saw Rachel lean over and look, pointing to this and that with her finger. Hewet unkindly compared Mr Flushing, who was extremely well dressed for a hot climate, and rather elaborate in his manner, to a very persuasive shopkeeper. Meanwhile, as he sat looking at them, he was entangled in the Thornburys and Miss Allan, who, after hovering about for a minute or two, settled in chairs round him, holding their cups in their hands. They wanted to know whether he could tell them anything about Mr Bax. Mr Thornbury as usual sat saying nothing, looking vaguely ahead of him, occasionally raising his eyeglasses, as if to put them on, but always thinking better of it at the last moment, and letting them fall again. After some discussion, the ladies put it beyond a doubt that Mr Bax was not the son of Mr William Bax. There was a pause. Then Mrs Thornbury remarked that she was still in the habit of saying Queen instead of King in the National Anthem. There was another pause. Then Miss Allan observed reflectively that going to church abroad always made her feel as if she had been to a sailor's funeral.

There was then a very long pause, which threatened to be final, when, mercifully, a bird about the size of a magpie, but of a metallic blue colour, appeared on the section of the terrace that could be seen from where they sat. Mrs Thornbury was led to enquire whether we should like it if all our rooks were blue – 'What do *you* think, William?' she asked, touching her husband on the knee.

'If all our rooks were blue,' he said – he raised his glasses; he actually placed them on his nose – 'they would not live long in Wiltshire,' he concluded; he dropped his glasses to his side again. The three elderly people now gazed meditatively at the bird, which was so obliging as to stay in the middle of the view for a considerable space of time, thus making it unnecessary for them to speak again. Hewet began to wonder whether he might not cross over to the Flushings' corner, when Hirst appeared from the background, slipped into a chair by Rachel's side, and began to talk to her with every appearance of familiarity. Hewet could stand it no longer. He rose, took his hat and dashed out of doors.

Chapter 18

Everything he saw was distasteful to him. He hated the blue and white, the intensity and definiteness, the hum and heat of the south; the landscape seemed to him as hard and as romantic as a cardboard background on the stage, and the mountain but a wooden screen against a sheet painted blue. He walked fast in spite of the heat of the sun.

Two roads led out of the town on the eastern side: one branched off towards the Ambroses' villa, the other struck into the country, eventually reaching a village on the plain, but many footpaths, which had been stamped in the earth when it was wet, led off from it, across great dry fields, to scattered farmhouses, and the villas of rich natives. Hewet stepped off the road on to one of these, in order to avoid the hardness and heat of the main road, the dust of which was always being raised in small clouds by carts and ramshackle flies which carried parties of festive peasants, or turkeys swelling unevenly like a bundle of air balls beneath a net, or the brass bedstead and black wooden boxes of some newly wedded pair.

The exercise indeed served to clear away the superficial irritations of the morning, but he remained miserable. It seemed proved beyond a doubt that Rachel was indifferent to him, for she had scarcely looked at him, and she had talked to Mr Flushing with just the same interest with which she talked to him. Finally, Hirst's odious words flicked his mind like a whip, and he remembered that he had left her talking to Hirst. She was at this moment talking to him, and it might be true, as he said, that she was in love with him. He went over all the evidence for this supposition – her sudden interest in Hirst's writing, her way of quoting his opinions respectfully, or with only half a laugh; her very nickname for him, 'the great Man', might have some serious meaning in it. Supposing that there were an understanding between them, what would it mean to him?

'Damn it all!' he demanded, 'am I in love with her?' To that he could only return himself one answer. He certainly was in love with her, if he knew what love meant. Ever since he had first seen her he had been interested and attracted, more and more interested and attracted, until he was scarcely able to think of anything except Rachel. But just as he was sliding into one of the long feasts of meditation about them both, he checked himself by asking whether he wanted to marry her? That was the real problem, for these miseries and agonies could not be endured, and it was necessary that he should make up his mind. He instantly decided that he did not want to marry anyone. Partly because he was irritated by Rachel the idea of marriage irritated him. It immediately suggested the picture of two people sitting alone over the fire; the man was reading, the woman sewing. There was a second picture. He saw a man jump up, say good-night, leave the company and hasten away with the quiet secret look of one who is stealing to certain happiness. Both these pictures were very unpleasant, and even more so was a third picture, of husband and wife and friend; and the married people glancing at each other as though they were content to let something pass unquestioned, being themselves possessed of the deeper truth. Other pictures – he was walking very fast in his irritation, and they came before him without any conscious effort, like pictures on a sheet – succeeded these. Here were the worn husband and wife sitting with their children round them, very patient, tolerant and wise. But that too, was an unpleasant picture. He tried all sorts of pictures, taking them from the lives of friends of his, for he knew many different married couples; but he saw them, always, walled up in a warm firelit room. When, on the other hand, he began to think of unmarried people, he saw them active in an unlimited world; above all, standing on the same ground as the rest, without shelter or advantage. All the most individual and humane of his friends were bachelors and spinsters; indeed he was surprised to find that the women he most admired and knew best were unmarried women. Marriage seemed to be worse for them than it was for men. Leaving these general pictures he considered the people whom he had been observing lately at the hotel. He had often revolved these questions in his mind as he watched Susan and Arthur, or Mr and Mrs Thornbury, or Mr and Mrs Elliot. He had observed how the shy happiness and surprise of the engaged couple had gradually been replaced by a comfortable, tolerant state of mind, as if they had already done with the adventure of intimacy and were taking up their parts. Susan used to pursue Arthur about with a sweater, because he had one day let slip that a brother of his had died of pneumonia. The sight amused him, but was not pleasant if you substituted Terence and Rachel for Arthur and Susan; and Arthur was far less eager to get you in a corner and talk about flying and the mechanics of aeroplanes. They would settle down. He then looked at the couples who had been married for several years. It was true that Mrs Thornbury had a husband, and that for the most part she was wonderfully successful in bringing him into the conversation, but one could not imagine what they said to each other when they were alone. There was the same difficulty with regard to the Elliots, except that they probably bickered openly in private. They sometimes bickered in public, though these disagreements were painfully covered over by little insincerities on the part of the wife, who was afraid of public opinion, because she was much stupider than her husband, and had to make efforts to keep hold of him. There could be no doubt, he decided, that it would have been far better for the world if these couples had separated. Even the Ambroses, whom he admired and respected profoundly – in spite of all the love between them, was not their marriage too a compromise? She gave way to him; she spoilt him; she arranged things for him; she who was all truth to others was not true to her husband, was not true to her friends if they came in conflict with her husband. It was a strange and piteous flaw in her nature. Perhaps Rachel had been right, then, when she said that night in the garden, 'We bring out what's worst in each other – we should live separate.'

No, Rachel had been utterly wrong! Every argument seemed to be against undertaking the burden of marriage until he came to Rachel's argument, which was manifestly absurd. From having been the pursued, he turned and became the pursuer. Allowing the case against marriage to lapse, he began to consider the peculiarities of character which had led to her saying that. Had she meant it? Surely one ought to know the character of the person with whom one might spend all one's life; being a novelist, let him try to discover what sort of person she was. When he was with her he could not analyse her qualities, because he seemed to know them instinctively, but when he was away from her it sometimes seemed to him that he did not know her at all. She was young, but she was also old; she had little self-confidence, and yet she was a good judge of people. She was happy; but what made her happy? If they were alone and the excitement had worn off, and they had to deal with the ordinary facts of the day, what would happen? Casting his eye upon his own character, two things appeared to him: that he was very unpunctual, and that he disliked answering notes. As far as he knew Rachel was inclined to be punctual, but he could not remember that he had ever seen her with a pen in her hand. Let him next imagine a dinner-party, say at the Crooms, and Wilson, who had taken her down, talking about the state of the Liberal party. She would say – of course – she was absolutely ignorant of politics. Nevertheless she was intelligent certainly, and honest too. Her temper was uncertain – that he had noticed – and she was not domestic, and she was not easy, and she was not quiet, or beautiful, except in some dresses in some lights. But the great gift she had was that she understood what was said to her; there had never been anyone like her for talking to. You could say anything – you could say everything, and yet she was never servile. Here he pulled himself up, for it seemed to him suddenly that he knew less about her than about anyone. All these thoughts had occurred to him many times already; often had he tried to argue and reason; and again he had reached the old state of doubt. He did not know her, and he did not know what she felt, or whether they could live together, or whether he wanted to marry her, and yet he was in love with her.

Supposing he went to her and said (he slackened his pace and began to speak aloud, as if he were speaking to Rachel): 'I worship you, but I loathe marriage, I hate its smugness, its safety, its compromise, and the thought of you interfering in my work, hindering me;' what would she answer?

He stopped, leant against the trunk of a tree, and gazed without seeing them at some stones scattered on the bank of the dry riverbed. He saw Rachel's face distinctly, the grey eyes, the hair, the mouth; the face that could look so many things – plain, vacant, almost insignificant, or wild, passionate, almost beautiful, yet in his eyes was always the same because of the extraordinary freedom with which she looked at him, and spoke as she felt. What would she answer? What did she feel? Did she love him, or did she feel nothing at all for him or for any other man, being, as she had said that afternoon, free, like the wind or the sea?

'Oh, you're free!' he exclaimed, in exultation at the thought of her, 'and I'd keep you free. We'd be free together. We'd share everything together. No happiness would be like ours. No lives would compare with ours.' He opened his arms wide as if to hold her and the world in one embrace.

No longer able to consider marriage, or to weigh coolly what her nature was, or how it would be if they lived together, he dropped to the ground and sat absorbed in the thought of her, and was soon tormented by the desire to be in her presence again.

Chapter 19

But Hewet need not have increased his torments by imagining that Hirst was still talking to Rachel. The party very soon broke up, the Flushings going in one direction, Hirst in another, and Rachel remaining in the hall, pulling the illustrated papers about, turning from one to another, her movements expressing the unformed restless desire in her mind. She did not know whether to go or to stay, though Mrs Flushing had commanded her to appear at tea. The hall was empty, save for Miss Willett who was playing scales with her fingers upon a sheet of sacred music, and the Carters, an opulent couple who disliked the girl, because her shoelaces were untied, and she did not look sufficiently cheery, which by some indirect process of thought led them to think that she would not like them. Rachel certainly would not have liked them, if she had seen them, for the excellent reason that Mr Carter waxed his moustache, and Mrs Carter wore bracelets, and they were evidently the kind of people who would not like her; but she was too much absorbed by her own restlessness to think or to look.

She was turning over the slippery pages of an American magazine, when the hall door swung, a wedge of light fell upon the floor, and a small white figure upon whom the light seemed focused made straight across the room to her.

'What! You here?' Evelyn exclaimed. 'Just caught a glimpse of you at lunch; but you wouldn't condescend to look at *me*.'

It was part of Evelyn's character that in spite of many snubs which she received or imagined, she never gave up the pursuit of people she wanted to know, and in the long run generally succeeded in knowing them and even in making them like her.

She looked round her. 'I hate this place. I hate these people,' she said. 'I wish you'd come up to my room with me. I do want to talk to you.'

As Rachel had no wish to go or to stay, Evelyn took her by the wrist and drew her out of the hall and up the stairs. As they went upstairs two steps at a time, Evelyn, who still kept hold of Rachel's hand, ejaculated broken sentences about not caring a hang what people said. 'Why should one, if one knows one's right? And let 'em all go to blazes! Them's my opinions!'

She was in a state of great excitement, and the muscles of her arms were twitching nervously. It was evident that she was only waiting for the door to shut to tell Rachel all about it. Indeed, directly they were inside her room, she sat on the end of the bed and said, 'I suppose you think I'm mad?'

Rachel was not in the mood to think clearly about anyone's state of mind. She was however in the mood to say straight out whatever occurred to her without fear of the consequences.

'Somebody's proposed to you,' she remarked.

'How on earth did you guess that?' Evelyn exclaimed, some pleasure mingling with her surprise. 'Do as I look as if I'd just had a proposal?'

'You look as if you had them every day,' Rachel replied.

'But I don't suppose I've had more than you've had,' Evelyn laughed rather insincerely.

'I've never had one.'

'But you will – lots – it's the easiest thing in the world – But that's not what's happened this afternoon exactly. It's – Oh, it's a muddle, a detestable, horrible, disgusting muddle!'

She went to the washstand and began sponging her cheeks with cold water; for they were burning hot. Still sponging them and trembling slightly she turned and explained in the high-pitched voice of nervous excitement: 'Alfred Perrott says I've promised to marry him, and I say I never did. Sinclair says he'll shoot himself if I don't marry him, and I say, "Well, shoot yourself!" But of course he doesn't – they never do. And Sinclair got hold of me this afternoon and began bothering me to give an answer, and accusing me of flirting with Alfred Perrott, and told me I'd no heart, and was merely a Siren, oh, and quantities of pleasant things like that. So at last I said to him, "Well, Sinclair, you've said enough now. You can just let me go." And then he caught me and kissed me – the disgusting brute – I can still feel his nasty hairy face just there – as if he'd any right to, after what he'd said!'

She sponged a spot on her left cheek energetically.

'I've never met a man that was fit to compare with a woman!' she cried; 'they've no dignity, they've no courage, they've nothing but their beastly passions and their brute strength! Would any woman have behaved like that – if a man had said he didn't want her? We've too much self-respect; we're infinitely finer than they are.'

She walked about the room, dabbing her wet cheeks with a towel. Tears were now running down with the drops of cold water.

'It makes me angry,' she explained, drying her eyes.

Rachel sat watching her. She did not think of Evelyn's position; she only thought that the world was full or people in torment.

'There's only one man here I really like,' Evelyn continued; 'Terence Hewet. One feels as if one could trust him.'

At these words Rachel suffered an indescribable chill; her heart seemed to be pressed together by cold hands.

'Why?' she asked. 'Why can you trust him?'

'I don't know,' said Evelyn. 'Don't you have feelings about people? Feelings you're absolutely certain are right? I had a long talk with Terence the other night. I felt we were really friends after that. There's something of a woman in him – ' She paused as though she were thinking of very intimate things that Terence had told her, so at least Rachel interpreted her gaze.

She tried to force herself to say, 'Has he proposed to you?' but the question was too tremendous, and in another moment Evelyn was saying that the finest men were like women, and women were nobler than men – for example, one couldn't imagine a woman like Lillah Harrison thinking a mean thing or having anything base about her.

'How I'd like you to know her!' she exclaimed.

She was becoming much calmer, and her cheeks were now quite dry. Her eyes had regained their usual expression of keen vitality, and she seemed to have forgotten Alfred and Sinclair and her emotion. 'Lillah runs a home for inebriate women in the Deptford Road,' she continued. 'She started it, managed it, did everything off her own bat, and it's now the biggest of its kind in England. You can't think what those women are like – and their homes. But she goes among them at all hours of the day and night. I've often been with her . . . That's what's the matter with us . . . We don't *do* things. What do you *do*?' she demanded, looking at Rachel with a slightly ironical smile. Rachel had scarcely listened to any of this, and her expression was vacant and unhappy. She had conceived an equal dislike for Lillah Harrison and her work in the Deptford Road, and for Evelyn M. and her profusion of love affairs.

'I play,' she said with an affection of stolid composure.

'That's about it!' Evelyn laughed. 'We none of us do anything but play. And that's why women like Lillah Harrison, who's worth twenty of you and me, have to work themselves to the bone. But I'm tired of playing,' she went on, lying flat on the bed, and raising her arms above her head. Thus stretched out, she looked more diminutive than ever.

'I'm going to do something. I've got a splendid idea. Look here, you must join. I'm sure you've got any amount of stuff in you, though you look – well, as if you'd lived all your life in a garden.' She sat up, and began to explain with animation. 'I belong to a club in London. It meets every Saturday, so it's called the Saturday Club. We're supposed to talk about art, but I'm sick of talking about art – what's the good of it? With all kinds of real things going on round one? It isn't as if they'd got anything to say about art, either. So what I'm going to tell 'em is that we've talked enough about art, and we'd better talk about life for a change. Questions that really matter to people's lives, the White Slave Traffic, Women Suffrage, the Insurance Bill, and so on. And when we've made up our mind what we want to do we could form ourselves into a society for doing it . . . I'm certain that if people like ourselves were to take things in hand instead of leaving it to policemen and magistrates, we could put a stop to – prostitution' – she lowered her voice at the ugly word – 'in six months. My idea is that men and women ought to join in these matters. We ought to go into Piccadilly and stop one of these poor wretches and say: "Now, look here, I'm no better than you are, and I don't pretend to be any better, but you're doing what you know to be beastly, and I won't have you doing beastly things, because we're all the same under our skins, and if you do a beastly thing it does matter to me." That's what Mr Bax was saying this morning, and it's true, though you clever people – you're clever too, aren't you? – don't believe it.'

When Evelyn began talking – it was a fact she often regretted – her thoughts came so quickly that she never had any time to listen to other people's thoughts. She continued without more pause than was needed for taking breath.

'I don't see why the Saturday Club people shouldn't do a really great work in that way,' she went on. 'Of course it would want organisation, someone to give their life to it, but I'm ready to do that. My notion's to think of the human beings first and let the abstract ideas take care of themselves. What's wrong with Lillah – if there is anything wrong – is that she thinks of Temperance[102] first and the women afterwards. Now there's one thing I'll say to my credit,' she continued; 'I'm not intellectual or artistic or anything of that sort, but I'm jolly human.' She slipped off the bed and sat on the floor, looking up at Rachel. She searched up into her face as if she were trying to read what kind of character was concealed behind the face. She put her hand on Rachel's knee.

'It *is* being human that counts, isn't it?' she continued. 'Being real, whatever Mr Hirst may say. Are you real?'

Rachel felt, much as Terence had felt, that Evelyn was too close to her, and that there was something exciting in this closeness, although it was also disagreeable. She was spared the need of finding an answer to the question, for Evelyn proceeded, 'Do you *believe* in anything?'

In order to put an end to the scrutiny of these bright blue eyes, and to relieve her own physical restlessness, Rachel pushed back her chair and exclaimed, 'In everything!' and began to finger different objects, the books on the table, the photographs, the fleshly-leaved plant with the stiff bristles, which stood in a large earthenware pot in the window.

'I believe in the bed, in the photographs, in the pot, in the balcony, in the sun, in Mrs Flushing,' she remarked, still speaking recklessly, with something at the back of her mind forcing her to say the things that one usually does not say. 'But I don't believe in God, I don't believe in Mr Bax, I don't believe in the hospital nurse. I don't believe – ' She took up a photograph and, looking at it, did not finish her sentence.

'That's my mother,' said Evelyn, who remained sitting on the floor binding her knees together with her arms, and watching Rachel curiously.

Rachel considered the portrait. 'Well, I don't much believe in her,' she remarked after a time in a low tone of voice.

Mrs Murgatroyd looked indeed as if the life had been crushed out of her; she knelt on a chair, gazing piteously from behind the body of a Pomeranian dog which she clasped to her cheek, as if for protection.

'And that's my dad,' said Evelyn, for there were two photographs in one frame. The second photograph represented a handsome soldier with high regular features and a heavy black moustache; his hand rested on the hilt of his sword; there was a decided likeness between him and Evelyn.

'And it's because of them,' said Evelyn, 'that I'm going to help the other women. You've heard about me, I suppose? They weren't married, you see; I'm not anybody in particular. I'm not a bit ashamed of it. They loved each other anyhow, and that's more than most people can say of their parents.'

Rachel sat down on the bed, with the two pictures in her hands, and compared them – the man and the woman who had, so Evelyn said, loved each other. That fact interested her more than the campaign on behalf of unfortunate women which Evelyn was once more beginning to describe. She looked again from one to the other.

'What d'you think it's like,' she asked, as Evelyn paused for a minute, 'being in love?'

'Have you never been in love?' Evelyn asked. 'Oh no – one's only got to look at you to see that,' she added. She considered. 'I really was in love once,' she said. She fell into reflection, her eyes losing their bright vitality and approaching something like an expression of tenderness. 'It was heavenly! – while it lasted. The worst of it is it don't last, not with me. That's the bother.'

She went on to consider the difficulty with Alfred and Sinclair about which she had pretended to ask Rachel's advice. But she did not want advice; she wanted intimacy. When she looked at Rachel, who was still looking at the photographs on the bed, she could not help seeing that Rachel was not thinking about her. What was she thinking about, then? Evelyn was tormented by the little spark of life in her which was always trying to work through to other people, and was always being rebuffed. Falling silent she looked at her visitor, her shoes, her stockings, the combs in her hair, all the details of her dress in short, as though by seizing every detail she might get closer to the life within.

Rachel at last put down the photographs, walked to the window and remarked, 'It's odd. People talk as much about love as they do about religion.'

'I wish you'd sit down and talk,' said Evelyn impatiently.

Instead Rachel opened the window, which was made in two long panes, and looked down into the garden below.

'That's where we got lost the first night,' she said. 'It must have been in those bushes.'

'They kill hens down there,' said Evelyn. 'They cut their heads off with a knife – disgusting! But tell me – what – '

'I'd like to explore the hotel,' Rachel interrupted. She drew her head in and looked at Evelyn, who still sat on the floor.

'It's just like other hotels,' said Evelyn.

That might be, although every room and passage and chair in the place had a character of its own in Rachel's eyes; but she could not bring herself to stay in one place any longer. She moved slowly towards the door.

'What is it you want?' said Evelyn. 'You make me feel as if you were always thinking of something you don't say . . . Do say it!'

But Rachel made no response to this invitation either. She stopped with her fingers on the handle of the door, as if she remembered that some sort of pronouncement was due from her.

'I suppose you'll marry one of them,' she said, and then turned the handle and shut the door behind her. She walked slowly down the passage, running her hand along the wall beside her. She did not think which way she was going, and therefore walked down a passage which only led to a window and a balcony. She looked down at the kitchen premises, the wrong side of hotel life, which was cut off from the right side by a maze of small bushes. The ground was bare, old tins were scattered about, and the bushes wore towels and aprons upon their heads to dry. Every now and then a waiter came out in a white apron and threw rubbish on to a heap. Two large women in cotton dresses were sitting on a bench with blood-smeared tin trays in front of them and yellow bodies across their knees. They were plucking the birds, and talking as they plucked. Suddenly a chicken came floundering, half flying, half running into the space, pursued by a third woman whose age could hardly be under eighty. Although wizened and unsteady on her legs she kept up the chase, egged on by the laughter of the others; her face was expressive of furious rage, and as she ran she swore in Spanish. Frightened by hand-clapping here, a napkin there, the bird ran this way and that in sharp angles, and finally fluttered straight at the old woman, who opened her scanty grey skirts to enclose it, dropped upon it in a bundle, and then holding it out cut its head off with an expression of vindictive energy and triumph combined. The blood and the ugly wriggling fascinated Rachel, so that although she knew that someone had come up behind and was standing beside her, she did not turn round until the old woman had settled down on the bench beside the others. Then she looked up sharply, because of the ugliness of what she had seen. It was Miss Allan who stood beside her.

'Not a pretty sight,' said Miss Allan, 'although I dare say it's really more humane than our method . . . I don't believe you've ever been in my room,' she added, and turned away as if she meant Rachel to follow her. Rachel followed, for it seemed possible that each new person might remove the mystery which burdened her.

The bedrooms at the hotel were all on the same pattern, save that some were larger and some smaller; they had a floor of dark red tiles; they had a high bed, draped in mosquito curtains; they had each a writing-table and a dressing-table, and a couple of armchairs. But directly a box was unpacked the rooms became very different, so that Miss Allan's room was very unlike Evelyn's room. There were no variously coloured hatpins on her dressing-table; no scent-bottles; no narrow curved pairs of scissors; no great variety of shoes and boots; no silk petticoats lying on the chairs. The room was extremely neat. There seemed to be two pairs of everything. The writing-table, however, was piled with manuscript, and a table was drawn out to stand by the armchair on which were two separate heaps of dark library books, in which there were many slips of paper sticking out at different degrees of thickness. Miss Allan had asked Rachel to come in out of kindness, thinking that she was waiting about with nothing to do. Moreover, she liked young women, for she had taught many of them, and having received so much hospitality from the Ambroses she was glad to be able to repay a minute part of it. She looked about accordingly for something to show her. The room did not provide much entertainment. She touched her manuscript. 'Age of Chaucer;[103]

Age of Elizabeth; Age of Dryden [104],' she reflected; 'I'm glad there aren't many more ages. I'm still in the middle of the eighteenth century. Won't you sit down, Miss Vinrace? The chair, though small, is firm . . . *Euphues*.[105] The germ of the English novel,' she continued, glancing at another page. 'Is that the kind of thing that interests you?'

She looked at Rachel with great kindness and simplicity, as though she would do her utmost to provide anything she wished to have. This expression had a remarkable charm in a face otherwise much lined with care and thought.

'Oh no, it's music with you, isn't it?' she continued, recollecting, 'and I generally find that they don't go together. Sometimes of course we have prodigies – ' She was looking about her for something and now saw a jar on the mantelpiece which she reached down and gave to Rachel. 'If you put your finger into this jar you may be able to extract a piece of preserved ginger. Are you a prodigy?'

But the ginger was deep and could not be reached.

'Don't bother,' she said, as Miss Allan looked about for some other implement. 'I dare say I shouldn't like preserved ginger.'

'You've never tried?' enquired Miss Allan. 'Then I consider that it is your duty to try now. Why, you may add a new pleasure to life, and as you are still young – ' She wondered whether a button-hook would do. 'I make it a rule to try everything,' she said. 'Don't you think it would be very annoying if you tasted ginger for the first time on your deathbed, and found you never liked anything so much? I should be so exceedingly annoyed that I think I should get well on that account alone.'

She was now successful, and a lump of ginger emerged on the end of the button-hook. While she went to wipe the button-hook, Rachel bit the ginger and at once cried, 'I must spit it out!'

'Are you sure you have really tasted it?' Miss Allan demanded.

For answer Rachel threw it out of the window.

'An experience anyhow,' said Miss Allan calmly. 'Let me see – I have nothing else to offer you, unless you would like to taste this.' A small cupboard hung above her bed, and she took out of it a slim elegant jar filled with a bright green fluid.

'Crème de menthe,' she said. 'Liqueur, you know. It looks as if I drank, doesn't it? As a matter of fact it goes to prove what an exceptionally abstemious person I am. I've had that jar for six-and-twenty years,' she added, looking at it with pride, as she tipped it over, and from the height of the liquid it could be seen that the bottle was still untouched.

'Twenty-six years?' Rachel exclaimed.

Miss Allan was gratified, for she had meant Rachel to be surprised.

'When I went to Dresden six-and-twenty years ago,' she said, 'a certain friend of mine announced her intention of making me a present. She thought that in the event of shipwreck or accident a stimulant might be useful. However, as I had no occasion for it, I gave it back on my return. On the eve of any foreign journey the same bottle always makes its appearance, with the same note; on my return in safety it is always handed back. I consider it a kind of charm against accidents. Though I was once detained twenty-four hours by an accident to the train in front of me, I have never met with any accident myself. Yes,' she continued, now addressing the bottle, 'we have seen many climes and cupboards together, have we not? I intend one of these days to have a silver label made with an inscription. It is a gentleman, as you may observe, and his name is Oliver . . . I do not think I could forgive you, Miss Vinrace, if you broke my Oliver,' she said, firmly taking the bottle out of Rachel's hands and replacing it in the cupboard.

Rachel was swinging the bottle by the neck. She was interested by Miss Allan to the point of forgetting the bottle.

'Well,' she exclaimed, 'I do think that odd; to have had a friend for twenty-six years, and a bottle, and – to have made all those journeys.'

'Not at all; I call it the reverse of odd,' Miss Allan replied. 'I always consider myself the most ordinary person I know. It's rather distinguished to be as ordinary as I am. I forget – are you a prodigy, or did you say you were not a prodigy?'

She smiled at Rachel very kindly. She seemed to have known and experienced so much, as she moved cumbrously about the room, that surely there must be balm for all anguish in her words, could one induce her to have recourse to them. But Miss Allan, who was now locking the cupboard door, showed no signs of breaking the reticence which had snowed her under for years. An uncomfortable sensation kept Rachel silent; on the one hand, she wished to whirl high and strike a spark out of the cool pink flesh; on the other she perceived there was nothing to be done but to drift past each other in silence.

'I'm not a prodigy. I find it very difficult to say what I mean – ' she observed at length.

'It's a matter of temperament, I believe,' Miss Allan helped her. 'There are some people who have no difficulty; for myself I find there are a great many things I simply cannot say. But then I consider myself very slow. One of my colleagues, now, knows whether she likes you or not – let me see, how does she do it? – by the way you say good-morning at breakfast. It is sometimes a matter of years before I can make up my mind. But most young people seem to find it easy?'

'Oh no,' said Rachel. 'It's hard!'

Miss Allan looked at Rachel quietly, saying nothing; she suspected that there were difficulties of some kind. Then she put her hand to the back of her head, and discovered that one of the grey coils of hair had come loose.

'I must ask you to be so kind as to excuse me,' she said, rising, 'if I do my hair. I have never yet found a satisfactory type of hairpin. I must change my dress, too, for the matter of that; and I should be particularly glad of your assistance, because there is a tiresome set of hooks which I *can* fasten for myself, but it takes from ten to fifteen minutes; whereas with your help – '

She slipped off her coat and skirt and blouse, and stood doing her hair before the glass, a massive homely figure, her petticoat being so short that she stood on a pair of thick slate-grey legs.

'People say youth is pleasant; I myself find middle age far pleasanter,' she remarked, removing hairpins and combs, and taking up her brush. When it fell loose her hair only came down to her neck.

'When one was young,' she continued, 'things could seem so very serious if one was made that way . . . And now my dress.'

In a wonderfully short space of time her hair had been reformed in its usual loops. The upper half of her body now became dark green with black stripes on it; the skirt, however, needed hooking at various angles, and Rachel had to kneel on the floor, fitting the eyes to the hooks.

'Our Miss Johnson used to find life very unsatisfactory, I remember,' Miss Allan continued. She turned her back to the light. 'And then she took to breeding guinea-pigs for their spots, and became absorbed in that. I have just heard that the yellow guinea-pig has had a black baby. We had a bet of sixpence on about it. She will be very triumphant.'

The skirt was fastened. She looked at herself in the glass with the curious stiffening of her face generally caused by looking in the glass.

'Am I in a fit state to encounter my fellow-beings?' she asked. 'I forget which way it is – but they find black animals very rarely have coloured babies – it may be the other way round. I have had it so often explained to me that it is very stupid of me to have forgotten again.'

She moved about the room acquiring small objects with quiet force, and fixing them about her – a locket, a watch and chain, a heavy gold bracelet, and the parti-coloured button of a suffrage society. Finally, completely equipped for Sunday tea, she stood before Rachel, and smiled at her kindly. She was not an impulsive woman, and her life had schooled her to restrain her tongue. At the same time, she was possessed of an amount of good-will towards others, and in particular towards the young, which often made her regret that speech was so difficult.

'Shall we descend?' she said.

She put one hand upon Rachel's shoulder, and stooping, picked up a pair of walking-shoes with the other, and placed them neatly side by side outside her door. As they walked down the passage they passed many pairs of boots and shoes, some black and some brown, all side by side, and all different, even to the way in which they lay together.

'I always think that people are so like their boots,' said Miss Allan. 'That is Mrs Paley's – ' but as she spoke the door opened, and Mrs Paley rolled out in her chair, equipped also for tea.

She greeted Miss Allan and Rachel.

'I was just saying that people are so like their boots,' said Miss Allan. Mrs Paley did not hear. She repeated it more loudly still. Mrs Paley did not hear. She repeated it a third time. Mrs Paley heard, but she did not understand. She was apparently about to repeat it for the fourth time, when Rachel suddenly said something inarticulate, and disappeared down the corridor. This misunderstanding, which involved a complete block in the passage, seemed to her unbearable. She walked quickly and blindly in the opposite direction, and found herself at the end of a *cul de sac*. There was a window, and a table and a chair in the window, and upon the table stood a rusty inkstand, an ashtray, an old copy of a French newspaper and a pen with a broken nib. Rachel sat down, as if to study the French newspaper, but a tear fell on the blurred French print, raising a soft blot. She lifted her head sharply, exclaiming aloud, 'It's intolerable!' Looking out of the window with eyes that would have seen nothing even had they not been dazed by tears, she indulged herself at last in violent abuse of the entire day. It had been miserable from start to finish; first, the service in the chapel; then luncheon; then Evelyn; then Miss Allan; then old Mrs Paley blocking up the passage. All day long she had been tantalised and put off. She had now reached one of those eminences, the result of some crisis, from which the world is finally displayed in its true proportions. She disliked the look of it immensely – churches, politicians, misfits and huge impostures – men like Mr Dalloway, men like Mr Bax, Evelyn and her chatter, Mrs Paley blocking up the passage. Meanwhile the steady beat of her own pulse represented the hot current of feeling that ran down beneath; beating, struggling, fretting. For the time, her own body was the source of all the life in the world, which tried to burst forth here – there – and was repressed now by Mr Bax, now by Evelyn, now by the imposition of ponderous stupidity, the weight of the entire world. Thus tormented, she would twist her hands together, for all things were wrong, all people stupid. Vaguely seeing that there were people down in the garden beneath she represented them as aimless masses of matter, floating hither and thither, without aim except to impede her. What were they doing, those other people in the world?

'Nobody knows,' she said. The force of her rage was beginning to spend itself, and the vision of the world which had been so vivid became dim.

'It's a dream,' she murmured. She considered the rusty inkstand, the pen, the ashtray and the old French newspaper. These small and worthless objects seemed to her to represent human lives.

'We're asleep and dreaming,' she repeated. But the possibility which now suggested itself that one of the shapes might be the shape of Terence roused her from her melancholy lethargy. She became as restless as she had been before she sat down. She was no longer able to see the world as a town laid out beneath her. It was covered instead by a haze of feverish red mist. She had returned to the state in which she had been all day. Thinking was no escape. Physical movement was the only refuge, in and out of rooms, in and out of people's minds, seeking she knew not what. Therefore she rose, pushed back the table, and went downstairs. She went out of the hall door, and, turning the corner of the hotel, found herself among the people whom she had seen from the window. But owing to the broad sunshine after shaded passages, and to the substance of living people after dreams, the group appeared with startling intensity, as though the dusty surface had been peeled off everything, leaving only the reality and the instant. It had the look of a vision printed on the dark at night. White and grey and purple figures were scattered on the green, round wicker tables, in the middle the flame of the tea-urn made the air waver like a faulty sheet of glass, a massive green tree stood over them as if it were a moving force held at rest. As she approached, she could hear Evelyn's voice repeating monotonously, 'Here then – here – good doggie, come here'; for a moment nothing seemed to happen; it all stood still, and then she realised that one of the figures was Helen Ambrose; and the dust again began to settle.

The group indeed had come together in a miscellaneous way; one tea-table joining to another tea-table, and deckchairs serving to connect two groups. But even at a distance it could be seen that Mrs Flushing, upright and imperious, dominated the party. She was talking vehemently to Helen across the table.

'Ten days under canvas,' she was saying. 'No comforts. If you want comforts, don't come. But I may tell you, if you don't come you'll regret it all your life. You say yes?'

At this moment Mrs Flushing caught sight of Rachel.

'Ah, there's your niece. She's promised. You're coming, aren't you?' Having adopted the plan, she pursued it with the energy of a child.

Rachel took her part with eagerness.

'Of course I'm coming. So are you, Helen. And Mr Pepper too.' As she sat she realised that she was surrounded by people she knew, but that Terence was not among them. From various angles people began saying what they thought of the proposed expedition. According to some it would be hot, but the nights would be cold; according to others, the difficulties would lie rather in getting a boat, and in speaking the language. Mrs Flushing disposed of all objections, whether due to man or due to nature, by announcing that her husband would settle all that.

Meanwhile, Mr Flushing quietly explained to Helen that the expedition was really a simple matter; it took five days at the outside; and the place – a native village – was certainly well worth seeing before she returned to England. Helen murmured ambiguously, and did not commit herself to one answer rather than to another.

The tea-party, however, included too many different kinds of people for general conversation to flourish; and from Rachel's point of view possessed the great advantage that it was quite unnecessary for her to talk. Over there Susan and Arthur were explaining to Mrs Paley that an expedition had been proposed; and Mrs Paley having grasped the fact, gave the advice of an old traveller that they should take nice canned vegetables, fur cloaks and insect powder. She leant over to Mrs Flushing and whispered something which from the twinkle in her eyes probably had reference to bugs. Then Helen was reciting 'Toll for the Brave'[106] to St John Hirst, in order apparently to win a sixpence which lay upon the table; while Mr Hughling Elliot imposed silence upon his section of the audience by his fascinating anecdote of Lord Curzon[107] and the undergraduate's bicycle. Mrs Thornbury was trying to remember the name of a man who might have been another Garibaldi, and had written a book which they ought to read; and Mr Thornbury recollected that he had a pair of binoculars at anybody's service. Miss Allan meanwhile murmured, with the curious intimacy which a spinster often achieves with dogs, to the fox-terrier which Evelyn had at last induced to come over to them. Little particles of dust or blossom fell on the plates now and then when the branches sighed above. Rachel seemed to see and hear a little of everything, much as a river feels the twigs that fall into it and sees the sky above, but her eyes were too vague for Evelyn's liking. She came across, and sat on the ground at Rachel's feet.

'Well?' she asked suddenly. 'What are you thinking about?'

'Miss Warrington,' Rachel replied rashly, because she had to say something. She did indeed see Susan murmuring to Mrs Elliot, while Arthur stared at her with complete confidence in his own love. Both Rachel and Evelyn then began to listen to what Susan was saying.

'There's the ordering and the dogs and the garden, and the children coming to be taught,' her voice proceeded rhythmically as if checking the list, 'and my tennis, and the village, and letters to write for father, and a thousand little things that don't sound much; but I never have a moment to myself, and when I go to bed, I'm so sleepy I'm off before my head touches the pillow. Besides I like to be a great deal with my aunts – I'm a great bore, aren't I, Aunt Emma?' (she smiled at old Mrs Paley, who with head slightly drooped was regarding the cake with speculative affection), 'and father has to be very careful about chills in winter which means a great deal of running about, because he won't look after himself, any more than you will, Arthur! So it all mounts up!'

Her voice mounted too, in a mild ecstasy of satisfaction with her life and her own nature. Rachel suddenly took a violent dislike to Susan, ignoring all that was kindly, modest and even pathetic about her. She appeared insincere and cruel; she saw her grown stout and prolific, the kind blue eyes now shallow and watery, the bloom of the cheeks congealed to a network of dry red canals.

Helen turned to her. 'Did you go to church?' she asked. She had won her sixpence and seemed making ready to go.

'Yes,' said Rachel. 'For the last time,' she added.

In preparing to put on her gloves, Helen dropped one.

'You're not going?' Evelyn asked, taking hold of one glove as if to keep them.

'It's high time we went,' said Helen. 'Don't you see how silent every one's getting – ?'

A silence had fallen upon them all, caused partly by one of the accidents of talk, and partly because they saw someone approaching. Helen could not see who it was, but keeping her eyes fixed upon Rachel observed something which made her say to herself, 'So it's Hewet.' She drew on her gloves with a curious sense of the significance of the moment. Then she rose, for Mrs Flushing had seen Hewet too, and was demanding information about rivers and boats which showed that the whole conversation would now come over again.

Rachel followed her, and they walked in silence down the avenue. In spite of what Helen had seen and understood, the feeling that was uppermost in her mind was now curiously perverse: if she went on this expedition, she would not be able to have a bath; the effort appeared to her to be great and disagreeable.

'It's so unpleasant, being cooped up with people one hardly knows,' she remarked. 'People who mind being seen naked.'

'You don't mean to go?' Rachel asked.

The intensity with which this was spoken irritated Mrs Ambrose.

'I don't mean to go, and I don't mean not to go,' she replied. She became more and more casual and indifferent. 'After all, I dare say we've seen all there is to be seen; and there's the bother of getting there, and whatever they may say it's bound to be vilely uncomfortable.'

For some time Rachel made no reply; but every sentence Helen spoke increased her bitterness. At last she broke out – 'Thank God, Helen, I'm not like you! I sometimes think you don't think or feel or care to do anything but exist! You're like Mr Hirst. You see that things are bad, and you pride yourself on saying so. It's what you call being honest; as a matter of fact it's being lazy, being dull, being nothing. You don't help; you put an end to things.'

Helen smiled as if she rather enjoyed the attack.

'Well?' she enquired.

'It seems to me bad – that's all,' Rachel replied.

'Quite likely,' said Helen.

At any other time Rachel would probably have been silenced by her aunt's candour; but this afternoon she was not in the mood to be silenced by anyone. A quarrel would be welcome.

'You're only half alive,' she continued.

'Is that because I didn't accept Mr Flushing's invitation?' Helen asked, 'or do you always think that?'

At the moment it appeared to Rachel that she had always seen the same faults in Helen, from the very first night on board the *Euphrosyne*, in spite of her beauty, in spite of her magnanimity and their love.

'Oh, it's only what's the matter with everyone!' she exclaimed. 'No one feels – no one does anything but hurt. I tell you, Helen, the world's bad. It's an agony, living, wanting – '

Here she tore a handful of leaves from a bush and crushed them to control herself.

'The lives of these people,' she tried to explain, 'the aimlessness, the way they live. One goes from one to another, and it's all the same. One never gets what one wants out of any of them.'

Her emotional state and her confusion would have made her an easy prey if Helen had wished to argue or had wished to draw confidences. But instead of talking she fell into a profound silence as they walked on. Aimless, trivial, meaningless, oh no – what she had seen at tea made it impossible for her to believe that. The little jokes, the chatter, the inanities of the afternoon had shrivelled up before her eyes. Underneath the likings and spites, the comings together and partings, great things were happening – terrible things, because they were so great. Her sense of safety was shaken, as if beneath twigs and dead leaves she had seen the movement of a snake. It seemed to her that a moment's respite was allowed, a moment's make-believe, and then again the profound and reasonless law asserted itself, moulding them all to its liking, making and destroying.

She looked at Rachel walking beside her, still crushing the leaves in her fingers and absorbed in her own thoughts. She was in love, and she pitied her profoundly. But she roused herself from these thoughts and apologised. 'I'm very sorry,' she said, 'but if I'm dull, it's my nature, and it can't be helped.' If it was a natural defect, however, she found an easy remedy, for she went on to say that she thought Mr Flushing's scheme a very good one, only needing a little consideration, which it appeared she had given it by the time they reached home. By that time they had settled that if anything more was said, they would accept the invitation.

Chapter 20

When considered in detail by Mr Flushing and Mrs Ambrose the expedition proved neither dangerous nor difficult. They found also that it was not even unusual. Every year at this season English people made parties which steamed a short way up the river, landed and looked at the native village, bought a certain number of things from the natives, and returned again without damage done to mind or body. When it was discovered that six people really wished the same thing the arrangements were soon carried out.

Since the time of Elizabeth very few people had seen the river, and nothing has been done to change its appearance from what it was to the eyes of the Elizabethan voyagers. The time of Elizabeth was only distant from the present time by a moment of space compared with the ages which had passed since the water had run between those banks, and the green thickets swarmed there, and the small trees had grown to huge wrinkled trees in solitude. Changing only with the change of the sun and the clouds, the waving green mass had stood there for century after century, and the water had run between its banks ceaselessly, sometimes washing away earth and sometimes the branches of trees, while in other parts of the world one town had risen upon the ruins of another town, and the men in the towns had become more and more articulate and unlike each other. A few miles of this river were visible from the top of the mountain where some weeks before the party from the hotel had picnicked. Susan and Arthur had seen it as they kissed each other, and Terence and Rachel as they sat talking about Richmond, and Evelyn and Perrott as they strolled about, imagining that they were great captains sent to colonise the world. They had seen the broad blue mark across the sand where it flowed into the sea, and the green cloud of trees mass themselves about it farther up, and finally hide its waters altogether from sight. At intervals for the first twenty miles or so houses were scattered on the bank; by degrees the houses became huts, and later still there was neither hut nor house, but trees and grass, which were seen only by hunters, explorers or merchants, marching or sailing, but making no settlement.

By leaving Santa Marina early in the morning, driving twenty miles and riding eight, the party, which was composed finally of six English people, reached the riverside as the night fell. They came cantering through the trees – Mr and Mrs Flushing, Helen Ambrose, Rachel, Terence and St John. The tired little horses then stopped automatically, and the English dismounted. Mrs Flushing strode to the riverbank in high spirits. The day had been long and hot, but she had enjoyed the speed and the open air; she had left the hotel which she hated, and she found the company to her liking. The river was swirling past in the darkness; they could just distinguish the smooth moving surface of the water, and the air was full of the sound of it. They stood in an empty space in the midst of great tree-trunks, and out there a little green light moving slightly up and down showed them where the steamer lay in which they were to embark.

When they all stood upon its deck they found that it was a very small boat which throbbed gently beneath them for a few minutes, and then shoved smoothly through the water. They seemed to be driving into the heart of the night, for the trees closed in front of them, and they could hear all round them the rustling of leaves. The great darkness had the usual effect of taking away all desire for communication by making their words sound thin and small; and, after walking round the deck three or four times, they clustered together, yawning deeply, and looking at the same spot of deep gloom on the banks. Murmuring very low in the rhythmical tone of one oppressed by the air, Mrs Flushing began to wonder where they were to sleep, for they could not sleep downstairs, they could not sleep in a doghole smelling of oil, they could not sleep on deck, they could not sleep – she yawned profoundly. It was as Helen had foreseen; the question of nakedness had arisen already, although they were half asleep, and almost invisible to each other. With St John's help she stretched an awning, and persuaded Mrs Flushing that she could take off her clothes behind this, and that no one would notice if by chance some part of her which had been concealed for forty-five years was laid bare to the human eye. Mattresses were thrown down, rugs provided, and the three women lay near each other in the soft open air.

The gentlemen, having smoked a certain number of cigarettes, dropped the glowing ends into the river, and looked for a time at the ripples wrinkling the black water beneath them, undressed too, and lay down at the other end of the boat. They were very tired, and curtained from each other by the darkness. The light from one lantern fell upon a few ropes, a few planks of the deck, and the rail of the boat, but beyond that there was unbroken darkness, no light reached their faces, or the trees which were massed on the sides of the river.

Soon Wilfrid Flushing slept, and Hirst slept. Hewet alone lay awake looking straight up into the sky. The gentle motion and the black shapes that were drawn ceaselessly across his eyes had the effect of making it impossible for him to think. Rachel's presence so near him lulled thought asleep. Being so near him, only a few paces off at the other end of the boat, she made it as impossible for him to think about her as it would have been impossible to see her if she had stood quite close to him, her forehead against his forehead. In some strange way the boat became identified with himself, and just as it would have been useless for him to get up and steer the boat, so was it useless for him to struggle any longer with the irresistible force of his own feelings. He was drawn on and on away from all he knew, slipping over barriers and past landmarks into unknown waters as the boat glided over the smooth surface of the river. In profound peace, enveloped in deeper unconsciousness than had been his for many nights, he lay on deck watching the tree-tops change their position slightly against the sky, and arch themselves, and sink and tower huge, until he passed from seeing them into dreams where he lay beneath the shadow of the vast trees, looking up into the sky.

When they woke next morning they had gone a considerable way up the river; on the right was a high yellow bank of sand tufted with trees, on the left a swamp quivering with long reeds and tall bamboos on the top of which, swaying slightly, perched vivid green and yellow birds. The morning was hot and still. After breakfast they drew chairs together and sat in an irregular semicircle in the bow. An awning above their heads protected them from the heat of the sun, and the breeze which the boat made aired them softly. Mrs Flushing was already dotting and striping her canvas, her head jerking this way and that with the action of a bird nervously picking up grain; the others had books or pieces of paper or embroidery on their knees, at which they looked fitfully and again looked at the river ahead. At one point Hewet read part of a poem aloud, but the number of moving things entirely vanquished his words. He ceased to read, and no one spoke. They moved on under the shelter of the trees. There was now a covey of red birds feeding on one of the little islets to the left, or again a blue-green parrot flew shrieking from tree to tree. As they moved on the country grew wilder and wilder. The trees and the undergrowth seemed to be strangling each other near the ground in a multitudinous wrestle; while here and there a splendid tree towered high above the swarm, shaking its thin green umbrellas lightly in the upper air. Hewet looked at his books again. The morning was peaceful as the night had been, only it was very strange because he could see it was light, and he could see Rachel and hear her voice and be near to her. He felt as if he were waiting, as if somehow he were stationary among things that passed over him and around him, voices, people's bodies, birds, only Rachel too was waiting with him. He looked at her sometimes as if she must know that they were waiting together, and being drawn on together, without being able to offer any resistance. Again he read from his book:

> Whoever you are holding me now in your hand,
> Without one thing all will be useless.[108]

A bird gave a wild laugh, a monkey chuckled a malicious question, and as fire fades in the hot sunshine, his words flickered and went out.

By degrees, as the river narrowed and the high sandbanks fell to level ground thickly grown with trees, the sounds of the forest could be heard. It echoed like a hall. There were sudden cries; and then long spaces of silence, such as there are in a cathedral when a boy's voice has ceased and the echo of it still seems to haunt about the remote places of the roof. Once Mr Flushing rose and spoke to a sailor, and even announced that some time after luncheon the steamer would stop, and they could walk a little way through the forest.

'There are tracks all through the trees there,' he explained. 'We're no distance from civilisation yet.'

He scrutinised his wife's painting. Too polite to praise it openly, he contented himself with cutting off one half of the picture with one hand, and giving a flourish in the air with the other.

'God!' Hirst exclaimed, staring straight ahead. 'Don't you think it's amazingly beautiful?'

'Beautiful?' Helen enquired. It seemed a strange little word, and Hirst and herself both so small that she forgot to answer him.

Hewet felt that he must speak.

'That's where the Elizabethans got their style,' he mused, staring into the profusion of leaves and blossoms and prodigious fruits.

'Shakespeare? I hate Shakespeare!' Mrs Flushing exclaimed; and Wilfrid returned admiringly, 'I believe you're the only person who dares to say that, Alice.' But Mrs Flushing went on painting. She did not appear to attach much value to her husband's compliment, and painted steadily, sometimes muttering a half-audible word or groan.

The morning was now very hot.

'Look at Hirst!' Mr Flushing whispered. His sheet of paper had slipped on to the deck, his head lay back, and he drew a long snoring breath.

Terence picked up the sheet of paper and spread it out before Rachel.

It was a continuation of the poem on God which he had begun in the chapel, and it was so indecent that Rachel did not understand half of it although she saw that it was indecent. Hewet began to fill in words where Hirst had left spaces, but he soon ceased; his pencil rolled on deck. Gradually they approached nearer and nearer to the bank on the right-hand side, so that the light which covered them became definitely green, falling through a shade of green leaves, and Mrs Flushing set aside her sketch and stared ahead of her in silence. Hirst woke up; they were then called to luncheon, and while they ate it, the steamer came to a standstill a little way out from the bank. The boat which was towed behind them was brought to the side, and the ladies were helped into it.

For protection against boredom, Helen put a book of memoirs beneath her arm, and Mrs Flushing her paintbox, and, thus equipped, they allowed themselves to be set on shore on the verge of the forest.

They had not strolled more than a few hundred yards along the track which ran parallel with the river before Helen professed to find it was unbearably hot. The river breeze had ceased, and a hot steamy atmosphere, thick with scents, came from the forest.

'I shall sit down here,' she announced, pointing to the trunk of a tree which had fallen long ago and was now laced across and across by creepers and thong-like brambles. She seated herself, opened her parasol, and looked at the river which was barred by the stems of trees. She turned her back to the trees which disappeared in black shadow behind her.

'I quite agree,' said Mrs Flushing, and proceeded to undo her paintbox. Her husband strolled about to select an interesting point of view for her. Hirst cleared a space on the ground by Helen's side, and seated himself with great deliberation, as if he did not mean to move until he had talked to her for a long time. Terence and Rachel were left standing by themselves without occupation. Terence saw that the time had come as it was fated to come, but although he realised this he was completely calm and master of himself. He chose to stand for a few moments talking to Helen, and persuading her to leave her seat. Rachel joined him too in advising her to come with them.

'Of all the people I've ever met,' he said, 'you're the least adventurous. You might be sitting on green chairs in Hyde Park. Are you going to sit there the whole afternoon? Aren't you going to walk?'

'Oh, no,' said Helen, 'one's only got to use one's eye. There's everything here – everything,' she repeated in a drowsy tone of voice. 'What will you gain by walking?'

'You'll be hot and disagreeable by teatime; we shall be cool and sweet,' put in Hirst. Into his eyes as he looked up at them had come yellow and green reflections from the sky and the branches, robbing them of their intentness, and he seemed to think what he did not say. It was thus taken for granted by them both that Terence and Rachel proposed to walk into the woods together; with one look at each other they turned away.

'Goodbye!' cried Rachel.

'Goodbye. Beware of snakes,' Hirst replied. He settled himself still more comfortably under the shade of the fallen tree and Helen's figure. As they went, Mr Flushing called after them, 'We must start in an hour. Hewet, please remember that. An hour.'

Whether made by man, or for some reason preserved by nature, there was a wide pathway striking through the forest at right angles to the river. It resembled a drive in an English forest, save that tropical bushes with their sword-like leaves grew at the side, and the ground was covered with an unmarked springy moss instead of grass, starred with little yellow flowers. As they passed into the depths of the forest the light grew dimmer, and the noises of the ordinary world were replaced by those creaking and sighing sounds which suggest to the traveller in a forest that he is walking at the bottom of the sea. The path narrowed and turned; it was hedged in by dense creepers which knotted tree to tree, and burst here and there into star-shaped crimson blossoms. The sighing and creaking up above were broken every now and then by the jarring cry of some startled animal. The atmosphere was close and the air came at them in languid puffs of scent. The vast green light was broken here and there by a round of pure yellow sunlight which fell through some gap in the immense umbrella of green above, and in these yellow spaces crimson and black butterflies were circling and settling. Terence and Rachel hardly spoke.

Not only did the silence weigh upon them, but they were both unable to frame any thoughts. There was something between them which had to be spoken of. One of them had to begin, but which of them was it to be? Then Hewet picked up a red fruit and threw it as high as he could. When it dropped, he would speak. They heard the flapping of great wings; they heard the fruit go pattering through the leaves and eventually fall with a thud. The silence was again profound.

'Does this frighten you?' Terence asked when the sound of the fruit falling had completely died away.

'No,' she answered. 'I like it.'

She repeated, 'I like it.' She was walking fast, and holding herself more erect than usual. There was another pause.

'You like being with me?' Terence asked.

'Yes, with you,' she replied.

He was silent for a moment. Silence seemed to have fallen upon the world.

'That is what I have felt ever since I knew you,' he replied. 'We are happy together.' He did not seem to be speaking, or she to be hearing.

'Very happy,' she answered.

They continued to walk for some time in silence. Their steps unconsciously quickened.

'We love each other,' Terence said.

'We love each other,' she repeated.

The silence was then broken by their voices which joined in tones of strange unfamiliar sound which formed no words. Faster and faster they walked; simultaneously they stopped, clasped each other in their arms, then releasing themselves, dropped to the earth. They sat side by side. Sounds stood out from the background making a bridge across their silence; they heard the swish of the trees and some beast croaking in a remote world.

'We love each other,' Terence repeated, searching into her face. Their faces were both very pale and quiet, and they said nothing. He was afraid to kiss her again. By degrees she drew close to him, and rested against him. In this position they sat for some time. She said, 'Terence,' once; he answered, 'Rachel.'

'Terrible – terrible,' she murmured after another pause, but in saying this she was thinking as much of the persistent churning of the water as of her own feeling. On and on it went in the distance, the senseless and cruel churning of the water. She observed that the tears were running down Terence's cheeks.

The next movement was on his part. A very long time seemed to have passed. He took out his watch.

'Flushing said an hour. We've been gone more than half an hour.'

'And it takes that to get back,' said Rachel. She raised herself very slowly. When she was standing up she stretched her arms and drew a deep breath, half a sigh, half a yawn. She appeared to be very tired. Her cheeks were white. 'Which way?' she asked.

'There,' said Terence.

They began to walk back down the mossy path again. The sighing and creaking continued far overhead, and the jarring cries of animals. The butterflies were circling still in the patches of yellow sunlight. At first Terence was certain of his way, but as they walked he became doubtful. They had to stop to consider, and then to return and start once more, for although he was certain of the direction of the river he was not certain of striking the point where they had left the others. Rachel followed him, stopping where he stopped, turning where he turned, ignorant of the way, ignorant why he stopped or why he turned.

'I don't want to be late,' he said, 'because – ' He put a flower into her hand and her fingers closed upon it quietly. 'We're so late – so late – so horribly late,' he repeated as if he were talking in his sleep. 'Ah – this is right. We turn here.'

They found themselves again in the broad path, like the drive in the English forest, where they had started when they left the others. They walked on in silence as people walking in their sleep, and were oddly conscious now and again of the mass of their bodies. Then Rachel exclaimed suddenly, 'Helen!'

In the sunny space at the edge of the forest they saw Helen still sitting on the tree-trunk, her dress showing very white in the sun, with Hirst still propped on his elbow by her side. They stopped instinctively. At the sight of other people they could not go on. They stood hand in hand for a minute or two in silence. They could not bear to face other people.

'But we must go on,' Rachel insisted at last, in the curious dull tone of voice in which they had both been speaking, and with a great effort they forced themselves to cover the short distance which lay between them and the pair sitting on the tree-trunk.

As they approached, Helen turned round and looked at them. She looked at them for some time without speaking, and when they were close to her she said quietly: 'Did you meet Mr Flushing? He has gone to find you. He thought you must be lost, though I told him you weren't lost.'

Hirst half turned round and threw his head back so that he looked at the branches crossing themselves in the air above him.

'Well, was it worth the effort?' he enquired dreamily.

Hewet sat down on the grass by his side and began to fan himself.

Rachel had balanced herself near Helen on the end of the tree trunk. 'Very hot,' she said.

'You look exhausted anyhow,' said Hirst.

'It's fearfully close in those trees,' Helen remarked, picking up her book and shaking it free from the dried blades of grass which had fallen between the leaves. Then they were all silent, looking at the river swirling past in front of them between the trunks of the trees until Mr Flushing interrupted them. He broke out of the trees a hundred yards to the left, exclaiming sharply: 'Ah, so you found the way after all. But it's late – much later than we arranged, Hewet.'

He was slightly annoyed, and in his capacity as leader of the expedition, inclined to be dictatorial. He spoke quickly, using curiously sharp, meaningless words.

'Being late wouldn't matter normally, of course,' he said, 'but when it's a question of keeping the men up to time – '

He gathered them together and made them come down to the river-bank, where the boat was waiting to row them out to the steamer.

The heat of the day was going down, and over their cups of tea the Flushings tended to become communicative. It seemed to Terence as he listened to them talking that existence now went on in two different layers. Here were the Flushings talking, talking somewhere high up in the air above him, and he and Rachel had dropped to the bottom of the world together. But with something of a child's directness, Mrs Flushing had also the instinct which leads a child to suspect what its elders wish to keep hidden. She fixed Terence with her vivid blue eyes and addressed herself to him in particular. What would he do, she wanted to know, if the boat ran upon a rock and sank.

'Would you care for anythin' but savin' yourself? Should I? No, no,' she laughed, 'not one scrap – don't tell me. There's only two creatures the ordinary woman cares about,' she continued, 'her child and her dog; and I don't believe it's even two with men. One reads a lot about love – that's why poetry's so dull. But what happens in real life, eh? It ain't love!' she cried.

Terence murmured something unintelligible. Mr Flushing, however, had recovered his urbanity. He was smoking a cigarette, and he now answered his wife.

'You must always remember, Alice,' he said, 'that your upbringing was very unnatural – unusual, I should say. They had no mother,' he explained, dropping something of the formality of his tone; 'and a father – he was a very delightful man, I've no doubt, but he cared only for racehorses and Greek statues. Tell them about the bath, Alice.'

'In the stable-yard,' said Mrs Flushing. 'Covered with ice in winter. We had to get in; if we didn't, we were whipped. The strong ones lived – the others died. What you call survival of the fittest – a most excellent plan, I dare say, if you've thirteen children!'

'And all this going on in the heart of England, in the nineteenth century!' Mr Flushing exclaimed, turning to Helen.

'I'd treat my children just the same if I had any,' said Mrs Flushing.

Every word sounded quite distinctly in Terence's ears; but what were they saying, and who were they talking to, and who were they, these fantastic people, detached somewhere high up in the air? Now that they had drunk their tea, they rose and leant over the bow of the boat. The sun was going down, and the water was dark and crimson. The river had widened again, and they were passing a little island set like a dark wedge in the middle of the stream. Two great white birds with red lights on them stood there on stilt-like legs, and the beach of the island was unmarked, save by the skeleton prints of birds' feet. The branches of the trees on the bank looked more twisted and angular than ever, and the green of the leaves was lurid and splashed with gold. Then Hirst began to talk, leaning over the bow.

'It makes one awfully queer, don't you find?' he complained. 'These trees get on one's nerves – it's all so crazy. God's undoubtedly mad. What sane person could have conceived a wilderness like this, and peopled it with apes and alligators? I should go mad if I lived here – raving mad.'

Terence attempted to answer him, but Mrs Ambrose replied instead. She bade him look at the way things massed themselves – look at the amazing colours, look at the shapes of the trees. She seemed to be protecting Terence from the approach of the others.

'Yes,' said Mr Flushing. 'And in my opinion,' he continued, 'the absence of population to which Hirst objects is precisely the significant touch. You must admit, Hirst, that a little Italian town even would vulgarise the whole scene, would detract from the vastness – the sense of elemental grandeur.' He swept his hands towards the forest, and paused for a moment, looking at the great green mass, which was now falling silent. 'I own it makes us seem pretty small – us, not them.' He nodded his head at a sailor who leant over the side spitting into the river. 'And that, I think, is what my wife feels, the essential superiority of the peasant – ' Under cover of Mr Flushing's words, which continued now gently reasoning with St John and persuading him, Terence drew Rachel to the side, pointing ostensibly to a great gnarled tree-trunk which had fallen and lay half in the water. He wished, at any rate, to be near her, but he found that he could say nothing. They could hear Mr Flushing flowing on, now about his wife, now about art, now about the future of the country, little meaningless words floating high in air. As it was becoming cold he began to pace the deck with Hirst. Fragments of their talk came out distinctly as they passed – art, emotion, truth, reality.

'Is it true, or is it a dream?' Rachel murmured, when they had passed.

'It's true, it's true,' he replied.

But the breeze freshened, and there was a general desire for movement. When the party rearranged themselves under cover of rugs and cloaks, Terence and Rachel were at opposite ends of the circle, and could not speak to each other. But as the dark descended, the words of the others seemed to curl up and vanish as the ashes of burnt paper, and left them sitting perfectly silent at the bottom of the world. Occasional starts of exquisite joy ran through them, and then they were peaceful again.

Chapter 21

Thanks to Mr Flushing's discipline, the right stages of the river were reached at the right hours, and when next morning after breakfast the chairs were again drawn out in a semicircle in the bow, the launch was within a few miles of the native camp which was the limit of the journey. Mr Flushing, as he sat down, advised them to keep their eyes fixed on the left bank, where they would soon pass a clearing, and in that clearing was a hut where Mackenzie, the famous explorer, had died of fever some ten years ago, almost within reach of civilisation – 'Mackenzie,' he repeated, 'the man who went farther inland than anyone's been yet. Their eyes turned that way obediently. The eyes of Rachel saw nothing. Yellow and green shapes did, it is true, pass before them, but she only knew that one was large and another small; she did not know that they were trees. These directions to look here and there irritated her, as interruptions irritate a person absorbed in thought, although she was not thinking of anything. She was annoyed with all that was said, and with the aimless movements of people's bodies, because they seemed to interfere with her and to prevent her from speaking to Terence. Very soon Helen saw her staring moodily at a coil of rope, and making no effort to listen. Mr Flushing and St John were engaged in more or less continuous conversation about the future of the country from a political point of view, and the degree to which it had been explored; the others, with legs stretched out, or chins poised on hands, gazed in silence.

Mrs Ambrose looked and listened obediently enough, but inwardly she was prey to an uneasy mood not readily to be ascribed to any one cause. Looking on shore as Mr Flushing bade her, she thought the country very beautiful, but also sultry and alarming. She did not like to feel herself the victim of unclassified emotions, and certainly as the launch slipped on and on, in the hot morning sun, she felt herself unreasonably moved. Whether the unfamiliarity of the forest was the cause of it, or something less definite, she could not determine. Her mind left the scene and occupied itself with anxieties for Ridley, for her children, for far-off things, such as old age and poverty and death. Hirst, too, was depressed. He had been looking forward to this expedition as to a holiday, for, once away from the hotel, surely wonderful things would happen, instead of which nothing happened, and here they were as uncomfortable, as restrained, as self-conscious as ever. That, of course, was what came of looking forward to anything: one was always disappointed. He blamed Wilfrid Flushing, who was so well dressed and so formal; he blamed Hewet and Rachel. Why didn't they talk? He looked at them sitting silent and self-absorbed, and the sight annoyed him. He supposed that they were engaged, or about to become engaged, but instead of being in the least romantic or exciting, that was as dull as everything else; it annoyed him, too, to think that they were in love. He drew close to Helen and began to tell her how uncomfortable his night had been, lying on the deck, sometimes too hot, sometimes too cold, and the stars so bright that he couldn't get to sleep. He had lain awake all night thinking, and when it was light enough to see, he had written twenty lines of his poem on God, and the awful thing was that he'd practically proved the fact that God did not exist. He did not see that he was teasing her, and he went on to wonder what would happen if God did exist – 'an old gentleman in a beard and a long blue dressing-gown, extremely testy and disagreeable, as he's bound to be? Can you suggest a rhyme? God, rod, sod – all used; any others?'

Although he spoke much as usual, Helen could have seen, had she looked, that he was also impatient and disturbed. But she was not called upon to answer, for Mr Flushing now exclaimed, 'There!' They looked at the hut on the bank, a desolate place with a large rent in the roof, and the ground round it yellow, scarred with fires and scattered with rusty open tins.

'Did they find his dead body there?' Mrs Flushing exclaimed, leaning forward in her eagerness to see the spot where the explorer had died.

'They found his body and his skins and a notebook,' her husband replied. But the boat had soon carried them on and left the place behind.

It was so hot that they scarcely moved, except now to change a foot or, again, to strike a match. Their eyes, concentrated upon the bank, were full of the same green reflections, and their lips were slightly pressed together as though the sights they were passing gave rise to thoughts, save that Hirst's lips moved intermittently as half consciously he sought rhymes for God. Whatever the thoughts of the others, no one said anything for a considerable space. They had grown so accustomed to the wall of trees on either side that they looked up with a start when the light suddenly widened out and the trees came to an end.

'It almost reminds one of an English park,' said Mr Flushing.

Indeed no change could have been greater. On both banks of the river lay an open lawn-like space, grass covered and planted, for the gentleness and order of the place suggested human care, with graceful trees on the top of little mounds. As far as they could gaze, this lawn rose and sank with the undulating motion of an old English park. The change of scene naturally suggested a change of position, grateful to most of them. They rose and leant over the rail.

'It might be Arundel or Windsor,' Mr Flushing continued, 'if you cut down that bush with the yellow flowers; and, by Jove, look!'

Rows of brown backs paused for a moment and then leapt with a motion as if they were springing over waves out of sight. For a moment no one of them could believe that they had really seen live animals in the open – a herd of wild deer, and the sight aroused a childlike excitement in them, dissipating their gloom.

'I've never in my life seen anything bigger than a hare!' Hirst exclaimed with genuine excitement. 'What an ass I was not to bring my Kodak!' [109]

Soon afterwards the launch came gradually to a standstill, and the captain explained to Mr Flushing that it would be pleasant for the passengers if they now went for a stroll on shore; if they chose to return within an hour, he would take them on to the village; if they chose to walk – it was only a mile or two farther on – he would meet them at the landing-place.

The matter being settled, they were once more put on shore; the sailors, producing raisins and tobacco, leant upon the rail and watched the six English, whose coats and dresses looked so strange upon the green, wander off. A joke that was by no means proper set them all laughing, and then they turned round and lay at their ease upon the deck.

Directly they landed, Terence and Rachel drew together slightly in advance of the others.

'Thank God!' Terence exclaimed, drawing a long breath. 'At last we're alone.'

'And if we keep ahead we can talk,' said Rachel.

Nevertheless, although their position some yards in advance of the others made it possible for them to say anything they chose, they were both silent.

'You love me?' Terence asked at length, breaking the silence painfully. To speak or to be silent was equally an effort, for when they were silent they were keenly conscious of each other's presence, and yet words were either too trivial or too large.

She murmured inarticulately, ending, 'And you?'

'Yes, yes,' he replied; but there were so many things to be said, and now that they were alone it seemed necessary to bring themselves still more near, and to surmount a barrier which had grown up since they had last spoken. It was difficult, frightening even, oddly embarrassing. At one moment he was clear-sighted, and at the next, confused.

'Now I'm going to begin at the beginning,' he said resolutely. 'I'm going to tell you what I ought to have told you before. In the first place, I've never been in love with other women, but I've had other women. Then I've great faults. I'm very lazy, I'm moody – ' He persisted, in spite of her exclamation, 'You've got to know the worst of me. I'm lustful. I'm overcome by a sense of futility – incompetence. I ought never to have asked you to marry me, I expect. I'm a bit of a snob; I'm ambitious – '

'Oh, our faults!' she cried. 'What do they matter?' Then she demanded, 'Am I in love – is this being in love – are we to marry each other?'

Overcome by the charm of her voice and her presence, he exclaimed, 'Oh, you're free, Rachel. To you, time will make no difference, or marriage, or – '

The voices of the others behind them kept floating, now farther, now nearer, and Mrs Flushing's laugh rose clearly by itself.

'Marriage?' Rachel repeated.

The shouts were renewed behind, warning them that they were bearing too far to the left. Improving their course, he continued, 'Yes, marriage.' The feeling that they could not be united until she knew all about him made him again endeavour to explain. 'All that's been bad in me, the things I've put up with – the second best – '

She murmured, considered her own life, but could not describe how it looked to her now.

'And the loneliness!' he continued. A vision of walking with her through the streets of London came before his eyes. 'We will go for walks together,' he said. The simplicity of the idea relieved them, and for the first time they laughed. They would have liked had they dared to take each other by the hand, but the consciousness of eyes fixed on them from behind had not yet deserted them.

'Books, people, sights – Mrs Nutt, Greeley, Hutchinson,' Hewet murmured.

With every word the mist which had enveloped them, making them seem unreal to each other, since the previous afternoon melted a little further, and their contact became more and more natural. Up through the sultry southern landscape they saw the world they knew appear clearer and more vividly than it had ever appeared before. As upon that occasion at the hotel when she had sat in the window, the world once more arranged itself beneath her gaze very vividly and in its true proportions. She glanced curiously at Terence from time to time, observing his grey coat and his purple tie; observing the man with whom she was to spend the rest of her life.

After one of these glances she murmured, 'Yes, I'm in love. There's no doubt; I'm in love with you.'

Nevertheless, they remained uncomfortably apart; drawn so close together, as she spoke, that there seemed no division between them, and the next moment separate and far away again. Feeling this painfully, she exclaimed, 'It will be a fight.'

But as she looked at him she perceived from the shape of his eyes, the lines about his mouth and other peculiarities, that he pleased her, and she added: 'Where I want to fight, you have compassion. You're finer than I am; you're much finer.'

He returned her glance and smiled, perceiving, much as she had done, the very small individual things about her which made her delightful to him. She was his for ever. This barrier being surmounted, innumerable delights lay before them both.

'I'm not finer,' he answered. 'I'm only older, lazier; a man, not a woman.'

'A man,' she repeated, and a curious sense of possession coming over her, it struck her that she might now touch him; she put out her hand and lightly touched his cheek. His fingers followed where hers had been, and the touch of his hand upon his face brought back the overpowering sense of unreality. This body of his was unreal; the whole world was unreal.

'What's happened?' he began. 'Why did I ask you to marry me? How did it happen?'

'Did you ask me to marry you?' she wondered. They faded far away from each other, and neither of them could remember what had been said.

'We sat upon the ground,' he recollected.

'We sat upon the ground,' she confirmed him. The recollection of sitting upon the ground, such as it was, seemed to unite them again, and they walked on in silence, their minds sometimes working with difficulty and sometimes ceasing to work, their eyes alone perceiving the things round them. Now he would attempt again to tell her his faults, and why he loved her; and she would describe what she had felt at this time or at that time, and together they would interpret her feeling. So beautiful was the sound of their voices that by degrees they scarcely listened to the words they framed. Long silences came between their words, which were no longer silences of struggle and confusion but refreshing silences, in which trivial thoughts moved easily. They began to speak naturally of ordinary things, of the flowers and the trees, how they grew there so red, like garden flowers at home, and there bent and crooked like the arm of a twisted old man.

Very gently and quietly, almost as if it were the blood singing in her veins, or the water of the stream running over stones, Rachel became conscious of a new feeling within her. She wondered for a moment what it was, and then said to herself, with a little surprise at recognising in her own person so famous a thing: 'This is happiness, I suppose.' And aloud to Terence she spoke, 'This is happiness.'

On the heels of her words he answered, 'This is happiness,' upon which they guessed that the feeling had sprung in both of them at the same time. They began therefore to describe how this felt and that felt, how like it was and yet how different; for they were very different.

Voices crying behind them never reached through the waters in which they were now sunk. The repetition of Hewet's name in short, dissevered syllables was to them the crack of a dry branch or the laughter of a bird. The grasses and breezes sounding and murmuring all round them, they never noticed that the swishing of the grasses grew louder and louder, and did not cease with the lapse of the breeze. A hand dropped abrupt as iron on Rachel's shoulder; it might have been a bolt from heaven. She fell beneath it, and the grass whipped across her eyes and filled her mouth and ears. Through the waving stems she saw a figure, large and shapeless against the sky. Helen was upon her. Rolled this way and that, now seeing only forests of green, and now the high blue heaven, she was speechless and almost without sense. At last she lay still, all the grasses shaken round her and before her by her panting. Over her loomed two great heads, the heads of a man and woman, of Terence and Helen.

Both were flushed, both laughing, and the lips were moving; they came together and kissed in the air above her. Broken fragments of speech came down to her on the ground. She thought she heard them speak of love and then of marriage. Raising herself and sitting up, she too realised Helen's soft body, the strong and hospitable arms, and happiness swelling and breaking in one vast wave. When this fell away, and the grasses once more lay low, and the sky became horizontal, and the earth rolled out flat on each side, and the trees stood upright, she was the first to perceive a little row of human figures standing patiently in the distance. For the moment she could not remember who they were.

'Who are they?' she asked, and then recollected.

Falling into line behind Mr Flushing, they were careful to leave at least three yards' distance between the toe of his boot and the rim of her skirt.

He led them across a stretch of green by the riverbank and then through a grove of trees, and bade them remark the signs of human habitation, the blackened grass, the charred tree-stumps, and there, through the trees, strange wooden nests, drawn together in an arch where the trees drew apart, the village which was the goal of their journey.

Stepping cautiously, they observed the women, who were squatting on the ground in triangular shapes, moving their hands either in plaiting straw or in kneading something in bowls. But when they had looked for a moment undiscovered, they were seen, and Mr Flushing, advancing into the centre of the clearing, was engaged in talk with a lean majestic man, whose bones and hollows at once made the shapes of the Englishman's body appear ugly and unnatural. The women took no notice of the strangers, except that their hands paused for a moment and their long narrow eyes slid round and fixed upon them with the motionless inexpensive gaze of those removed from each other far far beyond the plunge of speech. Their hands moved again, but the stare continued. It followed them as they walked, as they peered into the huts where they could distinguish guns leaning in the corner, and bowls upon the floor, and stacks of rushes; in the dusk the solemn eyes of babies regarded them, and old women stared out too. As they sauntered about, the stare followed them, passing over their legs, their bodies, their heads, curiously not without hostility, like the crawl of a winter fly. As she drew apart her shawl and uncovered her breast to the lips of her baby, the eyes of a woman never left their faces, although they moved uneasily under her stare, and finally turned away, rather than stand there looking at her any longer. When sweetmeats were offered them, they put out great red hands to take them, and felt themselves treading cumbrously like tight-coated soldiers among these soft instinctive people. But soon the life of the village took no notice of them; they had become absorbed in it. The women's hands became busy again with the straw; their eyes dropped. If they moved, it was to fetch something from the hut, or to catch a straying child, or to cross the space with a jar balanced on their heads; if they spoke, it was to cry some harsh unintelligible cry. Voices rose when a child was beaten, and fell again; voices rose in song, which slid up a little way and down a little way, and settled again upon the same low and melancholy note. Seeking each other, Terence and Rachel drew together under a tree. Peaceful and even beautiful at first, the sight of the women, who had given up looking at them, made them now feel very cold and melancholy.

'Well,' Terence sighed at length, 'it makes us seem insignificant, doesn't it?'

Rachel agreed. So it would go on for ever and ever, she said, those women sitting under the trees, the trees and the river. They turned away and began to walk through the trees, leaning, without fear of discovery, upon each other's arms. They had not gone far before they began to assure each other once more that they were in love, were happy, were content; but why was it so painful being in love, why was there so much pain in happiness?

The sight of the village indeed affected them all curiously though all differently. St John had left the others and was walking slowly down to the river, absorbed in his own thoughts, which were bitter and unhappy, for he felt himself alone; and Helen, standing by herself in the sunny space among the native women, was exposed to presentiments of disaster. The cries of the senseless beasts rang in her ears high and low in the air as they ran from tree-trunk to tree-top. How small the little figures looked wandering through the trees! She became acutely conscious of the little limbs, the thin veins, the delicate flesh of men and women, which breaks so easily and lets the life escape, compared with these great trees and deep waters. A falling branch, a foot that slips, and the earth has crushed them or the water drowned them. Thus thinking, she kept her eyes anxiously fixed upon the lovers, as if by doing so she could protect them from their fate. Turning, she found the Flushings by her side.

They were talking about the things they had bought and arguing whether they were really old, and whether there were not signs here and there of European influence. Helen was appealed to. She was made to look at a brooch, and then at a pair of earrings. But all the time she blamed them for having come on this expedition, for having ventured too far and exposed themselves. Then she roused herself and tried to talk, but in a few moments she caught herself seeing a picture of a boat upset on the river in England, at midday. It was morbid, she knew, to imagine such things; nevertheless she sought out the figures of the others between the trees, and whenever she saw them she kept her eyes fixed on them, so that she might be able to protect them from disaster.

But when the sun went down and the steamer turned and began to steam back towards civilisation, again her fears were calmed. In the semi-darkness the chairs on deck and the people sitting in them were angular shapes, the mouth being indicated by a tiny burning spot, and the arm by the same spot moving up or down as the cigar or cigarette was lifted to and from the lips. Words crossed the darkness, but, not knowing where they fell, seemed to lack energy and substance. Deep sighs proceeded regularly, although with some attempt at suppression, from the large white mound which represented the person of Mrs Flushing. The day had been long and very hot, and now that all the colours were blotted out the cool night air seemed to press soft fingers upon the eyelids, sealing them down. Some philosophical remark directed, apparently, at St John Hirst missed its aim, and hung so long suspended in the air until it was engulfed by a yawn, that it was considered dead, and this gave the signal for stirring of legs and murmurs about sleep. The white mound moved, finally lengthened itself and disappeared, and after a few turns and paces St John and Mr Flushing withdrew, leaving three chairs still occupied by three silent bodies. The light which came from a lamp high on the mast and a sky pale with stars left them with shapes but without features; but even in this darkness the withdrawal of the others made them feel each other very near, for they were all thinking of the same thing. For some time no one spoke, then Helen said with a sigh, 'So you're both very happy?'

As if washed by the air her voice sounded more spiritual and softer than usual. Voices at a little distance answered her, 'Yes.'

Through the darkness she was looking at them both, and trying to distinguish him. What was there for her to say? Rachel had passed beyond her guardianship. A voice might reach her ears, but never again would it carry as far as it had carried twenty-four hours ago. Nevertheless, speech seemed to be due from her before she went to bed. She wished to speak, but she felt strangely old and depressed.

'D'you realise what you're doing?' she demanded. 'She's young, you're both young; and marriage – ' Here she ceased. They begged her, however, to continue, with such earnestness in their voices, as if they only craved advice, that she was led to add: 'Marriage! well, it's not easy.'

'That's what we want to know,' they answered, and she guessed that now they were looking at each other.

'It depends on both of you,' she stated. Her face was turned towards Terence, and although he could hardly see her, he believed that her words really covered a genuine desire to know more about him. He raised himself from his semi-recumbent position and proceeded to tell her what she wanted to know. He spoke as lightly as he could in order to take away her depression.

'I'm twenty-seven, and I've about seven hundred a year,' he began. 'My temper is good on the whole, and health excellent, though Hirst detects a gouty tendency. Well, then, I think I'm very intelligent.' He paused as if for confirmation.

Helen agreed.

'Though, unfortunately, rather lazy. I intend to allow Rachel to be a fool if she wants to, and – Do you find me on the whole satisfactory in other respects?' he asked shyly.

'Yes, I like what I know of you,' Helen replied. 'But then – one knows so little.'

'We shall live in London,' he continued, 'and – '

With one voice they suddenly enquired whether she did not think them the happiest people that she had ever known.

'Hush,' she checked them, 'Mrs Flushing, remember. She's behind us.'

Then they fell silent, and Terence and Rachel felt instinctively that their happiness had made her sad, and, while they were anxious to go on talking about themselves, they did not like to.

'We've talked too much about ourselves,' Terence said. 'Tell us – '

'Yes, tell us – ' Rachel echoed. They were both in the mood to believe that everyone was capable of saying something very profound.

'What can I tell you?' Helen reflected, speaking more to herself in a rambling style than as a prophetess delivering a message. She forced herself to speak. 'After all, though I scold Rachel, I'm not much wiser myself. I'm older, of course, I'm halfway through, and you're just beginning. It's puzzling – sometimes, I think, disappointing; the great things aren't as great, perhaps, as one expects – but it's interesting – Oh, yes, you're certain to find it interesting – And so it goes on,' they became conscious here of the procession of dark trees into which, as far as they could see, Helen was now looking, 'and there are pleasures where one doesn't expect them (you must write to your father), and you'll be very happy, I've no doubt. But I must go to bed, and if you are sensible you will follow in ten minutes. And so,' she rose and stood before them, almost featureless and very large, 'good-night.' She passed behind the curtain.

After sitting in silence for the greater part of the ten minutes she allowed them, they rose and hung over the rail. Beneath them the smooth black water slipped away very fast and silently. The spark of a cigarette vanished behind them. 'A beautiful voice,' Terence murmured.

Rachel assented. Helen had a beautiful voice.

After a silence, she asked, looking up into the sky, 'Are we on the deck of a steamer on a river in South America? Am I Rachel, are you Terence?'

The great black world lay round them. As they were drawn smoothly along it seemed possessed of immense thickness and endurance. They could discern pointed tree-tops and blunt rounded tree-tops. Raising their eyes above the trees, they fixed them on the stars in the pale border of sky above the trees. The little points of frosty light infinitely far away drew their eyes and held them fixed, so that it seemed as if they stayed a long time and fell a great distance when once more they realised their hands grasping the rail and their separate bodies standing side by side.

'You'd forgotten completely about me,' Terence reproached her, taking her arm and beginning to pace the deck, 'and I never forget you.'

'Oh, no,' she whispered, she had not forgotten – only the stars – the night – the dark –

'You're like a bird half asleep in its nest, Rachel. You're asleep. You're talking in your sleep.'

Half asleep, and murmuring broken words, they stood in the angle made by the bow of the boat. It slipped on down the river. Now a bell struck on the bridge, and they heard the lapping of water as it rippled away on either side, and once a bird startled in its sleep creaked, flew on to the next tree, and was silent again. The darkness poured down profusely, and left them with scarcely any feeling of life, except that they were standing there together in the darkness.

Chapter 22

The darkness fell, but rose again, and as each day spread widely over the earth and parted them from the strange day in the forest when they had been forced to tell each other what they wanted, this wish of theirs was revealed to other people, and in the process became slightly strange to themselves. Apparently it was not anything unusual that had happened; it was that they had become engaged to marry each other. The world, which consisted for the most part of the hotel and the villa, expressed itself glad on the whole that two people should marry, and allowed them to see that they were not expected to take part in the work which has to be done in order that the world shall go on, but might absent themselves for a time. They were accordingly left alone until they felt the silence – as if, playing in a vast church, the door had been shut on them. They were driven to walk alone, and sit alone, to visit secret places where the flowers had never been picked and the trees were solitary. In solitude they could express those beautiful but too vast desires which were so oddly uncomfortable to the ears of other men and women – desires for a world, such as their own world which contained two people seemed to them to be, where people knew each other intimately and thus judged each other by what was good, and never quarrelled, because that was waste of time.

They would talk of such questions among books, or out in the sun, or sitting in the shade of a tree undisturbed. They were no longer embarrassed, or half-choked with meaning which could not express itself; they were not afraid of each other, or, like travellers down a twisting river, dazzled with sudden beauties when the corner is turned; the unexpected happened, but even the ordinary was lovable, and in many ways preferable to the ecstatic and mysterious, for it was refreshingly solid, and called out effort, and effort under such circumstances was not effort but delight.

While Rachel played the piano, Terence sat near her, engaged, as far as the occasional writing of a word in pencil testified, in shaping the world as it appeared to him now that he and Rachel were going to be married. It was different certainly. The book called *Silence* would not now be the same book that it would have been. He would then put down his pencil and stare in front of him, and wonder in what respects the world was different – it had, perhaps, more solidity, more coherence, more importance, greater depth. Why, even the earth sometimes seemed to him very deep; not carved into hills and cities and fields, but heaped in great masses. He would look out of the window for ten minutes at a time; but no, he did not care for the earth swept of human beings. He liked human beings – he liked them, he suspected, better than Rachel did. There she was, swaying enthusiastically over her music, quite forgetful of him – but he liked that quality in her. He liked the impersonality which it produced in her. At last, having written down a series of little sentences, with notes of interrogation attached to them, he observed aloud, ' "Women – " under the heading Women I've written: "Not really vainer than men? Lack of self-confidence at the base of most serious faults? Dislike of own sex traditional or founded on fact? Every woman not so much a rake at heart as an optimist, because they don't think." What do you say, Rachel?' He paused with his pencil in his hand and a sheet of paper on his knee.

Rachel said nothing. Up and up the steep spiral of a very late Beethoven sonata she climbed, like a person ascending a ruined staircase, energetically at first, then more laboriously advancing her feet with effort until she could go no higher and returned with a run to begin at the very bottom again.

' "Again, it's the fashion now to say that women are more practical and less idealistic than men, also that they have considerable organising ability but no sense of honour" – query, what is meant by masculine term, honour? – what corresponds to it in your sex? Eh?'

Attacking her staircase once more, Rachel again neglected this opportunity of revealing the secrets of her sex. She had, indeed, advanced so far in the pursuit of wisdom that she allowed these secrets to rest undisturbed; it seemed to be reserved for a later generation to discuss them philosophically.

Crashing down a final chord with her left hand, she exclaimed at last, swinging round upon him: 'No, Terence, it's no good; here am I, the best musician in South America, not to speak of Europe and Asia, and I can't play a note because of you in the room interrupting me every other second.'

'You don't seem to realise that that's what I've been aiming at for the last half-hour,' he remarked. 'I've no objection to nice simple tunes – indeed, I find them very helpful to my literary composition, but that kind of thing is merely like an unfortunate old dog going round on its hind legs in the rain.'

He began turning over the little sheets of notepaper which were scattered on the table, conveying the congratulations of their friends.

' " – all possible wishes for all possible happiness",' he read; 'Correct, but not very vivid, are they?'

'They're sheer nonsense!' Rachel exclaimed. 'Think of words compared with sounds!' she continued. 'Think of novels and plays and histories – ' Perched on the edge of the table, she stirred the red and yellow volumes contemptuously. She seemed to herself to be in a position where she could despise all human learning. Terence looked at them too.

'God, Rachel, you do read trash!' he exclaimed. 'And you're behind the times too, my dear. No one dreams of reading this kind of thing now – antiquated problem plays, harrowing descriptions of life in the East End – oh, no, we've exploded all that. Read poetry, Rachel, poetry, poetry, poetry!'

Picking up one of the books, he began to read aloud, his intention being to satirise the short sharp bark of the writer's English; but she paid no attention, and after an interval of meditation exclaimed: 'Does it ever seem to you, Terence, that the world is composed entirely of vast blocks of matter, and that we're nothing but patches of light – ' she looked at the soft spots of sun wavering over the carpet and up the wall – 'like that?'

'No,' said Terence, 'I feel solid; immensely solid; the legs of my chair might be rooted in the bowels of the earth. But at Cambridge, I can remember, there were times when one fell into ridiculous states of semi-coma about five o'clock in the morning. Hirst does now, I expect – oh, no, Hirst wouldn't.'

Rachel continued, 'The day your note came, asking us to go on the picnic, I was sitting where you're sitting now, thinking that; I wonder if I could think that again? I wonder if the world's changed? and if so, when it'll stop changing, and which is the real world?'

'When I first saw you,' he began, 'I thought you were like a creature who'd lived all its life among pearls and old bones. Your hands were wet, d'you remember, and you never said a word until I gave you a bit of bread, and then you said, "Human Beings!" '

'And I thought you – a prig,' she recollected. 'No; that's not quite it. There were the ants who stole the tongue, and I thought you and St John were like those ants – very big, very ugly, very energetic, with all your virtues on your backs. However, when I talked to you I liked you – '

'You fell in love with me,' he corrected her. 'You were in love with me all the time, only you didn't know it.'

'No, I never fell in love with you,' she asserted.

'Rachel – what a lie – didn't you sit here looking at my window – didn't you wander about the hotel like an owl in the sun – ?'

'No,' she repeated, 'I never fell in love, if falling in love is what people say it is, and it's the world that tells the lies and I tell the truth. Oh, what lies – what lies!'

She crumpled together a handful of letters from Evelyn M., from Mr Pepper, from Mrs Thornbury and Miss Allan, and Susan Warrington. It was strange, considering how very different these people were, that they used almost the same sentences when they wrote to congratulate her upon her engagement.

That any one of these people had ever felt what she felt, or could ever feel it, or had even the right to pretend for a single second that they were capable of feeling it, appalled her much as the church service had done, much as the face of the hospital nurse had done; and if they didn't feel a thing why did they go and pretend to? The simplicity and arrogance and hardness of her youth, now concentrated into a single spark as it was by her love of him, puzzled Terence; being engaged had not that effect on him; the world was different, but not in that way; he still wanted the things he had always wanted, and in particular he wanted the companionship of other people more than ever perhaps. He took the letters out of her hand, and protested: 'Of course they're absurd, Rachel; of course they say things just because other people say them, but even so, what a nice woman Miss Allan is; you can't deny that; and Mrs Thornbury too; she's got too many children I grant you, but if half a dozen of them had gone to the bad instead of rising infallibly to the tops of their trees – hasn't she a kind of beauty – of elemental simplicity as Flushing would say? Isn't she rather like a large old tree murmuring in the moonlight, or a river going on and on and on? By the way, Ralph's been made governor of the Carroway Islands – the youngest governor in the service; very good, isn't it?'

But Rachel was at present unable to conceive that the vast majority of the affairs of the world went on unconnected by a single thread with her own destiny.

'I won't have eleven children,' she asserted; 'I won't have the eyes of an old woman. She looks at one up and down, up and down, as if one were a horse.'

'We must have a son and we must have a daughter,' said Terence, putting down the letters, 'because, let alone the inestimable advantage of being our children, they'd be so well brought up.' They went on to sketch an outline of the ideal education – how their daughter should be required from infancy to gaze at a large square of cardboard painted blue, to suggest thoughts of infinity, for women were grown too practical; and their son – he should be taught to laugh at great men, that is, at distinguished successful men, at men who wore ribands and rose to the tops of their trees. He should in no way resemble (Rachel added) St John Hirst.

At this Terence professed the greatest admiration for St John Hirst. Dwelling upon his good qualities, he became seriously convinced of them; he had a mind like a torpedo, he declared, aimed at falsehood. Where should we all be without him and his like? Choked in weeds; Christians, bigots – why, Rachel herself would be a slave with a fan to sing songs to men when they felt drowsy.

'But you'll never see it!' he exclaimed; 'because with all your virtues you don't, and you never will, care with every fibre of your being for the pursuit of truth! You've no respect for facts, Rachel; you're essentially feminine.' She did not trouble to deny it, nor did she think it good to produce the one unanswerable argument against the merits which Terence admired. St John Hirst had said that she was in love with him; she would never forgive that; but the argument was not one to appeal to a man.

'But I like him,' she said, and she thought to herself that she also pitied him, as one pities those unfortunate people who are outside the warm mysterious globe full of changes and miracles in which we ourselves move about; she thought that it must be very dull to be St John Hirst.

She summed up what she felt about him by saying that she would not kiss him supposing he wished it, which was not likely.

As if some apology were due to Hirst for the kiss which she then bestowed upon him, Terence protested: 'And compared with Hirst I'm a perfect Zany.'[110]

The clock here struck twelve instead of eleven.

'We're wasting the morning – I ought to be writing my book, and you ought to be answering these.'

'We've only got twenty-one whole mornings left,' said Rachel. 'And my father'll be here in a day or two.'

However, she drew a pen and paper towards her and began to write laboriously, 'My dear Evelyn – '

Terence, meanwhile, read a novel which someone else had written, a process which he found essential to the composition of his own. For a considerable time nothing was to be heard but the ticking of the clock and the fitful scratch of Rachel's pen, as she produced phrases which bore a considerable likeness to those which she had condemned. She was struck by it herself, for she stopped writing and looked up; looked at Terence deep in the armchair, looked at the different pieces of furniture, at her bed in the corner, at the window-pane which showed the branches of a tree filled in with sky, heard the clock ticking, and was amazed at the gulf which lay between all that and her sheet of paper. Would there ever be a time when the world was one and indivisible? Even with Terence himself – how far apart they could be, how little she knew what was passing in his brain now! She then finished her sentence, which was awkward and ugly, and stated that they were 'both very happy, and going to be married in the autumn probably and hope to live in London, where we hope you will come and see us when we get back'. Choosing 'affectionately', after some further speculation, rather than sincerely, she signed the letter and was doggedly beginning on another when Terence remarked, quoting from his book: 'Listen to this, Rachel.

' "It is probable that Hugh" (he's the hero, a literary man), "had not realised at the time of his marriage, any more than the young man of parts and imagination usually does realise, the nature of the gulf which separates the needs and desires of the male from the needs and desires of the female . . . At first they had been very happy. The walking tour in Switzerland had been a time of jolly companionship and stimulating revelations for both of them. Betty had proved herself the ideal comrade . . . They had shouted *Love in the Valley* to each other across the snowy slopes of the Riffelhorn" (and so on, and so on – I'll skip the descriptions) . . . "But in London, after the boy's birth, all was changed. Betty was an admirable mother; but it did not take her long to find out that motherhood, as that function is understood by the mother of the upper middle classes, did not absorb the whole of her energies. She was young and strong, with healthy limbs and a body and brain that called urgently for exercise . . . " (In short she began to give tea-parties.) . . . "Coming in late from this singular talk with old Bob Murphy in his smoky, book-lined room, where the two men had each unloosened his soul to the other, with the sound of the traffic humming in his ears, and the foggy London sky slung tragically across his mind . . . he found women's hats dotted about among his papers. Women's wraps and absurd little feminine shoes and umbrellas were in the hall . . . Then the bills began to come in . . . He tried to speak frankly to her. He found her lying on the great polar-bear skin in their bedroom, half-undressed, for they were dining with the Greens in Wilton Crescent, the ruddy firelight making the diamonds wink and twinkle on her bare arms and in the delicious curve of her breast – a vision of adorable femininity. He forgave her all." (Well, this goes from bad to worse, and finally, about fifty pages later, Hugh takes a weekend ticket to Swanage and "has it out with himself on the downs above Corfe" ... Here there's fifteen pages or so which we'll skip.) The conclusion is ... "They were different. Perhaps, in the far future, when generations of men had struggled and failed as he must now struggle and fail, woman would be, indeed, what she now made a pretence of being – the friend and companion – not the enemy and parasite of man."

'The end of it is, you see, Hugh went back to his wife, poor fellow. It was his duty, as a married man. Lord, Rachel,' he concluded, 'will it be like that when we're married?'

Instead of answering him she asked, 'Why don't people write about the things they do feel?'

'Ah, that's the difficulty!' he sighed, tossing the book away.

'Well, then, what will it be like when we're married? What are the things people do feel?' She seemed doubtful.

'Sit on the floor and let me look at you,' he commanded.

Resting her chin on his knee, she looked straight at him.

He examined her curiously.

'You're not beautiful,' he began, 'but I like your face. I like the way your hair grows down in a point, and your eyes too – they never see anything. Your mouth's too big, and your cheeks would be better if they had more colour in them. But what I like about your face is that it makes one wonder what the devil you're thinking about – it makes me want to do that – ' He clenched his fist and shook it so near her that she started back, 'because now you look as if you'd blow my brains out. There are moments,' he continued, 'when, if we stood on a rock together, you'd throw me into the sea.'

Hypnotised by the force of his eyes in hers, she repeated, 'If we stood on a rock together – '

To be flung into the sea, to be washed hither and thither, and driven about the roots of the world – the idea was incoherently delightful. She sprang up, and began moving about the room, bending and thrusting aside the chairs and tables as if she were indeed striking through the waters. He watched her with pleasure; she seemed to be cleaving a passage for herself, and dealing triumphantly with the obstacles which would hinder their passage through life.

'It does seem possible!' he exclaimed, 'though I've always thought it the most unlikely thing in the world – I shall be in love with you all my life, and our marriage will be the most exciting thing that's ever been done! We'll never have a moment's peace – ' He caught her in his arms as she passed him, and they fought for mastery, imagining a rock and the sea heaving beneath them. At last she was thrown to the floor, where she lay gasping and crying for mercy.

'I'm a mermaid! I can swim,' she cried, 'so the game's up.' Her dress was torn across, and peace being established, she fetched a needle and thread and began to mend the tear.

'And now,' she said, 'be quiet and tell me about the world; tell me about everything that's ever happened, and I'll tell you – let me see, what can I tell you? – I'll tell you about Miss Montgomerie and the river party. She was left, you see, with one foot in the boat, and the other on shore.'

They had spent much time already in thus filling out for the other the course of their past lives, and the characters of their friends and relations, so that very soon Terence knew not only what Rachel's aunts might be expected to say upon every occasion, but also how their bedrooms were furnished, and what kind of bonnets they wore. He could sustain a conversation between Mrs Hunt and Rachel, and carry on a tea-party including the Revd William Johnson and Miss Macquoid, the Christian Scientists, with remarkable likeness to the truth. But he had known many more people, and was far more highly skilled in the art of narrative than Rachel was, whose experiences were, for the most part, of a curiously childlike and humorous kind, so that it generally fell to her lot to listen and ask questions.

He told her not only what had happened, but what he had thought and felt, and sketched for her portraits which fascinated her of what other men and women might be supposed to be thinking and feeling, so that she became very anxious to go back to England, which was full of people, where she could merely stand in the streets and look at them. According to him, too, there was an order, a pattern which made life reasonable, or if that word was foolish, made it of deep interest anyhow, for sometimes it seemed possible to understand why things happened as they did. Nor were people so solitary and uncommunicative as she believed. She should look for vanity – for vanity was a common quality – first in herself, and then in Helen, in Ridley, in St John, they all had their share of it – and she would find it in ten people out of every twelve she met; and once linked together by one such tie she would find them not separate and formidable, but practically indistinguishable, and she would come to love them when she found that they were like herself. If she denied this, she must defend her belief that human beings were as various as the beasts at the Zoo, which had stripes and manes, and horns and humps; and so, wrestling over the entire list of their acquaintances, and diverging into anecdote and theory and speculation, they came to know each other. The hours passed quickly, and seemed to them full to leaking-point. After a night's solitude they were always ready to begin again.

The virtues which Mrs Ambrose had once believed to exist in free talk between men and women did in truth exist for both of them, although not quite in the measure she prescribed. Far more than upon the nature of sex they dwelt upon the nature of poetry, but it was true that talk which had no boundaries deepened and enlarged the strangely small bright view of the girl. In return for what he could tell her, she brought him such curiosity and sensitiveness of perception that he was led to doubt whether any gift bestowed by much reading and living was quite the equal of that for pleasure and pain. What would experience give her after all, except a kind of ridiculous formal balance, like that of a drilled dog in the street? He looked at her face and wondered how it would look in twenty years' time, when the eyes had dulled, and the forehead wore those little persistent wrinkles which seem to show that the middle-aged are facing something hard which the young do not see? What would the hard thing be for them, he wondered? Then his thoughts turned to their life in England.

The thought of England was delightful, for together they would see the old things freshly; it would be England in June, and there would be June nights in the country; and the nightingales singing in the lanes, into which they could steal when the room grew hot; and there would be English meadows gleaming with water and set with stolid cows, and clouds dipping low and trailing across the green hills. As he sat in the room with her, he wished very often to be back again in the thick of life, doing things with Rachel.

He crossed to the window and exclaimed, 'Lord, how good it is to think of lanes, muddy lanes, with brambles and nettles, you know, and real grass fields, and farmyards with pigs and cows, and men walking beside carts with pitchforks – there's nothing to compare with that here – look at the stony red earth, and the bright blue sea, and the glaring white houses – how tired one gets of it! And the air, without a stain or a wrinkle. I'd give anything for a sea mist.'

Rachel, too, had been thinking of the English country: the flat land rolling away to the sea, and the woods and the long straight roads, where one can walk for miles without seeing anyone, and the great church towers and the curious houses clustered in the valleys, and the birds, and the dusk, and the rain falling against the windows.

'But London, London's the place,' Terence continued. They looked together at the carpet, as though London itself were to be seen there lying on the floor, with all its spires and pinnacles pricking through the smoke.

'On the whole, what I should like best at this moment,' Terence pondered, 'would be to find myself walking down Kingsway, by those big placards, you know, and turning into the Strand. Perhaps I might go and look over Waterloo Bridge for a moment. Then I'd go along the Strand, past the shops with all the new books in them, and through the little archway into the Temple. I always like the quiet after the uproar. You hear your own footsteps suddenly quite loud. The Temple's very pleasant. I think I should go and see if I could find dear old Hodgkin – the man who writes books about Van Eyck, you know. When I left England he was very sad about his tame magpie. He suspected that a man had poisoned it. And then Russell lives on the next staircase. I think you'd like him. He's a passion for Handel. Well, Rachel,' he concluded, dismissing the vision of London, 'we shall be doing that together in six weeks' time, and it'll be the middle of June then – and June in London – my God! how pleasant it all is!'

'And we're certain to have it too,' she said. 'It isn't as if we were expecting a great deal – only to walk about and look at things.'

'Only a thousand a year and perfect freedom,' he replied. 'How many people in London d'you think have that?'

'And now you've spoilt it,' she complained. 'Now we've got to think of the horrors.' She looked grudgingly at the novel which had once caused her perhaps an hour's discomfort, so that she had never opened it again, but kept it on her table, and looked at it occasionally, as some medieval monk kept a skull, or a crucifix to remind him of the frailty of the body.

'Is it true, Terence,' she demanded, 'that women die with bugs crawling across their faces?'

'I think it's very probable,' he said. 'But you must admit, Rachel, that we so seldom think of anything but ourselves that an occasional twinge is really rather pleasant.'

Accusing him of an affectation of cynicism which was just as bad as sentimentality itself, she left her position by his side and knelt upon the window sill, twisting the curtain tassels between her fingers. A vague sense of dissatisfaction filled her.

'What's so detestable in this country,' she exclaimed, 'is the blue – always blue sky and blue sea. It's like a curtain – all the things one wants are on the other side of that. I want to know what's going on behind it. I hate these divisions, don't you, Terence? One person all in the dark about another person. Now I liked the Dalloways,' she continued, 'and they're gone. I shall never see them again. Just by going on a ship we cut ourselves off entirely from the rest of the world. I want to see England there – London there – all sorts of people – why shouldn't one? why should one be shut up all by oneself in a room?'

While she spoke thus half to herself and with increasing vagueness, because her eye was caught by a ship that had just come into the bay, she did not see that Terence had ceased to stare contentedly in front of him, and was looking at her keenly and with dissatisfaction. She seemed to be able to cut herself adrift from him, and to pass away to unknown places where she had no need of him. The thought roused his jealousy.

'I sometimes think you're not in love with me and never will be,' he said energetically. She started and turned round at his words.

'I don't satisfy you in the way you satisfy me,' he continued. 'There's something I can't get hold of in you. You don't want me as I want you – you're always wanting something else.'

He began pacing up and down the room.

'Perhaps I ask too much,' he went on. 'Perhaps it isn't really possible to have what I want. Men and women are too different. You can't understand – you don't understand – '

He came up to where she stood looking at him in silence.

It seemed to her now that what he was saying was perfectly true, and that she wanted many more things than the love of one human being – the sea, the sky. She turned again and looked at the distant blue, which was so smooth and serene where the sky met the sea; she could not possibly want only one human being.

'Or is it only this damnable engagement?' he continued. 'Let's be married here, before we go back – or is it too great a risk? Are we sure we want to marry each other?'

They began pacing up and down the room, but although they came very near each other in their pacing, they took care not to touch each other. The hopelessness of their position overcame them both. They were impotent; they could never love each other sufficiently to over-come all these barriers, and they could never be satisfied with less. Realising this with intolerable keenness she stopped in front of him and exclaimed: 'Let's break it off, then.'

The words did more to unite them than any amount of argument. As if they stood on the edge of a precipice they clung together. They knew that they could not separate; painful and terrible it might be, but they were joined for ever. They lapsed into silence, and after a time crept together in silence. Merely to be so close soothed them, and sitting side by side the divisions disappeared, and it seemed as if the world were once more solid and entire, and as if, in some strange way, they had grown larger and stronger.

It was long before they moved, and when they moved it was with great reluctance. They stood together in front of the looking-glass, and with a brush tried to make themselves look as if they had been feeling nothing all the morning, neither pain nor happiness. But it chilled them to see themselves in the glass, for instead of being vast and indivisible they were really very small and separate, the size of the glass leaving a large space for the reflection of other things.

Chapter 23

But no brush was able to efface completely the expression of happiness, so that Mrs Ambrose could not treat them when they came downstairs as if they had spent the morning in a way that could be discussed naturally. This being so, she joined in the world's conspiracy to consider them for the time incapacitated from the business of life, struck by their intensity of feeling into enmity against life, and almost succeeded in dismissing them from her thoughts.

She reflected that she had done all that it was necessary to do in practical matters. She had written a great many letters, and had obtained Willoughby's consent. She had dwelt so often upon Mr Hewet's prospects, his profession, his birth, appearance and temperament, that she had almost forgotten what he was really like. When she refreshed herself by a look at him, she used to wonder again what he was like, and then, concluding that they were happy at any rate, thought no more about it.

She might more profitably consider what would happen in three years' time, or what might have happened if Rachel had been left to explore the world under her father's guidance. The result, she was honest enough to own, might have been better – who knows? She did not disguise from herself that Terence had faults. She was inclined to think him too easy and tolerant, just as he was inclined to think her perhaps a trifle hard – no, it was rather that she was uncompromising. In some ways she found St John preferable; but then, of course, he would never have suited Rachel. Her friendship with St John was established, for although she fluctuated between irritation and interest in a way that did credit to the candour of her disposition, she liked his company on the whole. He took her outside this little world of love and emotion. He had a grasp of facts. Supposing, for instance, that England made a sudden move towards some unknown port on the coast of Morocco, St John knew what was at the back of it, and to hear him engaged with her husband in argument about finance and the balance of power, gave her an odd sense of stability. She respected their arguments without always listening to them, much as she respected a solid brick wall, or one of those immense municipal buildings which, although they compose the greater part of our cities, have been built day after day and year after year by unknown hands. She liked to sit and listen, and even felt a little elated when the engaged couple, after showing their profound lack of interest, slipped from the room, and were seen pulling flowers to pieces in the garden. It was not that she was jealous of them, but she did undoubtedly envy them their great unknown future that lay before them. Slipping from one such thought to another, she was at the present moment wandering from drawing-room to dining-room with fruit in her hands. Sometimes she stopped to straighten a candle stooping with the heat, or disturbed some too rigid arrangement of the chairs. She had reason to suspect that Chailey had been balancing herself on the top of a ladder with a wet duster during their absence, and the room had never been quite like itself since. Returning from the dining-room for the third time, she perceived that one of the armchairs was now occupied by St John. He lay back in it, with his eyes half shut, looking, as he always did, curiously buttoned up in a neat grey suit and fenced against the exuberance of a foreign climate which might at any moment proceed to take liberties with him. Her eyes rested on him gently and then passed on over his head. Finally she took the chair opposite.

'I didn't want to come here,' he said at last, 'but I was positively driven to it . . . Evelyn M.,' he groaned.

He sat up, and began to explain with mock solemnity how the detestable woman was set upon marrying him.

'She pursues me about the place. This morning she appeared in the smoking-room. All I could do was to seize my hat and fly. I didn't want to come, but I couldn't stay and face another meal with her.'

'Well, we must make the best of it,' Helen replied philosophically. It was very hot, and they were indifferent to any amount of silence, so that they lay back in their chairs waiting for something to happen. The bell rang for luncheon, but there was no sound of movement in the house. Was there any news? Helen asked; anything in the papers? St John shook his head. Oh yes, he had had a letter from home, a letter from his mother, describing the suicide of the parlour-maid. She was called Susan Jane, and she came into the kitchen one afternoon, and said that she wanted cook to keep her money for her; she had twenty pounds in gold. Then she went out to buy herself a hat. She came in at half-past five and said that she had taken poison. They had only just time to get her into bed and call a doctor before she died.

'Well?' Helen enquired.

'There'll have to be an inquest,' said St John.

Why had she done it? He shrugged his shoulders. Why do people kill themselves? Why do the lower orders do any of the things they do do? Nobody knows. They sat in silence.

'The bell's rung fifteen minutes and they're not down,' said Helen at length.

When they appeared, St John explained why it had been necessary for him to come to luncheon. He imitated Evelyn's enthusiastic tone as she confronted him in the smoking-room. 'She thinks there can be nothing *quite* so thrilling as mathematics, so I've lent her a large work in two volumes. It'll be interesting to see what she makes of it.'

Rachel could now afford to laugh at him. She reminded him of Gibbon; she had the first volume somewhere still; if he were undertaking the education of Evelyn, that surely was the test; or she had heard that Burke, upon the American Rebellion – Evelyn ought to read them both simultaneously. When St John had disposed of her argument and had satisfied his hunger, he proceeded to tell them that the hotel was seething with scandals, some of the most appalling kind, which had happened in their absence; he was indeed much given to the study of his kind.

'Evelyn M., for example – but that was told me in confidence.'

'Nonsense!' Terence interposed.

'You've heard about poor Sinclair, too?'

'Oh, yes, I've heard about Sinclair. He's retired to his mine with a revolver. He writes to Evelyn daily that he's thinking of committing suicide. I've assured her that he's never been so happy in his life and, on the whole, she's inclined to agree with me.'

'But then she's entangled herself with Perrott,' St John continued; 'and I have reason to think, from something I saw in the passage, that everything isn't as it should be between Arthur and Susan. There's a young female lately arrived from Manchester. A very good thing if it were broken off, in my opinion. Their married life is something too horrible to contemplate. Oh, and I distinctly heard old Mrs Paley rapping out the most fearful oaths as I passed her bedroom door. It's supposed that she tortures her maid in private – it's practically certain she does. One can tell it from the look in her eyes.'

'When you're eighty and the gout tweezes you, you'll be swearing like a trooper,' Terence remarked. 'You'll be very fat, very testy, very disagreeable. Can't you imagine him – bald as a coot, with a pair of sponge-bag trousers, a little spotted tie, and a corporation?'

After a pause Hirst remarked that the worst infamy had still to be told. He addressed himself to Helen.

'They've hoofed out the prostitute. One night while we were away that old numskull Thornbury was doddering about the passages very late. (Nobody seems to have asked him what *he* was up to.) He saw the

Signora Lola Mendoza, as she calls herself, cross the passage in her nightgown. He communicated his suspicions next morning to Elliot, with the result that Rodriguez went to the woman and gave her twenty-four hours in which to clear out of the place. No one seems to have enquired into the truth of the story, or to have asked Thornbury and Elliot what business it was of theirs; they had it entirely their own way. I propose that we should all sign a Round Robin, go to Rodriguez in a body, and insist upon a full enquiry. Something's got to be done, don't you agree?'

Hewet remarked that there could be no doubt as to the lady's profession. 'Still,' he added, 'it's a great shame, poor woman; only I don't see what's to be done – '

'I quite agree with you, St John,' Helen burst out. 'It's monstrous. The hypocritical smugness of the English makes my blood boil. A man who's made a fortune in trade as Mr Thornbury has is bound to be twice as bad as any prostitute.'

She respected St John's morality, which she took far more seriously than anyone else did, and now entered into a discussion with him as to the steps that were to be taken to enforce their peculiar view of what was right. The argument led to some profoundly gloomy statements of a general nature. Who were they, after all – what authority had they – what power against the mass of superstition and ignorance? It was the English, of course; there must be something wrong in the English blood. Directly you met an English person, of the middle classes, you were conscious of an indefinable sensation of loathing; directly you saw the brown crescent of houses above Dover, the same thing came over you. But unfortunately, St John added, you couldn't trust these foreigners –

They were interrupted by sounds of strife at the farther end of the table. Rachel appealed to her aunt. 'Terence says we must go to tea with Mrs Thornbury because she's been so kind, but I don't see it; in fact, I'd rather have my right hand sawn in pieces – just imagine! the eyes of all those women!'

'Fiddlesticks, Rachel,' Terence replied. 'Who wants to look at you? You're consumed with vanity! You're a monster of conceit! Surely, Helen, you ought to have taught her by this time that she's a person of no conceivable importance whatever – not beautiful, or well dressed, or conspicuous for elegance or intellect, or deportment. A more ordinary sight than you are,' he concluded, 'except for the tear across your dress, has never been seen. However, stay at home if you want to. I'm going.'

She appealed again to her aunt. It wasn't the being looked at, she explained, but the things people were sure to say. The women in particular. She liked women, but where emotion was concerned they were as flies on a lump of sugar. They would be certain to ask her questions. Evelyn M. would say: 'Are you in love? Is it nice being in love?' And Mrs Thornbury – her eyes would go up and down, up and down – she shuddered at the thought of it. Indeed, the retirement of their life since their engagement had made her so sensitive that she was not exaggerating her case.

She found an ally in Helen, who proceeded to expound her views of the human race, as she regarded with complacency the pyramid of variegated fruits in the centre of the table. It wasn't that they were cruel, or meant to hurt, or were even stupid exactly; but she had always found that the ordinary person had so little emotion in his own life that the scent of it in the lives of others was like the scent of blood in the nostrils of a bloodhound. Warming to the theme, she continued: 'Directly anything happens – it may be a marriage, or a birth, or a death – on the whole they prefer it to be a death – everyone wants to see you. They insist upon seeing you. They've got nothing to say; they don't care a rap for you; but you've got to go to lunch or to tea or to dinner, and if you don't you're damned. It's the smell of blood,' she continued; 'I don't blame 'em; only they shan't have mine if I know it!'

She looked about her as if she had called up a legion of human beings, all hostile and all disagreeable, who encircled the table, with mouths gaping for blood, and made it appear a little island of neutral country in the midst of the enemy's country.

Her words roused her husband, who had been muttering rhythmically to himself, surveying his guests and his food and his wife with eyes that were now melancholy and now fierce, according to the fortunes of the lady in his ballad. He cut Helen short with a protest. He hated even the semblance of cynicism in women. 'Nonsense, nonsense,' he remarked abruptly.

Terence and Rachel glanced at each other across the table, which meant that when they were married they would not behave like that. The entrance of Ridley into the conversation had a strange effect. It became at once more formal and more polite. It would have been impossible to talk quite easily of anything that came into their heads and to say the word prostitute as simply as any other word. The talk now turned upon literature and politics, and Ridley told stories of the distinguished people he had known in his youth. Such talk was of the nature of an art, and the personalities and informalities of the young were silenced. As they rose to go, Helen stopped for a moment, leaning her elbows on the table.

'You've all been sitting here,' she said, 'for almost an hour, and you haven't noticed my figs, or my flowers, or the way the light comes through, or anything. I haven't been listening, because I've been looking at you. You looked very beautiful; I wish you'd go on sitting for ever.'

She led the way to the drawing-room, where she took up her embroidery, and began again to dissuade Terence from walking down to the hotel in this heat. But the more she dissuaded, the more he was determined to go. He became irritated and obstinate. There were moments when they almost disliked each other. He wanted other people; he wanted Rachel to see them with him. He suspected that Mrs Ambrose would now try to dissuade her from going. He was annoyed by all this space and shade and beauty, and Hirst, recumbent, drooping a magazine from his wrist.

'I'm going,' he repeated. 'Rachel needn't come unless she wants to.'

'If you go, Hewet, I wish you'd make enquiries about the prostitute,' said Hirst. 'Look here,' he added, 'I'll walk half the way with you.'

Greatly to their surprise he raised himself, looked at his watch, and remarked that, as it was now half an hour since luncheon, the gastric juices had had sufficient time to secrete; he was trying a system, he explained, which involved short spells of exercise interspaced by longer intervals of rest.

'I shall be back at four,' he remarked to Helen, 'when I shall lie down on the sofa and relax all my muscles completely.'

'So you're going, Rachel?' Helen asked. 'You won't stay with me?'

She smiled, but she might have been sad.

Was she sad, or was she really laughing? Rachel could not tell, and she felt for the moment very uncomfortable between Helen and Terence. Then she turned away, saying merely that she would go with Terence, on condition that he did all the talking.

A narrow border of shadow ran along the road, which was broad enough for two, but not broad enough for three. St John therefore dropped a little behind the pair, and the distance between them increased by degrees. Walking with a view to digestion, and with one eye upon his watch, he looked from time to time at the pair in front of him. They seemed to be so happy, so intimate, although they were walking side by side much as other people walk. They turned slightly towards each other now and then, and said something which he thought must be something very private. They were really disputing about Helen's character, and Terence was trying to explain why it was that she annoyed him so much sometimes. But St John thought that they were saying things which they did not want him to hear, and was led to think of his own isolation. These people were happy, and in some ways he despised them for being made happy so simply, and in other ways he envied them. He was much more remarkable than they were, but he was not happy. People never liked him; he doubted sometimes whether even Helen liked him. To be simple, to be able to say simply what one felt, without the terrific self-consciousness which possessed him, and showed him his own face and words perpetually in a mirror, that would be worth almost any other gift, for it made one happy. Happiness, happiness, what was happiness? He was never happy. He saw too clearly the little vices and deceits and flaws of life, and, seeing them, it seemed to him honest to take notice of them. That was the reason, no doubt, why people generally disliked him, and complained that he was heartless and bitter. Certainly they never told him the things he wanted to be told, that he was nice and kind, and that they liked him. But it was true that half the sharp things that he said about them were said because he was unhappy or hurt himself. But he admitted that he had very seldom told anyone that he cared for them, and when he had been demonstrative, he had generally regretted it afterwards. His feelings about Terence and Rachel were so complicated that he had never yet been able to bring himself to say that he was glad that they were going to be married. He saw their faults so clearly, and the inferior nature of a great deal of their feeling for each other, and he expected that their love would not last. He looked at them again, and, very strangely, for he was so used to thinking that he seldom saw anything, the look of them filled him with a simple emotion of affection in which there were some traces of pity also. What, after all, did people's faults matter in comparison with what was good in them? He resolved that he would now tell them what he felt. He quickened his pace and came up with them just as they reached the corner where the lane joined the main road. They stood still and began to laugh at him, and to ask him whether the gastric juices – but he stopped them and began to speak very quickly and stiffly.

'D'you remember the morning after the dance?' he demanded. 'It was here we sat, and you talked nonsense, and Rachel made little heaps of stones. I, on the other hand, had the whole meaning of life revealed to me in a flash.' He paused for a second, and drew his lips together in a tight little purse. 'Love,' he said. 'It seems to me to explain everything. So, on the whole, I'm very glad that you two are going to be married.' He then turned round abruptly, without looking at them, and walked back to the villa. He felt both exalted and ashamed of himself for having thus said what he felt. Probably they were laughing at him, probably they thought him a fool, and, after all, had he really said what he felt?

It was true that they laughed when he was gone; but the dispute about Helen which had become rather sharp, ceased, and they became peaceful and friendly.

Chapter 24

They reached the hotel rather early in the afternoon, so that most people were still lying down, or sitting speechless in their bedrooms, and Mrs Thornbury, although she had asked them to tea, was nowhere to be seen. They sat down, therefore, in the shady hall, which was almost empty, and full of the light swishing sounds of air going to and fro in a large empty space. Yes, this armchair was the same armchair in which Rachel had sat that afternoon when Evelyn came up, and this was the magazine she had been looking at, and this the very picture, a picture of New York by lamplight. How odd it seemed – nothing had changed.

By degrees a certain number of people began to come down the stairs and to pass through the hall, and in this dim light their figures possessed a sort of grace and beauty, although they were all unknown people. Sometimes they went straight through and out into the garden by the swing door, sometimes they stopped for a few minutes and bent over the tables and began turning over the newspapers. Terence and Rachel sat watching them through their half-closed eyelids – the Johnsons, the Parkers, the Baileys, the Simmonses, the Lees, the Morleys, the Campbells, the Gardiners. Some were dressed in white flannels and were carrying racquets under their arms, some were short, some tall, some were only children, and some perhaps were servants, but they all had their standing, their reason for following each other through the hall, their money, their position, whatever it might be. Terence soon gave up looking at them, for he was tired; and, closing his eyes, he fell half asleep in his chair. Rachel watched the people for some time longer; she was fascinated by the certainty and the grace of their movements, and by the inevitable way in which they seemed to follow each other, and loiter and pass on and disappear. But after a time her thoughts wandered, and she began to think of the dance, which had been held in this room, only then the room itself looked quite different. Glancing round, she could hardly believe that it was the same room. It had looked so bare and so bright and formal on that night when they came into it out of the darkness; it had been filled, too, with little red, excited faces, always moving, and people so brightly dressed and so animated that they did not seem in the least like real people, nor did you feel that you could talk to them. And now the room was dim and quiet, and beautiful silent people passed through it, to whom you could go and say anything you liked. She felt herself amazingly secure as she sat in her armchair, and able to review not only the night of the dance, but the entire past, tenderly and humorously, as if she had been turning in a fog for a long time, and could now see exactly where she had turned. For the methods by which she had reached her present position seemed to her very strange, and the strangest thing about them was that she had not known where they were leading her. That was the strange thing, that one did not know where one was going, or what one wanted, and followed blindly, suffering so much in secret, always unprepared and amazed and knowing nothing; but one thing led to another and by degrees something had formed itself out of nothing, and so one reached at last this calm, this quiet, this certainty, and it was this process that people called living. Perhaps, then, everyone really knew as she knew now where they were going; and things formed themselves into a pattern not only for her, but for them, and in that pattern lay satisfaction and meaning. When she looked back she could see that a meaning of some kind was apparent in the lives of her aunts, and in the brief visit of the Dalloways whom she would never see again, and in the life of her father.

The sound of Terence, breathing deep in his slumber, confirmed her in her calm. She was not sleepy although she did not see anything very distinctly, but although the figures passing through the hall became vaguer and vaguer, she believed that they all knew exactly where they were going, and the sense of their certainty filled her with comfort. For the moment she was as detached and disinterested as if she had no longer any lot in life, and she thought that she could now accept anything that came to her without being perplexed by the form in which it appeared. What was there to frighten or to perplex in the prospect of life? Why should this insight ever again desert her? The world was in truth so large, so hospitable, and after all it was so simple. 'Love,' St John had said, 'that seems to explain it all.' Yes, but it was not the love of man for woman, of Terence for Rachel. Although they sat so close together, they had ceased to be little separate bodies; they had ceased to struggle and desire one another. There seemed to be peace between them. It might be love, but it was not the love of man for woman.

Through her half-closed eyelids she watched Terence lying back in his chair, and she smiled as she saw how big his mouth was, and his chin so small, and his nose curved like a switchback with a knob at the end. Naturally, looking like that he was lazy, and ambitious, and full of moods and faults. She remembered their quarrels, and in particular how they had been quarrelling about Helen that very afternoon, and she thought how often they would quarrel in the thirty, or forty, or fifty years in which they would be living in the same house together, catching trains together, and getting annoyed because they were so different. But all this was superficial, and had nothing to do with the life that went on beneath the eyes and the mouth and the chin, for that life was independent of her, and independent of everything else. So too, although she was going to marry him and to live with him for thirty, or forty, or fifty years, and to quarrel, and to be so close to him, she was independent of him; she was independent of everything else. Nevertheless, as St John said, it was love that made her understand this, for she had never felt this independence, this calm, and this certainty until she fell in love with him, and perhaps this too was love. She wanted nothing else.

For perhaps two minutes Miss Allan had been standing at a little distance looking at the couple lying back so peacefully in their arm-chairs. She could not make up her mind whether to disturb them or not, and then, seeming to recollect something, she came across the hall. The sound of her approach woke Terence, who sat up and rubbed his eyes. He heard Miss Allan talking to Rachel.

'Well,' she was saying, 'this is very nice. It is very nice indeed. Getting engaged seems to be quite the fashion. It cannot often happen that two couples who have never seen each other before meet in the same hotel and decide to get married.' Then she paused and smiled, and seemed to have nothing more to say, so that Terence rose and asked her whether it was true that she had finished her book. Someone had said that she had really finished it. Her face lit up; she turned to him with a livelier expression than usual.

'Yes, I think I can fairly say I have finished it,' she said. 'That is, omitting Swinburne – *Beowulf to Browning* [111] – I rather like the two B's myself. *Beowulf to Browning*,' she repeated, 'I think that is the kind of title which might catch one's eye on a railway bookstall.'

She was indeed very proud that she had finished her book, for no one knew what an amount of determination had gone to the making of it. Also she thought that it was a good piece of work, and, considering what anxiety she had been in about her brother while she wrote it, she could not resist telling them a little more about it.

'I must confess,' she continued, 'that if I had known how many classics there are in English literature, and how verbose the best of them contrive to be, I should never have undertaken the work. They only allow one seventy thousand words, you see.'

'Only seventy thousand words!' Terence exclaimed.

'Yes, and one has to say something about everybody,' Miss Allan added. 'That is what I find so difficult, saying something different about everybody.' Then she thought that she had said enough about herself, and she asked whether they had come down to join the tennis tournament. 'The young people are very keen about it. It begins again in half an hour.'

Her gaze rested benevolently upon them both, and, after a momentary pause, she remarked, looking at Rachel as if she had remembered something that would serve to keep her distinct from other people, 'You're the remarkable person who doesn't like ginger.' But the kindness of the smile in her rather worn and courageous face made them feel that although she would scarcely remember them as individuals, she had laid upon them the burden of the new generation.

'And in that I quite agree with her,' said a voice behind; Mrs Thornbury had overheard the last few words about not liking ginger. 'It's associated in my mind with a horrid old aunt of ours (poor thing, she suffered dreadfully, so it isn't fair to call her horrid) who used to give it to us when we were small, and we never had the courage to tell her we didn't like it. We just had to put it out in the shrubbery – she had a big house near Bath.'

They had begun moving slowly across the hall, when they were stopped by the impact of Evelyn, who dashed into them, as though in running downstairs to catch them her legs had got beyond her control.

'Well,' she exclaimed, with her usual enthusiasm, seizing Rachel by the arm, 'I call this splendid! I guessed it was going to happen from the very beginning! I saw you two were made for each other. Now you've just got to tell me all about it – when's it to be, where are you going to live – are you both tremendously happy?'

But the attention of the group was diverted to Mrs Elliot, who was passing them with her eager but uncertain movement, carrying in her hands a plate and an empty hot-water bottle. She would have passed them, but Mrs Thornbury went up and stopped her.

'Thank you, Hughling's better,' she replied, in answer to Mrs Thornbury's enquiry, 'but he's not an easy patient. He wants to know what his temperature is, and if I tell him he gets anxious, and if I don't tell him he suspects. You know what men are when they're ill! And of course there are none of the proper appliances, and, though he seems very willing and anxious to help' (here she lowered her voice mysteriously), 'one can't feel that Dr Rodriguez is the same as a proper doctor. If you would come and see him, Mr Hewet,' she added, 'I know it would cheer him up – lying there in bed all day – and the flies – But I must go and find Angelo – the food here – of course, with an invalid, one wants things particularly nice.' And she hurried past them in search of the head waiter. The worry of nursing her husband had fixed a plaintive frown upon her forehead; she was pale and looked unhappy and more than usually inefficient, and her eyes wandered more vaguely than ever from point to point.

'Poor thing!' Mrs Thornbury exclaimed. She told them that for some days Hughling Elliot had been ill, and the only doctor available was the brother of the proprietor, or so the proprietor said, whose right to the title of doctor was not above suspicion.

'I know how wretched it is to be ill in a hotel,' Mrs Thornbury remarked, once more leading the way with Rachel to the garden. 'I spent six weeks on my honeymoon in having typhoid at Venice,' she continued. 'But even so, I look back upon them as some of the happiest weeks in my life. Ah, yes,' she said, taking Rachel's arm, 'you think yourself happy now, but it's nothing to the happiness that comes afterwards. And I assure you I could find it in my heart to envy you young people! You've a much better time than we had, I may tell you. When I look back upon it, I can hardly believe how things have changed. When we were engaged I wasn't allowed to go for walks with William alone – someone had always to be in the room with us – I really believe I had to show my parents all his letters! – though they were very fond of him too. Indeed, I may say they looked upon him as their own son. It amuses me,' she continued, 'to think how strict they were with us, when I see how they spoil their grandchildren!'

The table was laid under the tree again, and taking her place before the teacups, Mrs Thornbury beckoned and nodded until she had collected quite a number of people, like Susan and Arthur and Mr Pepper, who were strolling about, waiting for the tournament to begin. A murmuring tree, a river brimming in the moonlight, Terence's words came back to Rachel as she sat drinking the tea and listening to the words which flowed on so lightly, so kindly, and with such silvery smoothness. This long life and all these children had left her very smooth; they seemed to have rubbed away the marks of individuality, and to have left only what was old and maternal.

'And the things you young people are going to see!' Mrs Thornbury continued. She included them all in her forecast, she included them all in her maternity, although the party comprised William Pepper and Miss Allan, both of whom might have been supposed to have seen a fair share of the panorama. 'When I see how the world has changed in my lifetime,' she went on, 'I can set no limit to what may happen in the next fifty years. Ah, no, Mr Pepper, I don't agree with you in the least,' she laughed, interrupting his gloomy remark about things going steadily from bad to worse. 'I know I ought to feel that, but I don't, I'm afraid. They're going to be much better people than we were. Surely everything goes to prove that. All round me I see women, young women, women with household cares of every sort, going out and doing things that we should not have thought it possible to do.'

Mr Pepper thought her sentimental and irrational like all old women, but her manner of treating him as if he were a cross old baby baffled him and charmed him, and he could only reply to her with a curious grimace which was more a smile than a frown.

'And they remain women,' Mrs Thornbury added. 'They give a great deal to their children.'

As she said this she smiled slightly in the direction of Susan and Rachel. They did not like to be included in the same lot, but they both smiled a little self-consciously, and Arthur and Terence glanced at each other too. She made them feel that they were all in the same boat together, and they looked at the women they were going to marry and compared them. It was inexplicable how anyone could wish to marry Rachel, incredible that anyone should be ready to spend his life with Susan; but singular though the other's taste must be, they bore each other no ill-will on account of it; indeed, they liked each other rather the better for the eccentricity of their choice.

'I really must congratulate you,' Susan remarked, as she leant across the table for the jam.

There seemed to be no foundation for St John's gossip about Arthur and Susan. Sunburnt and vigorous they sat side by side, with their racquets across their knees, not saying much but smiling slightly all the time. Through the thin white clothes which they wore, it was possible to see the lines of their bodies and legs, the beautiful curves of their muscles, his leanness and her flesh, and it was natural to think of the firm-fleshed sturdy children that would be theirs. Their faces had too little shape in them to be beautiful, but they had clear eyes and an appearance of great health and power of endurance, for it seemed as if the blood would never cease to run in his veins, or to lie deeply and calmly in her cheeks. Their eyes at the present moment were brighter than usual, and wore the peculiar expression of pleasure and self-confidence which is seen in the eyes of athletes, for they had been playing tennis, and they were both first-rate at the game.

Evelyn had not spoken, but she had been looking from Susan to

Rachel. Well – they had both made up their minds very easily, they had done in a very few weeks what it sometimes seemed to her that she would never be able to do. Although they were so different, she thought that she could see in each the same look of satisfaction and completion, the same calmness of manner, and the same slowness of movement. It was that slowness, that confidence, that content which she hated, she thought to herself. They moved so slowly because they were not single but double, and Susan was attached to Arthur, and Rachel to Terence, and for the sake of this one man they had renounced all other men, and movement, and the real things of life. Love was all very well, and those snug domestic houses, with the kitchen below and the nursery above, which were so secluded and self-contained, like little islands in the torrents of the world; but the real things were surely the things that happened, the causes, the wars, the ideals, which happened in the great world outside, and went on independently of these women, turning so quietly and beautifully towards the men. She looked at them sharply. Of course they were happy and content, but there must be better things than that. Surely one could get nearer to life, one could get more out of life, one could enjoy more and feel more than they would ever do. Rachel in particular looked so young – what could she know of life? She became restless, and getting up, crossed over to sit beside Rachel. She reminded her that she had promised to join her club.

'The bother is,' she went on, 'that I mayn't be able to start work seriously till October. I've just had a letter from a friend of mine whose brother is in business in Moscow. They want me to stay with them, and as they're in the thick of all the conspiracies and anarchists, I've a good mind to stop on my way home. It sounds too thrilling.' She wanted to make Rachel see how thrilling it was. 'My friend knows a girl of fifteen who's been sent to Siberia for life merely because they caught her addressing a letter to an anarchist. And the letter wasn't from her, either. I'd give all I have in the world to help in a revolution against the Russian government, and it's bound to come.'

She looked from Rachel to Terence. They were both a little touched by the sight of her, remembering how lately they had been listening to evil words about her, and Terence asked her what her scheme was, and she explained that she was going to found a club – a club for doing things, really doing them. She became very animated, as she talked on and on, for she professed herself certain that if once twenty people – no, ten would be enough if they were keen – set about doing things instead of talking about doing them, they could abolish almost every evil that exists. It was brains that were needed. If only people with brains – of course they would want a room, a nice room, in Bloomsbury preferably, where they could meet once a week . . .

As she talked Terence could see the traces of fading youth in her face, the lines that were being drawn by talk and excitement round her mouth and eyes, but he did not pity her; looking into those bright, rather hard, and very courageous eyes, he saw that she did not pity herself, or feel any desire to exchange her own life for the more refined and orderly lives of people like himself and St John, although, as the years went by, the fight would become harder and harder. Perhaps, though, she would settle down; perhaps, after all, she would marry Perrott. While his mind was half occupied with what she was saying, he thought of her probable destiny, the light clouds of tobacco smoke serving to obscure his face from her eyes.

Terence smoked and Arthur smoked and Evelyn smoked, so that the air was full of the mist and fragrance of good tobacco. In the intervals when no one spoke, they heard far off the low murmur of the sea, as the waves quietly broke and spread the beach with a film of water, and withdrew to break again. The cool green light fell through the leaves of the tree, and there were soft crescents and diamonds of sunshine upon the plates and the tablecloth. Mrs Thornbury, after watching them all for a time in silence, began to ask Rachel kindly questions – When did they all go back? Oh, they expected her father. She must want to see her father – there would be a great deal to tell him, and (she looked sympathetically at Terence) he would be so happy, she felt sure. Years ago, she continued, it might have been ten or twenty years ago, she remembered meeting Mr Vinrace at a party, and being so much struck by his face, which was so unlike the ordinary face one sees at a party, that she had asked who he was, and she was told that it was Mr Vinrace, and she had always remembered the name – an uncommon name – and he had had a lady with him, a very sweet-looking woman, but it was one of those dreadful London crushes, where you don't talk – you only look at each other – and although she had shaken hands with Mr Vinrace, she didn't think they had said anything. She sighed very slightly, remembering the past.

Then she turned to Mr Pepper, who had become very dependent on her, so that he always chose a seat near her, and attended to what she was saying, although he did not often make any remark of his own.

'You who know everything, Mr Pepper,' she said, 'tell us how did those wonderful French ladies manage their salons? Did we ever do anything of the same kind in England, or do you think that there is some reason why we cannot do it in England?'

Mr Pepper was pleased to explain very accurately why there has never been an English salon. There were three reasons, and they were very good ones, he said. As for himself, when he went to a party, as one was sometimes obliged to, from a wish not to give offence – his niece, for example, had been married the other day – he walked into the middle of the room, said 'Ha! ha!' as loud as ever he could, considered that he had done his duty, and walked away again. Mrs Thornbury protested. She was going to give a party directly she got back, and they were all to be invited, and she should set people to watch Mr Pepper, and if she heard that he had been caught saying 'Ha! ha!' she would – she would do something very dreadful indeed to him. Arthur Venning suggested that what she must do was to rig up something in the nature of a surprise – a portrait, for example, of a nice old lady in a lace cap, concealing a bath of cold water, which at a signal could be sprung on Pepper's head; or they'd have a chair which shot him twenty feet high directly he sat on it.

Susan laughed. She had done her tea; she was feeling very well contented, partly because she had been playing tennis brilliantly, and then everyone was so nice; she was beginning to find it so much easier to talk, and to hold her own even with quite clever people, for somehow clever people did not frighten her any more. Even Mr Hirst, whom she had disliked when she first met him, really wasn't disagreeable; and, poor man, he always looked so ill; perhaps he was in love; perhaps he had been in love with Rachel – she really shouldn't wonder; or perhaps it was Evelyn – she was of course very attractive to men. Leaning forward, she went on with the conversation. She said that she thought that the reason why parties were so dull was mainly because gentlemen will not dress: even in London, she stated, it struck her very much how people don't think it necessary to dress in the evening, and of course if they don't dress in London they won't dress in the country. It was really quite a treat at Christmastime when there were the hunt balls, and the gentlemen wore nice red coats; but Arthur didn't care for dancing, so she supposed that they wouldn't go even to the ball in their little country town. She didn't think that people who were fond of one sport often cared for another, although her father was an exception. But then he was an exception in every way – such a gardener, and he knew all about birds and animals, and of course he was simply adored by all the old women in the village, and at the same time what he really liked best was a book. You always knew where to find him if he were wanted; he would be in his study with a book. Very likely it would be an old, old book, some fusty old thing that no one else would dream of reading. She used to tell him that he would have made a first-rate old bookworm if only he hadn't had a family of six to support, and six children, she added, charmingly confident of universal sympathy, didn't leave one much time for being a bookworm.

Still talking about her father, of whom she was very proud, she rose, for Arthur upon looking at his watch found that it was time they went back again to the tennis court. The others did not move.

'They're very happy!' said Mrs Thornbury, looking benignantly after them. Rachel agreed; they seemed to be so certain of themselves; they seemed to know exactly what they wanted.

'D'you think they *are* happy?' Evelyn murmured to Terence in an undertone, and she hoped that he would say that he did not think them happy; but, instead, he said that they must go too – go home, for they were always being late for meals, and Mrs Ambrose, who was very stern and particular, didn't like that. Evelyn laid hold of Rachel's skirt and protested. Why should they go? It was still early, and she had so many things to say to them. 'No,' said Terence, 'we must go, because we walk so slowly. We stop and look at things, and we talk.'

'What d'you talk about?' Evelyn enquired, upon which he laughed and said that they talked about everything.

Mrs Thornbury went with them to the gate, trailing very slowly and gracefully across the grass and the gravel, and talking all the time about flowers and birds. She told them that she had taken up the study of botany since her daughter married, and it was wonderful what a number of flowers there were which she had never seen, although she had lived in the country all her life and she was now seventy-two. It was a good thing to have some occupation which was quite independent of other people, she said, when one got old. But the odd thing was that one never felt old. She always felt that she was twenty-five, not a day more or a day less, but, of course, one couldn't expect other people to agree to that.

'It must be very wonderful to be twenty-five, and not merely to imagine that you're twenty-five,' she said, looking from one to the other with her smooth, bright glance. 'It must be very wonderful, very wonderful indeed.' She stood talking to them at the gate for a long time; she seemed reluctant that they should go.

Chapter 25

The afternoon was very hot, so hot that the breaking of the waves on the shore sounded like the repeated sigh of some exhausted creature, and even on the terrace under an awning the bricks were hot, and the air danced perpetually over the short dry grass. The red flowers in the stone basins were drooping with the heat, and the white blossoms which had been so smooth and thick only a few weeks ago were now dry, and their edges were curled and yellow. Only the stiff and hostile plants of the south, whose fleshy leaves seemed to be grown upon spines, still remained standing upright and defied the sun to beat them down. It was too hot to talk, and it was not easy to find any book that would withstand the power of the sun. Many books had been tried and then let fall, and now Terence was reading Milton aloud, because he said the words of Milton had substance and shape, so that it was not necessary to understand what he was saying; one could merely listen to his words; one could almost handle them.

> 'There is a gentle nymph not far from hence,'

he read,

> 'That with moist curb sways the smooth Severn stream.
> Sabrina is her name, a virgin pure;
> Whilom she was the daughter of Locrine,
> That had the sceptre from his father Brute.'

The words, in spite of what Terence had said, seemed to be laden with meaning, and perhaps it was for this reason that it was painful to listen to them; they sounded strange; they meant different things from what they usually meant. Rachel at any rate could not keep her attention fixed upon them, but went off upon curious trains of thought suggested by words such as 'curb' and 'Locrine' and 'Brute', which brought unpleasant sights before her eyes, independently of their meaning. Owing to the heat and the dancing air the garden too looked strange – the trees were either too near or too far, and her head almost certainly ached. She was not quite certain, and therefore she did not know whether to tell Terence now, or to let him go on reading. She decided that she would wait until he came to the end of a stanza, and if by that time she had turned her head this way and that, and it ached in every position undoubtedly, she would say very calmly that her head ached.

> 'Sabrina fair,
>   Listen where thou art sitting
> Under the glassy, cool, translucent wave,
>   In twisted braids of lilies knitting
> The loose train of thy amber dropping hair,
> Listen for dear honour's sake,
>   Goddess of the silver lake,
>   Listen and save! '[112]

But her head ached; it ached whichever way she turned it.

She sat up and said as she had determined, 'My head aches so that I shall go indoors.'

He was halfway through the next verse, but he dropped the book instantly.

'Your head aches?' he repeated.

For a few moments they sat looking at one another in silence, holding each other's hands. During this time his sense of dismay and catastrophe were almost physically painful; all round him he seemed to hear the shiver of broken glass which, as it fell to earth, left him sitting in the open air. But at the end of two minutes, noticing that she was not sharing his dismay, but was only rather more languid and heavy-eyed than usual, he recovered, fetched Helen, and asked her to tell him what they had better do, for Rachel had a headache.

Mrs Ambrose was not discomposed, but advised that she should go to bed, and added that she must expect her head to ache if she sat up to all hours and went out in the heat, but a few hours in bed would cure it completely. Terence was unreasonably reassured by her words, as he had been unreasonably depressed the moment before. Helen's sense seemed to have much in common with the ruthless good sense of nature, which avenged rashness by a headache, and, like nature's good sense, might be depended upon.

Rachel went to bed; she lay in the dark, it seemed to her, for a very long time, but at length, waking from a transparent kind of sleep, she saw the windows white in front of her, and recollected that some time before she had gone to bed with a headache, and that Helen had said it would be gone when she woke. She supposed, therefore, that she was now quite well again. At the same time the wall of her room was painfully white, and curved slightly, instead of being straight and flat. Turning her eyes to the window, she was not reassured by what she saw there. The movement of the blind as it filled with air and blew slowly out, drawing the cord with a little trailing sound along the floor, seemed to her terrifying, as if it were the movement of an animal in the room. She shut her eyes, and the pulse in her head beat so strongly that each thump seemed to tread upon a nerve, piercing her forehead with a little stab of pain. It might not be the same headache, but she certainly had a headache. She turned from side to side, in the hope that the coolness of the sheets would cure her, and that when she next opened her eyes to look the room would be as usual. After a considerable number of vain experiments, she resolved to put the matter beyond a doubt. She got out of bed and stood upright, holding on to the brass ball at the end of the bedstead. Ice-cold at first, it soon became as hot as the palm of her hand, and as the pains in her head and body and the instability of the floor proved that it would be far more intolerable to stand and walk than to lie in bed, she got into bed again; but though the change was refreshing at first, the discomfort of bed was soon as great as the discomfort of standing up. She accepted the idea that she would have to stay in bed all day long, and as she laid her head on the pillow, relinquished the happiness of the day.

When Helen came in an hour or two later, suddenly stopped her cheerful words, looked startled for a second and then unnaturally calm, the fact that she was ill was put beyond a doubt. It was confirmed that the whole household knew of it when the song that someone was singing in the garden stopped suddenly, and when Maria, as she brought water, slipped past the bed with averted eyes. There was all the morning to get through, and then all the afternoon, and at intervals she made an effort to cross over into the ordinary world, but she found that her heat and discomfort had put a gulf between her world and the ordinary world which she could not bridge. At one point the door opened, and Helen came in with a little dark man who had – it was the chief thing she noticed about him – very hairy hands. She was drowsy and intolerably hot, and as he seemed shy and obsequious she scarcely troubled to answer him, although she understood that he was a doctor. At another point the door opened and Terence came in very gently, smiling too steadily, as she realised, for it to be natural. He sat down and talked to her, stroking her hands until it became irksome to her to lie any more in the same position and she turned round, and when she looked up again Helen was beside her and Terence had gone. It did not matter; she would see him tomorrow when things would be ordinary again. Her chief occupation during the day was to try to remember how the lines went:

> Under the glassy, cool, translucent wave,
>   In twisted braids of lilies knitting
> The loose train of thy amber dropping hair;

and the effort worried her because the adjectives persisted in getting into the wrong places.

The second day did not differ very much from the first day, except that her bed had become very important, and the world outside, when she tried to think of it, appeared distinctly further off. The glassy, cool, translucent wave was almost visible before her, curling up at the end of the bed, and as it was refreshingly cool she tried to keep her mind fixed upon it. Helen was here, and Helen was there all day long; sometimes she said that it was lunchtime, and sometimes that it was teatime; but by the next day all landmarks were obliterated, and the outer world was so far away that the different sounds, such as the sounds of people moving overhead, could only be ascribed to their cause by a great effort of memory. The recollection of what she had felt, or of what she had been doing and thinking three days before, had faded entirely. On the other hand, every object in the room, and the bed itself, and her own body with its various limbs and their different sensations were more and more important each day. She was completely cut off, and unable to communicate with the rest of the world, isolated alone with her body.

Hours and hours would pass thus, without getting any further through the morning, or again a few minutes would lead from broad daylight to the depths of the night. One evening when the room appeared very dim, either because it was evening or because the blinds were drawn, Helen said to her, 'Someone is going to sit here tonight. You won't mind?'

Opening her eyes, Rachel saw not only Helen but a nurse in spectacles, whose face vaguely recalled something that she had once seen. She had seen her in the chapel. 'Nurse McInnis,' said Helen, and the nurse smiled steadily as they all did, and said that she did not find many people who were frightened of her. After waiting for a moment they both disappeared, and having turned on her pillow Rachel woke to find herself in the midst of one of those interminable nights which do not end at twelve, but go on into the double figures – thirteen, fourteen, and so on, until they reach the twenties, and then the thirties, and then the forties. She realised that there is nothing to prevent nights from doing this if they choose. At a great distance an elderly woman sat with her head bent down; Rachel raised herself slightly and saw with dismay that she was playing cards by the light of a candle which stood in the hollow of a newspaper. The sight had something inexplicably sinister about it, and she was terrified and cried out, upon which the woman laid down her cards and came across the room, shading the candle with her hands. Coming nearer and nearer across the great space of the room, she stood at last above Rachel's head and said, 'Not asleep? Let me make you comfortable.'

She put down the candle and began to arrange the bedclothes. It struck Rachel that a woman who sat playing cards in a cavern all night long would have very cold hands, and she shrank from the touch of them.

'Why, there's a toe all the way down there!' the woman said, proceeding to tuck in the bedclothes. Rachel did not realise that the toe was hers.

'You must try and lie still,' she proceeded, 'because if you lie still you will be less hot, and if you toss about you will make yourself more hot, and we don't want you to be any hotter than you are.' She stood looking down upon Rachel for an enormous length of time.

'And the quieter you lie the sooner you will be well,' she repeated.

Rachel kept her eyes fixed upon the peaked shadow on the ceiling, and all her energy was concentrated upon the desire that this shadow should move. But the shadow and the woman seemed to be eternally fixed above her. She shut her eyes. When she opened them again several more hours had passed, but the night still lasted interminably. The woman was still playing cards, only she sat now in a tunnel under a river, and the light stood in a little archway in the wall above her. She cried, 'Terence!' and the peaked shadow again moved across the ceiling, as the woman with an enormous slow movement rose, and they both stood still above her.

'It's just as difficult to keep you in bed as it was to keep Mr Forrest in bed,' the woman said, 'and he was such a tall gentleman.'

In order to get rid of this terrible stationary sight Rachel again shut her eyes, and found herself walking through a tunnel under the Thames, where there were little deformed women sitting in archways playing cards, while the bricks of which the wall was made oozed with damp, which collected into drops and slid down the wall. But the little old women became Helen and Nurse McInnis after a time, standing in the window together whispering, whispering incessantly.

Meanwhile outside her room the sounds, the movements and the lives of the other people in the house went on in the ordinary light of the sun, throughout the usual succession of hours. When, on the first day of her illness, it became clear that she would not be absolutely well, for her temperature was very high, until Friday, that day being Tuesday, Terence was filled with resentment, not against her, but against the force outside them which was separating them. He counted up the number of days that would almost certainly be spoilt for them. He realised, with an odd mixture of pleasure and annoyance, that, for the first time in his life, he was so dependent upon another person that his happiness was in her keeping. The days were completely wasted upon trifling, immaterial things, for after three weeks of such intimacy and intensity all the usual occupations were unbearably flat and beside the point. The least intolerable occupation was to talk to St John about Rachel's illness, and to discuss every symptom and its meaning, and, when this subject was exhausted, to discuss illness of all kinds, and what caused them, and what cured them.

Twice every day he went in to sit with Rachel, and twice every day the same thing happened. On going into her room, which was not very dark, where the music was lying about as usual, and her books and letters, his spirits rose instantly. When he saw her he felt completely reassured. She did not look very ill. Sitting by her side he would tell her what he had been doing, using his natural voice to speak to her, only a few tones lower down than usual; but by the time he had sat there for five minutes he was plunged into the deepest gloom. She was not the same; he could not bring them back to their old relationship; but although he knew that it was foolish he could not prevent himself from endeavouring to bring her back, to make her remember, and when this failed he was in despair. He always concluded as he left her room that it was worse to see her than not to see her, but by degrees, as the day wore on, the desire to see her returned and became almost too great to be borne.

On Thursday morning when Terence went into her room he felt the usual increase of confidence. She turned round and made an effort to remember certain facts from the world that was so many millions of miles away.

'You have come up from the hotel?' she asked.

'No; I'm staying here for the present,' he said. 'We've just had luncheon,' he continued, 'and the mail has come in. There's a bundle of letters for you – letters from England.'

Instead of saying, as he meant her to say, that she wished to see them, she said nothing for some time.

'You see, there they go, rolling off the edge of the hill,' she said suddenly.

'Rolling, Rachel? What do you see rolling? There's nothing rolling.'

'The old woman with the knife,' she replied, not speaking to Terence in particular and looking past him. As she appeared to be looking at a vase on the shelf opposite, he rose and took it down.

'Now they can't roll any more,' he said cheerfully. Nevertheless she lay gazing at the same spot, and paid him no further attention although he spoke to her. He became so profoundly wretched that he could not endure to sit with her but wandered about until he found St John, who was reading *The Times* in the verandah. He laid it aside patiently, and heard all that Terence had to say about delirium. He was very patient with Terence. He treated him like a child.

By Friday it could not be denied that the illness was no longer an attack that would pass off in a day or two; it was a real illness that required a good deal of organisation, and engrossed the attention of at least five people, but there was no reason to be anxious. Instead of lasting five days it was going to last ten days. Rodriguez was understood to say that there were well-known varieties of this illness. Rodriguez appeared to think that they were treating the illness with undue anxiety. His visits were always marked by the same show of confidence, and in his interviews with Terence he always waved aside his anxious and minute questions with a kind of flourish which seemed to indicate that they were all taking it much too seriously. He seemed curiously unwilling to sit down.

'A high temperature,' he said, looking furtively about the room, and appearing to be more interested in the furniture and in Helen's embroidery than in anything else; 'in this climate you must expect a high temperature. You need not be alarmed by that. It is the pulse we go by' (he tapped his own hairy wrist), 'and the pulse continues excellent.'

Thereupon he bowed and slipped out. The interview was conducted laboriously upon both sides in French, and this, together with the fact that he was optimistic, and that Terence respected the medical profession from hearsay, made him less critical than he would have been had he encountered the doctor in any other capacity. Unconsciously he took Rodriguez' side against Helen, who seemed to have taken an unreasonable prejudice against him.

When Saturday came it was evident that the hours of the day must be more strictly organised than they had been. St John offered his services; he said that he had nothing to do, and that he might as well spend the day at the villa if he could be of use. As if they were starting on a difficult expedition together, they parcelled out their duties between them, writing out an elaborate scheme of hours upon a large sheet of paper which was pinned to the drawing-room door. Their distance from the town, and the difficulty of procuring rare things with unknown names from the most unexpected places, made it necessary to think very carefully, and they found it unexpectedly difficult to do the simple but practical things that were required of them, as if they, being very tall, were asked to stoop down and arrange minute grains of sand in a pattern on the ground.

It was St John's duty to fetch what was needed from the town, so that Terence would sit all through the long hot hours alone in the drawing-room, near the open door, listening for any movement upstairs, or call from Helen. He always forgot to pull down the blinds, so that he sat in bright sunshine, which worried him without his knowing what was the cause of the worry. The room was terribly stiff and uncomfortable. There were hats in the chairs, and medicine bottles among the books. He tried to read, but good books were too good, and bad books were too bad, and the only thing he could tolerate was the newspaper, which with its news of London, and the movements of real people who were giving dinner-parties and making speeches, seemed to give a little background of reality to what was otherwise mere nightmare. Then, just as his attention was fixed on the print, a soft call would come from Helen, or Mrs Chailey would bring in something which was wanted upstairs, and he would run up very quietly in his socks, and put the jug on the little table which stood crowded with jugs and cups outside the bedroom door; or if he could catch Helen for a moment he would ask, 'How is she?'

'Rather restless . . . On the whole, quieter, I think.'

The answer would be one or the other.

As usual she seemed to reserve something which she did not say, and Terence was conscious that they disagreed, and, without saying it aloud, were arguing against each other. But she was too hurried and preoccupied to talk.

The strain of listening and the effort of making practical arrangements and seeing that things worked smoothly, absorbed all Terence's power. Involved in this long dreary nightmare, he did not attempt to think what it amounted to. Rachel was ill; that was all; he must see that there was medicine and milk, and that things were ready when they were wanted. Thought had ceased; life itself had come to a standstill. Sunday was rather worse than Saturday had been, simply because the strain was a little greater every day, although nothing else had changed. The separate feelings of pleasure, interest and pain, which combine to make up the ordinary day, were merged in one long-drawn sensation of sordid misery and profound boredom. He had never been so bored since he was shut up in the nursery alone as a child. The vision of Rachel as she was now, confused and heedless, had almost obliterated the vision of her as she had been once long ago; he could hardly believe that they had ever been happy, or engaged to be married, for what were feelings, what was there to be felt? Confusion covered every sight and person, and he seemed to see St John, Ridley and the stray people who came up now and then from the hotel to enquire, through a mist; the only people who were not hidden in this mist were Helen and Rodriguez, because they could tell him something definite about Rachel.

Nevertheless the day followed the usual forms. At certain hours they went into the dining-room, and when they sat round the table they talked about indifferent things. St John usually made it his business to start the talk and to keep it from dying out.

'I've discovered the way to get Sancho past the white house,' said St John on Sunday at luncheon. 'You crackle a piece of paper in his ear, then he bolts for about a hundred yards, but he goes on quite well after that.'

'Yes, but he wants corn. You should see that he has corn.'

'I don't think much of the stuff they give him; and Angelo seems a dirty little rascal.'

There was then a long silence. Ridley murmured a few lines of poetry under his breath, and remarked, as if to conceal the fact that he had done so, 'Very hot today.'

'Two degrees higher than it was yesterday,' said St John. 'I wonder where these nuts come from,' he observed, taking a nut out of the plate, turning it over in his fingers, and looking at it curiously.

'London, I should think,' said Terence, looking at the nut too.

'A competent man of business could make a fortune here in no time,' St John continued. 'I suppose the heat does something funny to people's brains. Even the English go a little queer. Anyhow they're hopeless people to deal with. They kept me three-quarters of an hour waiting at the chemist's this morning, for no reason whatever.'

There was another long pause. Then Ridley enquired, 'Rodriguez seems satisfied?'

'Quite,' said Terence with decision. 'It's just got to run its course.' Whereupon Ridley heaved a deep sigh. He was genuinely sorry for everyone, but at the same time he missed Helen considerably, and was a little aggrieved by the constant presence of the two young men.

They moved back into the drawing-room.

'Look here, Hirst,' said Terence, 'there's nothing to be done for two hours.' He consulted the sheet pinned to the door. 'You go and lie down. I'll wait here. Chailey sits with Rachel while Helen has her luncheon.'

It was asking a good deal of Hirst to tell him to go without waiting for a sight of Helen. These little glimpses of Helen were the only respites from strain and boredom, and very often they seemed to make up for the discomfort of the day, although she might not have anything to tell them. However, as they were on an expedition together, he had made up his mind to obey.

Helen was very late in coming down. She looked like a person who has been sitting for a long time in the dark. She was pale and thinner, and the expression of her eyes was harassed but determined. She ate her luncheon quickly, and seemed indifferent to what she was doing. She brushed aside Terence's enquiries, and at last, as if he had not spoken, she looked at him with a slight frown and said: 'We can't go on like this, Terence. Either you've got to find another doctor, or you must tell Rodriguez to stop coming, and I'll manage for myself. It's no use for him to say that Rachel's better; she's not better; she's worse.'

Terence suffered a terrific shock, like that which he had suffered when Rachel said, 'My head aches.' He stilled it by reflecting that Helen was overwrought, and he was upheld in this opinion by his obstinate sense that she was opposed to him in the argument.

'Do you think she's in danger?' he asked.

'No one can go on being as ill as that day after day – ' Helen replied. She looked at him, and spoke as if she felt some indignation with somebody.

'Very well, I'll talk to Rodriguez this afternoon,' he replied.

Helen went upstairs at once.

Nothing now could assuage Terence's anxiety. He could not read, nor could he sit still, and his sense of security was shaken, in spite of the fact that he was determined that Helen was exaggerating, and that Rachel was not very ill. But he wanted a third person to confirm him in his belief.

Directly Rodriguez came down he demanded, 'Well, how is she? Do you think her worse?'

'There is no reason for anxiety, I tell you – none,' Rodriguez replied in his execrable French, smiling uneasily, and making little movements all the time as if to get away.

Hewet stood firmly between him and the door. He was determined to see for himself what kind of man he was. His confidence in the man vanished as he looked at him and saw his insignificance, his dirty appearance, his shiftiness, and his unintelligent, hairy face. It was strange that he had never seen this before.

'You won't object, of course, if we ask you to consult another doctor?' he continued.

At this the little man became openly incensed.

'Ah!' he cried. 'You have not confidence in me? You object to my treatment? You wish me to give up the case?'

'Not at all,' Terence replied, 'but in serious illness of this kind – '

Rodriguez shrugged his shoulders.

'It is not serious, I assure you. You are over-anxious. The young lady is not seriously ill, and I am a doctor. The lady of course is frightened,' he sneered. 'I understand that perfectly.'

'The name and address of the doctor is – ?' Terence continued.

'There is no other doctor,' Rodriguez replied sullenly. 'Everyone has confidence in me. Look! I will show you.'

He took out a packet of old letters and began turning them over as if in search of one that would confute Terence's suspicions. As he searched, he began to tell a story about an English lord who had trusted him – a great English lord, whose name he had, unfortunately, forgotten.

'There is no other doctor in the place,' he concluded, still turning over the letters.

'Never mind,' said Terence shortly. 'I will make enquiries for myself.'

Rodriguez put the letters back in his pocket. 'Very well,' he remarked. 'I have no objection.'

He lifted his eyebrows, shrugged his shoulders, as if to repeat that they took the illness much too seriously and that there was no other doctor, and slipped out, leaving behind him an impression that he was conscious that he was distrusted, and that his malice was aroused.

After this Terence could no longer stay downstairs. He went up, knocked at Rachel's door, and asked Helen whether he might see her for a few minutes. He had not seen her yesterday. She made no objection, and went and sat at a table in the window.

Terence sat down by the bedside. Rachel's face was changed. She looked as though she were entirely concentrated upon the effort of keeping alive. Her lips were drawn, though without colour, and her cheeks were sunken and flushed. Her eyes were not entirely shut, the lower half of the white part showing, not as if she saw, but as if they remained open because she was too much exhausted to close them. She opened them completely when he kissed her. But she only saw an old woman slicing a man's head off with a knife.

'There it falls!' she murmured. She then turned to Terence and asked him anxiously some question about a man with mules, which he could not understand. 'Why doesn't he come? Why doesn't he come?' she repeated. He was appalled to think of the dirty little man downstairs in connection with illness like this, and turning instinctively to Helen, but she was doing something at a table in the window and did not seem to realise how great the shock to him must be. He rose to go, for he could not endure to listen any longer; his heart beat quickly and painfully with anger and misery. As he passed Helen she asked him in the same weary, unnatural, but determined voice to fetch her more ice, and to have the jug outside filled with fresh milk.

When he had done these errands he went to find Hirst. Exhausted and very hot, St John had fallen asleep on a bed, but Terence woke him without scruple.

'Helen thinks she's worse,' he said. 'There's no doubt she's frightfully ill. Rodriguez is useless. We must get another doctor.'

'But there is no other doctor,' said Hirst drowsily, sitting up and rubbing his eyes.

'Don't be a damned fool!' Terence exclaimed. 'Of course there's another doctor, and, if there isn't, you've got to find one. It ought to have been done days ago. I'm going down to saddle the horse.' He could not stay still in one place.

In less than ten minutes St John was riding to the town in the scorching heat in search of a doctor, his orders being to find one and bring him back even if he had to be fetched in a special train.

'We ought to have done it days ago,' Hewet repeated angrily.

When he went back into the drawing-room he found that Mrs Flushing was there, standing very erect in the middle of the room, having arrived, as people did in these days, by the kitchen or through the garden unannounced.

'She's better?' Mrs Flushing enquired abruptly; they did not attempt to shake hands.

'No,' said Terence. 'If anything, they think she's worse.'

Mrs Flushing seemed to consider for a moment or two, looking straight at Terence all the time.

'Let me tell you,' she said, speaking in nervous jerks, 'it's always about the seventh day one begins to get anxious. I dare say you've been sittin' here worryin' by yourself. You think she's bad, but anyone comin' with a fresh eye would see she was better. Mr Elliot's had fever; he's all right now,' she threw out. 'It wasn't anythin' she caught on the expedition. What's it matter – a few days' fever? My brother had fever for twenty-six days once. And in a week or two he was up and about. We gave him nothin' but milk and arrowroot – '

Here Mrs Chailey came in with a message.

'I'm wanted upstairs,' said Terence.

'You see – she'll be better,' Mrs Flushing jerked out as he left the room. Her anxiety to persuade Terence was very great, and when he left her without saying anything she felt dissatisfied and restless; she did not like to stay, but she could not bear to go. She wandered from room to room looking for someone to talk to, but all the rooms were empty.

Terence went upstairs, stood inside the door to take Helen's directions, looked over at Rachel, but did not attempt to speak to her. She appeared vaguely conscious of his presence, but it seemed to disturb her, and she turned, so that she lay with her back to him.

For six days indeed she had been oblivious of the world outside, because it needed all her attention to follow the hot, red, quick sights which passed incessantly before her eyes. She knew that it was of enormous importance that she should attend to these sights and grasp their meaning, but she was always being just too late to hear or see something which would explain it all. For this reason, the faces – Helen's face, the nurse's, Terence's, the doctor's – which occasionally forced themselves very close to her, were worrying because they distracted her attention and she might miss the clue. However, on the fourth afternoon she was suddenly unable to keep Helen's face distinct from the sights themselves; her lips widened as she bent down over the bed, and she began to gabble unintelligibly like the rest. The sights were all concerned in some plot, some adventure, some escape. The nature of what they were doing changed incessantly, although there was always a reason behind it, which she must endeavour to grasp. Now they were among trees and savages, now they were on the sea, now they were on the tops of high towers; now they jumped; now they flew. But just as the crisis was about to happen, something invariably slipped in her brain, so that the whole effort had to begin over again. The heat was suffocating. At last the faces went further away; she fell into a deep pool of sticky water, which eventually closed over her head. She saw nothing and heard nothing but a faint booming sound, which was the sound of the sea rolling over her head. While all her tormentors thought that she was dead, she was not dead, but curled up at the bottom of the sea. There she lay, sometimes seeing darkness, sometimes light, while every now and then someone turned her over at the bottom of the sea.

After St John had spent some hours in the heat of the sun wrangling with evasive and very garrulous natives, he extracted the information that there was a doctor, a French doctor, who was at present away on a holiday in the hills. It was quite impossible, so they said, to find him. With his experience of the country, St John thought it unlikely that a telegram would either be sent or received; but having reduced the distance of the hill town, in which he was staying, from a hundred miles to thirty miles, and having hired a carriage and horses, he started at once to fetch the doctor himself. He succeeded in finding him, and eventually forced the unwilling man to leave his young wife and return forthwith. They reached the villa at midday on Tuesday.

Terence came out to receive them, and St John was struck by the fact that he had grown perceptibly thinner in the interval; he was white too; his eyes looked strange. But the curt speech and the sulky masterful manner of Dr Lesage impressed them both favourably, although at the same time it was obvious that he was very much annoyed at the whole affair. Coming downstairs he gave his directions emphatically, but it never occurred to him to give an opinion either because of the presence of Rodriguez, who was now obsequious as well as malicious, or because he took it for granted that they knew already what was to be known.

'Of course,' he said with a shrug of his shoulders, when Terence asked him, 'Is she very ill?'

They were both conscious of a certain sense of relief when Dr Lesage was gone, leaving explicit directions, and promising another visit in a few hours' time; but, unfortunately, the rise of their spirits led them to talk more than usual, and in talking they quarrelled. They quarrelled about a road, the Portsmouth Road. St John said that it is macadamised where it passes Hindhead, and Terence knew as well as he knew his own name that it is not macadamised at that point. In the course of the argument they said some very sharp things to each other, and the rest of the dinner was eaten in silence, save for an occasional half-stifled reflection from Ridley.

When it grew dark and the lamps were brought in, Terence felt unable to control his irritation any longer. St John went to bed in a state of complete exhaustion, bidding Terence good-night with rather more affection than usual because of their quarrel, and Ridley retired to his books. Left alone, Terence walked up and down the room; he stood at the open window.

The lights were coming out one after another in the town beneath, and it was very peaceful and cool in the garden, so that he stepped out on to the terrace. As he stood there in the darkness, able only to see the shapes of trees through the fine grey light, he was overcome by a desire to escape, to have done with this suffering, to forget that Rachel was ill. He allowed himself to lapse into forgetfulness of everything. As if a wind that had been raging incessantly suddenly fell asleep, the fret and strain and anxiety which had been pressing on him passed away. He seemed to stand in an unvexed space of air, on a little island by himself; he was free and immune from pain. It did not matter whether Rachel was well or ill; it did not matter whether they were apart or together; nothing mattered – nothing mattered. The waves beat on the shore far away, and the soft wind passed through the branches of the trees, seeming to encircle him with peace and security, with dark and nothingness. Surely the world of strife and fret and anxiety was not the real world, but this was the real world, the world that lay beneath the superficial world, so that, whatever happened, one was secure. The quiet and peace seemed to lap his body in a fine cool sheet, soothing every nerve; his mind seemed once more to expand, and become natural.

But when he had stood thus for a time a noise in the house roused him; he turned instinctively and went into the drawing-room. The sight of the lamp-lit room brought back so abruptly all that he had forgotten that he stood for a moment unable to move. He remembered everything, the hour, the minute even, what point they had reached and what was to come. He cursed himself for making believe for a minute that things were different from what they were. The night was now harder to face than ever.

Unable to stay in the empty drawing-room, he wandered out and sat on the stairs halfway up to Rachel's room. He longed for someone to talk to, but Hirst was asleep, and Ridley was asleep; there was no sound in Rachel's room. The only sound in the house was the sound of Chailey moving in the kitchen. At last there was a rustling on the stairs overhead, and Nurse McInnis came down fastening the links in her cuffs, in preparation for the night's watch. Terence rose and stopped her. He had scarcely spoken to her, but it was possible that she might confirm him in the belief which still persisted in his own mind that Rachel was not seriously ill. He told her in a whisper that Dr Lesage had been and what he had said.

'Now, nurse,' he whispered, 'please tell me your opinion. Do you consider that she is very seriously ill? Is she in any danger?'

'The doctor has said – ' she began.

'Yes, but I want your opinion. You have had experience of many cases like this?'

'I could not tell you more than Dr Lesage, Mr Hewet,' she replied cautiously, as though her words might be used against her. 'The case is serious, but you may feel quite certain that we are doing all we can for Miss Vinrace.' She spoke with some professional self-approbation. But she realised perhaps that she did not satisfy the young man, who still blocked her way, for she shifted her feet slightly upon the stair and looked out of the window where they could see the moon over the sea.

'If you ask me,' she began in a curiously stealthy tone, 'I never like May for my patients.'

'May?' Terence repeated.

'It may be a fancy, but I don't like to see anybody fall ill in May,' she continued. 'Things seem to go wrong in May. Perhaps it's the moon. They say the moon affects the brain, don't they, sir?'

He looked at her but he could not answer her; like all the others, when one looked at her she seemed to shrivel beneath one's eyes and become worthless, malicious and untrustworthy.

She slipped past him and disappeared.

Though he went to his room he was unable even to take his clothes off. For a long time he paced up and down, and then leaning out of the window gazed at the earth which lay so dark against the paler blue of the sky. With a mixture of fear and loathing he looked at the slim black cypress trees which were still visible in the garden, and heard the unfamiliar creaking and grating sounds which show that the earth is still hot. All these sights and sounds appeared sinister and full of hostility and foreboding; together with the natives and the nurse and the doctor and the terrible force of the illness itself they seemed to be in conspiracy against him. They seemed to join together in their effort to extract the greatest possible amount of suffering from him. He could not get used to his pain, it was a revelation to him. He had never realised before that underneath every action, underneath the life of every day, pain lies, quiescent, but ready to devour; he seemed to be able to see suffering, as if it were a fire, curling up over the edges of all action, eating away the lives of men and women. He thought for the first time with understanding of words which had before seemed to him empty: the struggle of life; the hardness of life. Now he knew for himself that life is hard and full of suffering. He looked at the scattered lights in the town beneath, and thought of Arthur and Susan or Evelyn and Perrott, venturing out unwittingly and by their happiness laying themselves open to suffering such as this. How did they dare to love each other, he wondered; how had he himself dared to live as he had lived, rapidly and carelessly, passing from one thing to another, loving Rachel as he had loved her? Never again would he feel secure; he would never believe in the stability of life, or forget what depths of pain lie beneath small happiness and feelings of content and safety. It seemed to him as he looked back that their happiness had never been so great as his pain was now. There had always been something imperfect in their happiness, something they had wanted and had not been able to get. It had been fragmentary and incomplete, because they were so young and had not known what they were doing.

The light of his candle flickered over the boughs of a tree outside the window, and as a branch swayed in the darkness there came before his mind a picture of all the world that lay outside his window; he thought of the immense river and the immense forest, the vast stretches of dry earth and the plains of the sea that encircled the earth; from the sea the sky rose steep and enormous, and the air washed profoundly between the sky and the sea. How vast and dark it must be tonight, lying exposed to the wind; and in all this great space it was curious to think how few the towns were, and how small little rings of light, or single glowworms he figured them, scattered here and there, among the swelling uncultivated folds of the world. And in those towns were little men and women, tiny men and women. Oh, it was absurd, when one thought of it, to sit here in a little room suffering and caring. What did anything matter? Rachel, a tiny creature, lay ill beneath him, and here in his little room he suffered on her account. The nearness of their bodies in this vast universe, and the minuteness of their bodies, seemed to him absurd and laughable. Nothing mattered, he repeated; they had no power, no hope. He leant on the window-sill, thinking, until he almost forgot the time and the place. Nevertheless, although he was convinced that it was absurd and laughable, and that they were small and hopeless, he never lost the sense that these thoughts somehow formed part of a life which he and Rachel would live together.

Owing perhaps to the change of doctor, Rachel appeared to be rather better next day. Terribly pale and worn though Helen looked, there was a slight lifting of the cloud which had hung all these days in her eyes.

'She talked to me,' she said voluntarily. 'She asked me what day of the week it was, like herself.'

Then suddenly, without any warning or any apparent reason, the tears formed in her eyes and rolled steadily down her cheeks. She cried with scarcely any attempt at movement of her features, and without any attempt to stop herself, as if she did not know that she was crying. In spite of the relief which her words gave him, Terence was dismayed by the sight; had everything given way? Were there no limits to the power of this illness? Would everything go down before it? Helen had always seemed to him strong and determined, and now she was like a child. He took her in his arms, and she clung to him like a child, crying softly and quietly upon his shoulder. Then she roused herself and wiped her tears away; it was silly to behave like that, she said; very silly, she repeated, when there could be no doubt that Rachel was better. She asked Terence to forgive her for her folly. She stopped at the door and came back and kissed him without saying anything.

On this day indeed Rachel was conscious of what went on round her. She had come to the surface of the dark, sticky pool, and a wave seemed to bear her up and down with it; she had ceased to have any will of her own; she lay on the top of the wave conscious of some pain, but chiefly of weakness. The wave was replaced by the side of a mountain. Her body became a drift of melting snow, above which her knees rose in huge peaked mountains of bare bone. It was true that she saw Helen and saw her room, but everything had become very pale and semi-transparent. Sometimes she could see through the wall in front of her. Sometimes when Helen went away she seemed to go so far that Rachel's eyes could hardly follow her. The room also had an odd power of expanding, and though she pushed her voice out as far as possible until sometimes it became a bird and flew away, she thought it doubtful whether it ever reached the person she was talking to. There were immense intervals or chasms, for things still had the power to appear visibly before her, between one moment and the next; it sometimes took an hour for Helen to raise her arm, pausing long between each jerky movement, and pour out medicine. Helen's form stooping to raise her in bed appeared of gigantic size, and came down upon her like the ceiling falling. But for long spaces of time she would merely lie conscious of her body floating on the top of the bed and her mind driven to some remote corner of her body, or escaped and gone flitting round the room. All sights were something of an effort, but the sight of Terence was the greatest effort, because he forced her to join mind to body in the desire to remember something. She did not wish to remember; it troubled her when people tried to disturb her loneliness; she wished to be alone. She wished for nothing else in the world.

Although she had cried, Terence observed Helen's greater hopefulness with something like triumph; in the argument between them she had made the first sign of admitting herself in the wrong. He waited for Dr Lesage to come down that afternoon with considerable anxiety, but with the same certainty at the back of his mind that he would in time force them all to admit that they were in the wrong.

As usual, Dr Lesage was sulky in his manner and very short in his answers. To Terence's demand, 'She seems to be better?' he replied, looking at him in an odd way, 'She has a chance of life.'

The door shut and Terence walked across to the window. He leant his forehead against the pane.

'Rachel,' he repeated to himself. 'She has a chance of life. Rachel.'

How could they say these things of Rachel? Had anyone yesterday seriously believed that Rachel was dying? They had been engaged for four weeks. A fortnight ago she had been perfectly well. What could fourteen days have done to bring her from that state to this? To realise what they meant by saying that she had a chance of life was beyond him, knowing as he did that they were engaged. He turned, still enveloped in the same dreary mist, and walked towards the door. Suddenly he saw it all. He saw the room and the garden, and the trees moving in the air, they could go on without her; she could die. For the first time since she fell ill he remembered exactly what she looked like and the way in which they cared for each other. The immense happiness of feeling her close to him mingled with a more intense anxiety than he had felt yet. He could not let her die; he could not live without her. But after a momentary struggle, the curtain fell again, and he saw nothing and felt nothing clearly. It was all going on – going on still, in the same way as before. Save for a physical pain when his heart beat, and the fact that his fingers were icy cold, he did not realise that he was anxious about anything. Within his mind he seemed to feel nothing about Rachel or about anyone or anything in the world. He went on giving orders, arranging with Mrs Chailey, writing out lists, and every now and then he went upstairs and put something quietly on the table outside Rachel's door. That night Dr Lesage seemed to be less sulky than usual. He stayed voluntarily for a few moments, and, addressing St John and Terence equally, as if he did not remember which of them was engaged to the young lady, said, 'I consider that her condition tonight is very grave.'

Neither of them went to bed or suggested that the other should go to bed. They sat in the drawing-room playing picquet with the door open. St John made up a bed upon the sofa, and when it was ready insisted that Terence should lie upon it. They began to quarrel as to who should lie on the sofa and who should lie upon a couple of chairs covered with rugs. St John forced Terence at last to lie down upon the sofa.

'Don't be a fool, Terence,' he said. 'You'll only get ill if you don't sleep. Old fellow – ' he began, as Terence still refused, and stopped

abruptly, fearing sentimentality; he found that he was on the verge
of tears.

He had begun to say what he had long been wanting to say, that he
was sorry for Terence, that he cared for him, that he cared for Rachel.
Did she know how much he cared for her – had she said anything, asked
perhaps? He was very anxious to say this, but he refrained, thinking that
it was a selfish question after all, and what was the use of bothering
Terence to talk about such things? He was already half asleep. But St
John could not sleep at once. If only, he thought to himself, as he lay in
the darkness, something would happen – if only this strain would come
to an end. He did not mind what happened, so long as the succession of
these hard and dreary days was broken; he did not mind if she died. He
felt himself disloyal in not minding it, but it seemed to him that he had
no feelings left.

All night long there was no call or movement, except the opening and
shutting of the bedroom door once. By degrees the light returned into
the untidy room. At six the servants began to move; at seven they crept
downstairs into the kitchen; and half an hour later the day began again.

Nevertheless it was not the same as the days that had gone before,
although it would have been hard to say in what the difference consisted.
Perhaps it was that they seemed to be waiting for something. There
were certainly fewer things to be done than usual. People drifted through
the drawing-room – Mr Flushing, Mr and Mrs Thornbury. They spoke
very apologetically in low tones, refusing to sit down, but remaining for
a considerable time standing up, although the only thing they had to say
was, 'Is there anything we can do?' and there was nothing they could do.

Feeling oddly detached from it all, Terence remembered how Helen
had said that whenever anything happened to you this was how people
behaved. Was she right, or was she wrong? He was too little interested
to frame an opinion of his own. He put things away in his mind, as if
one of these days he would think about them, but not now. The mist of
unreality had deepened and deepened until it had produced a feeling of
numbness all over his body. Was it his body? Were those really his
own hands?

This morning also for the first time Ridley found it impossible to sit
alone in his room. He was very uncomfortable downstairs, and, as he
did not know what was going on, constantly in the way; but he would
not leave the drawing-room. Too restless to read, and having nothing
to do, he began to pace up and down reciting poetry in an undertone.
Occupied in various ways – now in undoing parcels, now in uncorking
bottles, now in writing directions, the sound of Ridley's song and the

beat of his pacing worked into the minds of Terence and St John all the morning as a half comprehended refrain.

> They wrestled up, they wrestled down,
>   They wrestled sore and still:
> The fiend who blinds the eyes of men,
>   That night he had his will.
>
> Like stags full spent, among the bent
>   They dropped awhile to rest – [113]

'Oh, it's intolerable!' Hirst exclaimed, and then checked himself, as if it were a breach of their agreement. Again and again Terence would creep halfway up the stairs in case he might be able to glean news of Rachel. But the only news now was of a very fragmentary kind; she had drunk something; she had slept a little; she seemed quieter. In the same way, Dr Lesage confined himself to talking about details, save once when he volunteered the information that he had just been called in to ascertain, by severing a vein in the wrist, that an old lady of eighty-five was really dead. She had a horror of being buried alive.

'It is a horror,' he remarked, 'that we generally find in the very old, and seldom in the young.' They both expressed their interest in what he told them; it seemed to them very strange. Another strange thing about the day was that the luncheon was forgotten by all of them until it was late in the afternoon, and then Mrs Chailey waited on them, and looked strange too, because she wore a stiff print dress, and her sleeves were rolled up above her elbows. She seemed as oblivious of her appearance, however, as if she had been called out of her bed by a midnight alarm of fire, and she had forgotten, too, her reserve and her composure; she talked to them quite familiarly as if she had nursed them and held them naked on her knee. She assured them over and over again that it was their duty to eat.

The afternoon, being thus shortened, passed more quickly than they expected. Once Mrs Flushing opened the door, but on seeing them shut it again quickly; once Helen came down to fetch something, but she stopped as she left the room to look at a letter addressed to her. She stood for a moment turning it over, and the extraordinary and mournful beauty of her attitude struck Terence in the way things struck him now – as something to be put away in his mind and to be thought about afterwards. They scarcely spoke, the argument between them seeming to be suspended or forgotten.

Now that the afternoon sun had left the front of the house, Ridley paced up and down the terrace repeating stanzas of a long poem, in a subdued but suddenly sonorous voice. Fragments of the poem were wafted in at the open window as he passed and repassed.

> 'Peor and Baalim
> Forsake their temples dim,
>   With that twice batter'd God of Palestine
> And moonéd Astaroth – '[114]

The sound of these words were strangely discomforting to both the young men, but they had to be borne. As the evening drew on and the red light of the sunset glittered far away on the sea, the same sense of desperation attacked both Terence and St John at the thought that the day was nearly over and that another night was at hand. The appearance of one light after another in the town beneath them produced in Hirst a repetition of his terrible and disgusting desire to break down and sob. Then the lamps were brought in by Chailey. She explained that Maria, in opening a bottle, had been so foolish as to cut her arm badly, but she had bound it up; it was unfortunate when there was so much work to be done. Chailey herself limped because of the rheumatism in her feet, but it appeared to her mere waste of time to take any notice of the unruly flesh of servants. The evening went on. Dr Lesage arrived unexpectedly, and stayed upstairs a very long time. He came down once and drank a cup of coffee.

'She is very ill,' he said in answer to Ridley's question. All the annoyance had by this time left his manner; it was grave and formal, but at the same time it was full of consideration, which had not marked it before. He went upstairs again. The three men sat together in the drawing-room. Ridley was quite quiet now, and his attention seemed to be thoroughly awakened. Save for little half-voluntary movements and exclamations that were stifled at once, they waited in complete silence. It seemed as if they were at last brought together face to face with something definite.

It was nearly eleven o'clock when Dr Lesage again appeared in the room. He approached them very slowly, and did not speak at once. He looked first at St John and then at Terence, and said to Terence, 'Mr Hewet, I think you should go upstairs now.'

Terence rose immediately, leaving the others seated with Dr Lesage standing motionless between them.

Chailey was in the passage outside, repeating over and over again, 'It's wicked – it's wicked.'

Terence paid her no attention; he heard what she was saying, but it conveyed no meaning to his mind. All the way upstairs he kept saying to himself, 'This has not happened to me. It is not possible that this has happened to me.'

He looked curiously at his own hand on the banisters. The stairs were very steep, and it seemed to take him a long time to surmount them. Instead of feeling keenly, as he knew that he ought to feel, he felt nothing at all. When he opened the door he saw Helen sitting by the bedside. There were shaded lights on the table, and the room, though it seemed to be full of a great many things, was very tidy. There was a faint and not unpleasant smell of disinfectants. Helen rose and gave up her chair to him in silence. As they passed each other their eyes met in a peculiar level glance, he wondered at the extraordinary clearness of his eyes, and at the deep calm and sadness that dwelt in them. He sat down by the bedside, and a moment afterwards heard the door shut gently behind her. He was alone with Rachel, and a faint reflection of the sense of relief that they used to feel when they were left alone possessed him. He looked at her. He expected to find some terrible change in her, but there was none. She looked indeed very thin, and, as far as he could see, very tired, but she was the same as she had always been. Moreover, she saw him and knew him. She smiled at him and said, 'Hello, Terence.'

The curtain which had been drawn between them for so long vanished immediately.

'Well, Rachel,' he replied in his usual voice, upon which she opened her eyes quite widely and smiled with her familiar smile. He kissed her and took her hand. 'It's been wretched without you,' he said.

She still looked at him and smiled, but soon a slight look of fatigue or perplexity came into her eyes and she shut them again.

'But when we're together we're perfectly happy,' he said. He continued to hold her hand.

The light being dim, it was impossible to see any change in her face. An immense feeling of peace came over Terence, so that he had no wish to move or to speak. The terrible torture and unreality of the last days were over, and he had come out now into perfect certainty and peace. His mind began to work naturally again and with great ease. The longer he sat there the more profoundly was he conscious of the peace invading every corner of his soul. Once he held his breath and listened acutely; she was still breathing; he went on thinking for some time; they seemed to be thinking together; he seemed to be Rachel as well as himself; and then he listened again; no, she had ceased to breathe. So much the better – this was death. It was nothing; it was to cease to breathe. It was happiness, it was perfect happiness. They had now what they had always wanted to have, the union which had been impossible while they lived. Unconscious whether he thought the words or spoke them aloud, he said, 'No two people have ever been so happy as we have been. No one has ever loved as we have loved.'

It seemed to him that their complete union and happiness filled the room with rings eddying more and more widely. He had no wish in the world left unfulfilled. They possessed what could never be taken from them.

He was not conscious that anyone had come into the room, but later, moments later, or hours later perhaps, he felt an arm behind him. The arms were round him. He did not want to have arms round him, and the mysterious whispering voices annoyed him. He laid Rachel's hand, which was now cold, upon the counterpane, and rose from his chair, and walked across to the window. The windows were uncurtained, and showed the moon, and a long silver pathway upon the surface of the waves.

'Why,' he said, in his ordinary tone of voice, 'look at the moon. There's a halo round the moon. We shall have rain tomorrow.'

The arms, whether they were the arms of man or of woman, were round him again; they were pushing him gently towards the door. He turned of his own accord and walked steadily in advance of the arms, conscious of a little amusement at the strange way in which people behaved merely because someone was dead. He would go if they wished it, but nothing they could do would disturb his happiness.

As he saw the passage outside the room, and the table with the cups and the plates, it suddenly came over him that here was a world in which he would never see Rachel again.

'Rachel! Rachel!' he shrieked, trying to rush back to her. But they prevented him, and pushed him down the passage and into a bedroom far from her room. Downstairs they could hear the thud of his feet on the floor, as he struggled to break free; and twice they heard him shout, 'Rachel, Rachel!'

Chapter 26

For two or three hours longer the moon poured its light through the empty air. Unbroken by clouds it fell straightly, and lay almost like a chill white frost over the sea and the earth. During these hours the silence was not broken, and the only movement was caused by the movement of trees and branches which stirred slightly, and then the shadows that lay across the white spaces of the land moved too. In this profound silence one sound only was audible, the sound of a slight but continuous breathing which never ceased, although it never rose and never fell. It continued after the birds had begun to flutter from branch to branch, and could be heard behind the first thin notes of their voices. It continued all through the hours when the east whitened, and grew red, and a faint blue tinged the sky, but when the sun rose it ceased, and gave place to other sounds.

The first sounds that were heard were little inarticulate cries, the cries, it seemed, of children or of the very poor, of people who were very weak or in pain. But when the sun was above the horizon, the air which had been thin and pale grew every moment richer and warmer, and the sounds of life became bolder and more full of courage and authority. By degrees the smoke began to ascend in wavering breaths over the houses, and these slowly thickened, until they were as round and straight as columns, and instead of striking upon pale white blinds, the sun shone upon dark windows, beyond which there was depth and space.

The sun had been up for many hours, and the great dome of air was warmed through and glittering with thin gold threads of sunlight, before anyone moved in the hotel. White and massive it stood in the early light, half asleep with its blinds down.

At about half-past nine Miss Allan came very slowly into the hall, and walked very slowly to the table where the morning papers were laid, but she did not put out her hand to take one; she stood still, thinking, with her head a little sunk upon her shoulders. She looked curiously old, and from the way in which she stood, a little hunched together and very massive, you could see what she would be like when she was really old, how she would sit day after day in her chair looking placidly in front of her. Other people began to come into the room, and to pass her, but she did not speak to any of them or even look at them, and at last, as if it were necessary to do something, she sat down in a chair, and looked quietly and fixedly in front of her. She felt very old this morning, and useless too, as if her life had been a failure, as if it had been hard and laborious to no purpose. She did not want to go on living, and yet she knew that she would. She was so strong that she would live to be a very old woman. She would probably live to be eighty, and as she was now fifty, that left thirty years more for her to live. She turned her hands over and over in her lap and looked at them curiously; her old hands that had done so much work for her. There did not seem to be much point in it all; one went on, of course one went on . . . She looked up to see Mrs Thornbury standing beside her, with lines drawn upon her forehead, and her lips parted as if she were about to ask a question.

Miss Allan anticipated her.

'Yes,' she said. 'She died this morning, very early, about three o'clock.'

Mrs Thornbury made a little exclamation, drew her lips together, and the tears rose in her eyes. Through them she looked at the hall which was now laid with great breadths of sunlight, and at the careless, casual groups of people who were standing beside the solid armchairs and tables. They looked to her unreal, or as people look who remain unconscious that some great explosion is about to take place beside them. But there was no explosion, and they went on standing by the chairs and the tables. Mrs Thornbury no longer saw them, but, penetrating through them as though they were without substance, she saw the house, the people in the house, the room, the bed in the room, and the figure of the dead lying still in the dark beneath the sheets. She could almost see the dead. She could almost hear the voices of the mourners.

'They expected it?' she asked at length.

Miss Allan could only shake her head. 'I know nothing,' she replied, 'except what Mrs Flushing's maid told me. She died early this morning.'

The two women looked at each other with a quiet significant gaze, and then, feeling oddly dazed, and seeking she did not know exactly what, Mrs Thornbury went slowly upstairs and walked quietly along the passages, touching the wall with her fingers as if to guide herself. Housemaids were passing briskly from room to room, but Mrs Thornbury avoided them; she hardly saw them; they seemed to her to be in another world. She did not even look up directly when Evelyn stopped her. It was evident that Evelyn had been lately in tears, and when she looked at Mrs Thornbury she began to cry again. Together they drew into the hollow of a window, and stood there in silence. Broken words formed themselves at last among Evelyn's sobs. 'It was wicked,' she sobbed, 'it was cruel – they were so happy.'

Mrs Thornbury patted her on the shoulder.

'It seems hard – very hard,' she said. She paused and looked out over the slope of the hill at the Ambroses' villa; the windows were blazing in the sun, and she thought how the soul of the dead had passed from those windows. Something had passed from the world. It seemed to her strangely empty.

'And yet the older one grows,' she continued, her eyes regaining more than their usual brightness, 'the more certain one becomes that there is a reason. How could one go on if there were no reason?' she asked. She asked the question of someone, but she did not ask it of Evelyn. Evelyn's sobs were becoming quieter. 'There must be a reason,' she said. 'It can't only be an accident. For it was an accident – it need never have happened.'

Mrs Thornbury sighed deeply.

'But we must not let ourselves think of that,' she added, 'and let us hope that they don't either. Whatever they had done it might have been the same. These terrible illnesses – '

'There's no reason – I don't believe there's any reason at all!' Evelyn broke out, pulling the blind down and letting it fly back with a little snap. 'Why should these things happen? Why should people suffer? I honestly believe,' she went on, lowering her voice slightly, 'that Rachel's in heaven, but Terence . . .

'What's the good of it all?' she demanded.

Mrs Thornbury shook her head slightly but made no reply, and pressing Evelyn's hand she went on down the passage. Impelled by a strong desire to hear something, although she did not know exactly what there was to hear, she was making her way to the Flushings' room. As she opened their door she felt that she had interrupted some argument between husband and wife. Mrs Flushing was sitting with her back to the light, and Mr Flushing was standing near her, arguing and trying to persuade her of something.

'Ah, here is Mrs Thornbury,' he began with some relief in his voice. 'You have heard, of course. My wife feels that she was in some way responsible. She urged poor Miss Vinrace to come on the expedition. I'm sure you will agree with me that it is most unreasonable to feel that. We don't even know – in fact I think it most unlikely – that she caught her illness there. These diseases – Besides, she was set on going. She would have gone whether you asked her or not, Alice.'

'Don't, Wilfrid,' said Mrs Flushing, neither moving nor taking her eyes off the spot on the floor upon which they rested. 'What's the use of talking? What's the use – ?' She ceased.

'I was coming to ask you,' said Mrs Thornbury, addressing Wilfrid, for it was useless to speak to his wife. 'Is there anything you think that one could do? Has the father arrived? Could one go and see?'

The strongest wish in her being at this moment was to be able to do something for the unhappy people – to see them – to assure them – to help them. It was dreadful to be so far away from them. But Mr Flushing shook his head; he did not think that now – later perhaps one might be able to help. Here Mrs Flushing rose stiffly, turned her back to them, and walked to the dressing-room opposite. As she walked, they could see her breast slowly rise and slowly fall. But her grief was silent. She shut the door behind her.

When she was alone by herself she clenched her fists together, and began beating the back of a chair with them. She was like a wounded animal. She hated death; she was furious, outraged, indignant with death, as if it were a living creature. She refused to relinquish her friends to death. She would not submit to dark and nothingness. She began to pace up and down, clenching her hands, and making no attempt to stop the quick tears which raced down her cheeks. She sat still at last, but she did not submit. She looked stubborn and strong when she had ceased to cry.

In the next room, meanwhile, Wilfrid was talking to Mrs Thornbury with greater freedom now that his wife was not sitting there.

'That's the worst of these places,' he said. 'People will behave as though they were in England, and they're not. I've no doubt myself that Miss Vinrace caught the infection up at the villa itself. She probably ran risks a dozen times a day that might have given her the illness. It's absurd to say she caught it with us.'

If he had not been sincerely sorry for them he would have been annoyed. 'Pepper tells me,' he continued, 'that he left the house because he thought them so careless. He says they never washed their vegetables properly. Poor people! It's a fearful price to pay. But it's only what I've seen over and over again – people seem to forget that these things happen, and then they do happen, and they're surprised.'

Mrs Thornbury agreed with him that they had been very careless, and that there was no reason whatever to think that she had caught the fever on the expedition; and after talking about other things for a short time, she left him and went sadly along the passage to her own room. There must be some reason why such things happen, she thought to herself, as she shut the door. Only at first it was not easy to understand what it was. It seemed so strange – so unbelievable. Why, only three weeks ago – only a fortnight ago, she had seen Rachel; when she shut her eyes she could almost see her now, the quiet, shy girl who was going to be married. She thought of all that she would have missed had she died at Rachel's age, the children, the married life, the unimaginable depths and miracles that seemed to her, as she looked back, to have lain about her, day after day, and year after year. The stunned feeling, which had been making it difficult for her to think, gradually gave way to a feeling of the opposite nature; she thought very quickly and very clearly, and, looking back over all her experiences, tried to fit them into a kind of order. There was undoubtedly much suffering, much struggling, but, on the whole, surely there was a balance of happiness – surely order did prevail. Nor were the deaths of young people really the saddest things in life – they were saved so much; they kept so much. The dead – she called to mind those who had died early, accidentally – were beautiful; she often dreamt of the dead. And in time Terence himself would come to feel – She got up and began to wander restlessly about the room.

For an old woman of her age she was very restless, and for one of her clear, quick mind she was unusually perplexed. She could not settle to anything, so that she was relieved when the door opened. She went up to her husband, took him in her arms, and kissed him with unusual intensity, and then as they sat down together she began to pat him and question him as if he were a baby, an old, tired, querulous baby. She did not tell him about Miss Vinrace's death, for that would only disturb him, and he was put out already. She tried to discover why he was uneasy. Politics again? What were those horrid people doing? She spent the whole morning in discussing politics with her husband, and by degrees she became deeply interested in what they were saying. But every now and then what she was saying seemed to her oddly empty of meaning.

At luncheon it was remarked by several people that the visitors at the hotel were beginning to leave; there were fewer every day. There were only forty people at luncheon, instead of the sixty that there had been. So old Mrs Paley computed, gazing about her with her faded eyes, as she took her seat at her own table in the window. Her party generally consisted of Mr Perrott as well as Arthur and Susan, and today Evelyn was lunching with them also.

She was unusually subdued. Having noticed that her eyes were red, and guessing the reason, the others took pains to keep up an elaborate conversation between themselves. She suffered it to go on for a few minutes, leaning both elbows on the table, and leaving her soup untouched, when she exclaimed suddenly, 'I don't know how you feel, but I can simply think of nothing else!'

The gentlemen murmured sympathetically, and looked grave.

Susan replied, 'Yes – isn't it perfectly awful? When you think what a nice girl she was – only just engaged, and this need never have happened – it seems too tragic.' She looked at Arthur as though he might be able to help her with something more suitable.

'Hard lines,' said Arthur briefly. 'But it was a foolish thing to do – to go up that river.' He shook his head. 'They should have known better. You can't expect Englishwomen to stand roughing it as the natives do who've been acclimatised. I'd half a mind to warn them at tea that day when it was being discussed. But it's no good saying these sort of things – it only puts people's backs up – it never makes any difference.'

Old Mrs Paley, hitherto contented with her soup, here intimated, by raising one hand to her ear, that she wished to know what was being said.

'You heard, Aunt Emma, that poor Miss Vinrace has died of the fever,' Susan informed her gently. She could not speak of death loudly or even in her usual voice, so that Mrs Paley did not catch a word.

Arthur came to the rescue. 'Miss Vinrace is dead,' he said very distinctly.

Mrs Paley merely bent a little towards him and asked, 'Eh?'

'Miss Vinrace is dead,' he repeated. It was only by stiffening all the muscles round his mouth that he could prevent himself from bursting into laughter and force himself to repeat for the third time, 'Miss Vinrace . . . She's dead.'

Let alone the difficulty of hearing the exact words, facts that were outside her daily experience took some time to reach Mrs Paley's consciousness. A weight seemed to rest upon her brain, impeding, though not damaging its action. She sat vague-eyed for at least a minute before she realised what Arthur meant.

'Dead?' she said vaguely. 'Miss Vinrace dead? Dear me . . . that's very sad. But I don't at the moment remember which she was. We seem to have made so many new acquaintances here.' She looked at Susan for help. 'A tall dark girl, who just missed being handsome, with a high colour?'

'No,' Susan interposed. 'She was – ' then she gave it up in despair. There was no use in explaining that Mrs Paley was thinking of the wrong person.

'She ought not to have died,' Mrs Paley continued. 'She looked so strong. But people will drink the water. I can never make out why. It seems such a simple thing to tell them to put a bottle of Seltzer water in your bedroom. That's all the precaution I've ever taken, and I've been in every part of the world, I may say – Italy a dozen times over . . . But young people always think they know better, and then they pay the penalty. Poor thing – I am very sorry for her.' But the difficulty of peering into a dish of potatoes and helping herself engrossed her attention.

Arthur and Susan both secretly hoped that the subject was now disposed of, for there seemed to them something unpleasant in this discussion. But Evelyn was not ready to let it drop. Why would people never talk about the things that mattered?

'I don't believe you care a bit!' she said, turning savagely upon Mr Perrott, who had sat all this time in silence.

'I? Oh, yes, I do,' he answered awkwardly, but with obvious sincerity. Evelyn's questions made him too feel uncomfortable.

'It seems so inexplicable,' Evelyn continued. 'Death, I mean. Why should she be dead, and not you or I? It was only a fortnight ago that she was here with the rest of us. What d'you believe?' she demanded of Mr Perrott. 'D'you believe that things go on, that she's still somewhere – or d'you think it's simply a game – we crumble up to nothing when we die? I'm positive Rachel's not dead.'

Mr Perrott would have said almost anything that Evelyn wanted him to say, but to assert that he believed in the immortality of the soul was not in his power. He sat silent, more deeply wrinkled than usual, crumbling his bread.

Lest Evelyn should next ask him what he believed, Arthur, after making a pause equivalent to a full stop, started a completely different topic.

'Supposing,' he said, 'a man were to write and tell you that he wanted five pounds because he had known your grandfather, what would you do? It was this way. My grandfather – '

'Invented a stove,' said Evelyn. 'I know all about that. We had one in the conservatory to keep the plants warm.'

'Didn't know I was so famous,' said Arthur. 'Well,' he continued, determined at all costs to spin his story out at length, 'the old chap, being about the second best inventor of his day, and a capable lawyer too, died, as they always do, without making a will. Now Fielding, his clerk, with how much justice I don't know, always claimed that he meant to do something for him. The poor old boy's come down in the world through trying inventions on his own account, lives in Penge over a tobacconist's shop. I've been to see him there. The question is – must I stump up or not? What does the abstract spirit of justice require,

Perrott? Remember, I didn't benefit under my grandfather's will, and I've no way of testing the truth of the story.'

'I don't know much about the abstract spirit of justice,' said Susan, smiling complacently at the others, 'but I'm certain of one thing – he'll get his five pounds!'

As Mr Perrott proceeded to deliver an opinion, and Evelyn insisted that he was much too stingy, like all lawyers, thinking of the letter and not of the spirit, while Mrs Paley required to be kept informed between the courses as to what they were all saying, the luncheon passed with no interval of silence, and Arthur congratulated himself upon the tact with which the discussion had been smoothed over.

As they left the room it happened that Mrs Paley's wheeled chair ran into the Elliots, who were coming through the door as she was going out. Brought thus to a standstill for a moment, Arthur and Susan congratulated Hughling Elliot upon his convalescence – he was down, cadaverous enough, for the first time – and Mr Perrott took occasion to say a few words in private to Evelyn.

'Would there be any chance of seeing you this afternoon, about three-thirty say? I shall be in the garden, by the fountain.'

The block dissolved before Evelyn answered. But as she left them in the hall, she looked at him brightly and said, 'Half-past three, did you say? That'll suit me.'

She ran upstairs with the feeling of spiritual exaltation and quickened life which the prospect of an emotional scene always aroused in her. That Mr Perrott was again about to propose to her, she had no doubt, and she was aware that on this occasion she ought to be prepared with a definite answer, for she was going away in three days' time. But she could not bring her mind to bear upon the question. To come to a decision was very difficult for her, because she had a natural dislike of anything final and done with; she liked to go on and on – always on and on. She was leaving, and, therefore, she occupied herself in laying her clothes out side by side upon the bed. She observed that some were very shabby. She took the photograph of her father and mother, and before she laid it away in her box, she held it for a minute in her hand. Rachel had looked at it. Suddenly the keen feeling of someone's personality, which things that they have owned or handled sometimes preserves, overcame her; she felt Rachel in the room with her; it was as if she were on a ship at sea, and the life of the day was as unreal as the land in the distance. But by degrees the feeling of Rachel's presence passed away, and she could no longer realise her, for she had scarcely known her. But this momentary sensation left her depressed and fatigued. What had she done with her life? What future was there before her? What was make-believe, and what was real? Were these proposals and intimacies and adventures real, or was the contentment which she had seen on the faces of Susan and Rachel more real than anything she had ever felt?

She made herself ready to go downstairs, absent-mindedly, but her fingers were so well trained that they did the work of preparing her almost of their own accord. When she was actually on the way downstairs, the blood began to circle through her body of its own accord too, for her mind felt very dull.

Mr Perrott was waiting for her. Indeed, he had gone straight into the garden after luncheon, and had been walking up and down the path for more than half an hour, in a state of acute suspense.

'I'm late as usual!' she exclaimed, as she caught sight of him. 'Well, you must forgive me; I had to pack up . . . My word! It looks stormy! And that's a new steamer in the bay, isn't it?'

She looked at the bay, in which a steamer was just dropping anchor, the smoke still hanging about it, while a swift black shudder ran through the waves. 'One's quite forgotten what rain looks like,' she added.

But Mr Perrott paid no attention to the steamer or to the weather.

'Miss Murgatroyd,' he began with his usual formality, 'I asked you to come here from a very selfish motive, I fear. I do not think you need to be assured once more of my feelings; but, as you are leaving so soon, I felt that I could not let you go without asking you to tell me – have I any reason to hope that you will ever come to care for me?'

He was very pale, and seemed unable to say any more.

The little gush of vitality which had come into Evelyn as she ran downstairs had left her, and she felt herself impotent. There was nothing for her to say; she felt nothing. Now that he was actually asking her, in his elderly gentle words, to marry him, she felt less for him than she had ever felt before.

'Let's sit down and talk it over,' she said rather unsteadily.

Mr Perrott followed her to a curved green seat under a tree. They looked at the fountain in front of them, which had long ceased to play. Evelyn kept looking at the fountain instead of thinking of what she was saying; the fountain without any water seemed to be the type of her own being.

'Of course I care for you,' she began, rushing her words out in a hurry; 'I should be a brute if I didn't. I think you're quite one of the nicest people I've ever known, and one of the finest too. But I wish . . . I wish you didn't care for me in that way. Are you sure you do?' For the moment she honestly desired that he should say no.

'Quite sure,' said Mr Perrott.

'You see, I'm not as simple as most women,' Evelyn continued. 'I think I want more. I don't know exactly what I feel.'

He sat by her, watching her and refraining from speech.

'I sometimes think I haven't got it in me to care very much for one person only. Someone else would make you a better wife. I can imagine you very happy with someone else.'

'If you think that there is any chance that you will come to care for me, I am quite content to wait,' said Mr Perrott.

'Well – there's no hurry, is there?' said Evelyn. 'Suppose I thought it over and wrote and told you when I get back? I'm going to Moscow; I'll write from Moscow.'

But Mr Perrott persisted.

'You cannot give me any kind of idea? I do not ask for a date . . . that would be most unreasonable.' He paused, looking down at the gravel path. As she did not immediately answer, he went on. 'I know very well that I am not – that I have not much to offer you either in myself or in my circumstances. And I forget; it cannot seem the miracle to you that it does to me. Until I met you I had gone on in my own quiet way – we are both very quiet people, my sister and I – quite content with my lot. My friendship with Arthur was the most important thing in my life. Now that I know you, all that has changed. You seem to put such a spirit into everything. Life seems to hold so many possibilities that I had never dreamt of.'

'That's splendid!' Evelyn exclaimed, grasping his hand. 'Now you'll go back and start all kinds of things and make a great name in the world; and we'll go on being friends, whatever happens . . . we'll be great friends, won't we?'

'Evelyn!' he moaned suddenly, and took her in his arms, and kissed her. She did not resent it, although it made little impression on her.

As she sat upright again, she said, 'I never see why one shouldn't go on being friends – though some people do. And friendships do make a difference, don't they? They are the kind of things that matter in one's life?'

He looked at her with a bewildered expression as if he did not really understand what she was saying. With a considerable effort he collected himself, stood up, and said, 'Now I think I have told you what I feel, and I will only add that I can wait as long as ever you wish.'

Left alone, Evelyn walked up and down the path. What did matter then? What was the meaning of it all?

Chapter 27

All that evening the clouds gathered, until they closed entirely over the blue of the sky. They seemed to narrow the space between earth and heaven, so that there was no room for the air to move in freely; and the waves, too, lay flat, and yet rigid, as if they were restrained. The leaves on the bushes and trees in the garden hung closely together, and the feeling of pressure and restraint was increased by the short chirping sounds which came from birds and insects.

So strange were the light and the silence that the busy hum of voices which usually filled the dining-room at mealtimes had distinct gaps in it, and during these silences the clatter of the knives upon plates became audible. The first roll of thunder and the first heavy drop striking the pane caused a little stir.

'It's coming!' was said simultaneously in many different languages.

There was then a profound silence, as if the thunder had withdrawn into itself. People had just begun to eat again, when a gust of cold air came through the open windows, lifting tablecloths and skirts, a light flashed, and was instantly followed by a clap of thunder right over the hotel. The rain swished with it, and immediately there were all those sounds of windows being shut and doors slamming violently which accompany a storm.

The room grew suddenly several degrees darker, for the wind seemed to be driving waves of darkness across the earth. No one attempted to eat for a time, but sat looking out at the garden, with their forks in the air. The flashes now came frequently, lighting up faces as if they were going to be photographed, surprising them in tense and unnatural expressions. The clap followed close and violently upon them. Several women half rose from their chairs and then sat down again, but dinner was continued uneasily with eyes upon the garden. The bushes outside were ruffled and whitened, and the wind pressed upon them so that they seemed to stoop to the ground. The waiters had to press dishes upon the diners' notice; and the diners had to draw the attention of waiters, for they were all absorbed in looking at the storm. As the thunder showed no signs of withdrawing, but seemed massed right overhead, while the lightning aimed straight at the garden every time, an uneasy gloom replaced the first excitement.

Finishing the meal very quickly, people congregated in the hall, where they felt more secure than in any other place because they could retreat far from the windows, and although they heard the thunder, they could not see anything. A little boy was carried away sobbing in the arms of his mother.

While the storm continued, no one seemed inclined to sit down, but they collected in little groups under the central skylight, where they stood in a yellow atmosphere, looking upwards. Now and again their faces became white, as the lightning flashed, and finally a terrific crash came, making the panes of the skylight lift at the joints.

'Ah!' several voices exclaimed at the same moment.

'Something struck,' said a man's voice.

The rain rushed down. The rain seemed now to extinguish the lightning and the thunder, and the hall became almost dark.

After a minute or two, when nothing was heard but the rattle of water upon the glass, there was a perceptible slackening of the sound, and then the atmosphere became lighter.

'It's over,' said another voice.

At a touch, all the electric lights were turned on, and revealed a crowd of people all standing, all looking with rather strained faces up at the skylight, but when they saw each other in the artificial light they turned at once and began to move away. For some minutes the rain continued to rattle upon the skylight, and the thunder gave another shake or two; but it was evident from the clearing of the darkness and the light drumming of the rain upon the roof that the great confused ocean of air was travelling away from them, and passing high overhead, with its clouds and its rods of fire, out to sea. The building, which had seemed so small in the tumult of the storm, now became as square and spacious as usual.

As the storm drew away, the people in the hall of the hotel sat down and with a comfortable sense of relief began to tell each other stories about great storms, and produced in many cases their occupations for the evening. The chessboard was brought out, and Mr Elliot, who wore a stock instead of a collar as a sign of convalescence, but was otherwise much as usual, challenged Mr Pepper to a final contest. Round them gathered a group of ladies with pieces of needlework, or in default of needlework, with novels, to superintend the game, much as if they were in charge of two small boys playing marbles. Every now and then they looked at the board and made some encouraging remark to the gentlemen.

Mrs Paley just round the corner had her cards arranged in long ladders before her, with Susan sitting near to sympathise but not to correct, and the merchants and the miscellaneous people who had never been discovered to possess names were stretched in their armchairs with their newspapers on their knees. The conversation in these circumstances was very gentle, fragmentary and intermittent, but the room was full of the indescribable stir of life. Every now and then the moth, which was now grey of wing and shiny of thorax, whizzed over their heads and hit the lamps with a thud.

A young woman put down her needlework and exclaimed, 'Poor creature! it would be kinder to kill it.' But nobody seemed disposed to rouse himself in order to kill the moth. They watched it dash from lamp to lamp, because they were comfortable and had nothing to do.

On the sofa, beside the chess-players, Mrs Elliot was imparting a new stitch in knitting to Mrs Thornbury, so that their heads came very near together, and were only to be distinguished by the old lace cap which Mrs Thornbury wore in the evening. Mrs Elliot was an expert at knitting, and disclaimed a compliment to that effect with evident pride.

'I suppose we're all proud of something,' she said, 'and I'm proud of my knitting. I think things like that run in families. We all knit well. I had an uncle who knitted his own socks to the day of his death – and he did it better than any of his daughters, dear old gentleman. Now I wonder that you, Miss Allan, who use your eyes so much, don't take up knitting in the evenings. You'd find it such a relief, I should say – such a rest to the eyes – and the bazaars are so glad of things.' Her voice dropped into the smooth half-conscious tone of the expert knitter; the words came gently one after another. 'As much as I do I can always dispose of, which is a comfort, for then I feel that I am not wasting my time – '

Miss Allan, being thus addressed, shut her novel and observed the others placidly for a time. At last she said, 'It is surely not natural to leave your wife because she happens to be in love with you. But that – as far as I can make out – is what the gentleman in my story does.'

'Tut, tut, that doesn't sound good – no, that doesn't sound at all natural,' murmured the knitters in their absorbed voices.

'Still, it's the kind of book people call very clever,' Miss Allan added.

'*Maternity* – by Michael Jessop – I presume,' Mr Elliot put in, for he could never resist the temptation of talking while he played chess.

'D'you know,' said Mrs Elliot, after a moment, 'I don't think people *do* write good novels now – not as good as they used to, anyhow.'

No one took the trouble to agree with her or to disagree with her. Arthur Venning who was strolling about, sometimes looking at the game, sometimes reading a page of a magazine, looked at Miss Allan, who was half asleep, and said humorously, 'A penny for your thoughts, Miss Allan.'

The others looked up. They were glad that he had not spoken to them. But Miss Allan replied without any hesitation, 'I was thinking of my imaginary uncle. Hasn't everyone got an imaginary uncle?' she continued. 'I have one – a most delightful old gentleman. He's always giving me things. Sometimes it's a gold watch; sometimes it's a carriage and pair; sometimes it's a beautiful little cottage in the New Forest; sometimes it's a ticket to the place I most want to see.'

She set them all thinking vaguely of the things they wanted. Mrs Elliot knew exactly what she wanted: she wanted a child; and the usual little pucker deepened on her brow.

'We're such lucky people,' she said, looking at her husband. 'We really have no wants.' She was apt to say this, partly in order to convince herself, and partly in order to convince other people. But she was prevented from wondering how far she carried conviction by the entrance of Mr and Mrs Flushing, who came through the hall and stopped by the chessboard. Mrs Flushing looked wilder than ever. A great strand of black hair looped down across her brow, her cheeks were whipped a dark blood red, and drops of rain made wet marks upon them.

Mr Flushing explained that they had been on the roof watching the storm.

'It was a wonderful sight,' he said. 'The lightning went right out over the sea, and lit up the waves and the ships far away. You can't think how wonderful the mountains looked too, with the lights on them, and the great masses of shadow. It's all over now.'

He slid down into a chair, becoming interested in the final struggle of the game.

'And you go back tomorrow?' said Mrs Thornbury, looking at Mrs Flushing.

'Yes,' she replied.

'And indeed one is not sorry to go back,' said Mrs Elliot, assuming an air of mournful anxiety, 'after all this illness.'

'Are you afraid of dyin'?' Mrs Flushing demanded scornfully.

'I think we are all afraid of that,' said Mrs Elliot with dignity.

'I suppose we're all cowards when it comes to the point,' said Mrs Flushing, rubbing her cheek against the back of the chair. 'I'm sure I am.'

'Not a bit of it!' said Mr Flushing, turning round, for Mr Pepper took a very long time to consider his move. 'It's not cowardly to wish to live, Alice. It's the very reverse of cowardly. Personally, I'd like to go on for a hundred years – granted, of course, that I had the full use of my faculties. Think of all the things that are bound to happen!'

'That is what I feel,' Mrs Thornbury rejoined. 'The changes, the improvements, the inventions – and beauty. D'you know I feel sometimes that I couldn't bear to die and cease to see beautiful things about me?'

'It would certainly be very dull to die before they have discovered whether there is life in Mars,' Miss Allan added.

'Do you really believe there's life in Mars?' asked Mrs Flushing, turning to her for the first time with keen interest. 'Who tells you that? Someone who knows? D'you know a man called – ?'

Here Mrs Thornbury laid down her knitting, and a look of extreme solicitude came into her eyes.

'There is Mr Hirst,' she said quietly.

St John had just come through the swing door. He was rather blown about by the wind, and his cheeks looked terribly pale, unshorn and cavernous. After taking off his coat he was going to pass straight through the hall and up to his room, but he could not ignore the presence of so many people he knew, especially as Mrs Thornbury rose and went up to him, holding out her hand. But the shock of the warm lamp-lit room, together with the sight of so many cheerful human beings sitting together at their ease, after the dark walk in the rain, and the long days of strain and horror, overcame him completely. He looked at Mrs Thornbury and could not speak.

Everyone was silent. Mr Pepper's hand stayed upon his knight. Mrs Thornbury somehow moved him to a chair, sat herself beside him, and with tears in her own eyes said gently, 'You have done everything for your friend.'

Her action set them all talking again as if they had never stopped, and Mr Pepper finished the move with his knight.

'There was nothing to be done,' said St John. He spoke very slowly. 'It seems impossible – '

He drew his hand across his eyes as if some dream came between him and the others and prevented him from seeing where he was.

'And that poor fellow,' said Mrs Thornbury, the tears falling again down her cheeks.

'Impossible,' St John repeated.

'Did he have the consolation of knowing – ?' Mrs Thornbury began very tentatively.

But St John made no reply. He lay back in his chair, half-seeing the others, half-hearing what they said. He was terribly tired, and the light and warmth, the movements of the hands, and the soft communicative voices soothed him; they gave him a strange sense of quiet and relief. As he sat there, motionless, this feeling of relief became a feeling of profound happiness. Without any sense of disloyalty to Terence and Rachel he ceased to think about either of them. The movements and the voices seemed to draw together from different parts of the room, and to combine themselves into a pattern before his eyes; he was content to sit silently watching the pattern build itself up, looking at what he hardly saw.

The game was really a good one, and Mr Pepper and Mr Elliot were becoming more and more set upon the struggle. Mrs Thornbury, seeing that St John did not wish to talk, resumed her knitting.

'Lightning again!' Mrs Flushing suddenly exclaimed. A yellow light flashed across the blue window, and for a second they saw the green trees outside. She strode to the door, pushed it open, and stood half out in the open air.

But the light was only the reflection of the storm which was over. The rain had ceased, the heavy clouds were blown away, and the air was thin and clear, although vapourish mists were being driven swiftly across the moon. The sky was once more a deep and solemn blue, and the shape of the earth was visible at the bottom of the air, enormous, dark, and solid, rising into the tapering mass of the mountain, and pricked here and there on the slopes by the tiny lights of villas. The driving air, the drone of the trees and the flashing light which now and again spread a broad illumination over the earth filled Mrs Flushing with exultation. Her breasts rose and fell.

'Splendid! Splendid!' she muttered to herself. Then she turned back into the hall and exclaimed in a peremptory voice, 'Come outside and see, Wilfrid; it's wonderful.'

Some half-stirred; some rose; some dropped their balls of wool and began to stoop to look for them.

'To bed – to bed,' said Miss Allan.

'It was the move with your queen that gave it away, Pepper,' exclaimed Mr Elliot triumphantly, sweeping the pieces together and standing up. He had won the game.

'What? Pepper beaten at last? I congratulate you!' said Arthur Venning, who was wheeling old Mrs Paley to bed.

All these voices sounded gratefully in St John's ears as he lay half-asleep, and yet vividly conscious of everything around him. Across his eyes passed a procession of objects, black and indistinct, the figures of people picking up their books, their cards, their balls of wool, their work-baskets, and passing him one after another on their way to bed.

NOTES TO
The Voyage Out

Chapter 1

1 (p. 150) *Bluebeard* villain of the tale *Barbe-bleue* (1697) by Charles Perrault. The story of how he serially killed his wives has passed into popular myth.

2 (p. 150) *'Lars Porsena . . . '* the opening lines of 'Horatius', from *Lays of Ancient Rome* (1842) by Thomas Babington Macaulay

3 (p. 154) *Euphrosyne* the name of one of the three Graces (daughters of Zeus and Hera), signifying Joy

4 (p. 154) *Peterhouse* Cambridge college

5 (p. 155) *Cats* St Catharine's College, Cambridge

6 (p. 157) *Odysseus* the hero of Homer's epic poem the *Odyssey*

Chapter 2

7 (p. 161) *Pindar* Greek poet (*c.*522–*c.*440 BC) best known for his odes

8 (p. 162) *Petronius* (d. AD 66), Roman poet at the court of Nero, author of the *Satyricon*

9 (p. 162) *Catullus* (87–*c.*54 BC), Roman lyric poet

10 (p. 163) *Coryphaeus* not a known text, so possibly invented. The word is Greek for leader of the chorus in a play.

11 (p. 170) *Tristan* *Tristan und Isolde* (1865), Richard Wagner's opera, based on the medieval narrative, *Tristan and Iseult*

12 (p. 170) *Cowper's Letters* William Cowper (1731–1800), poet

Chapter 3

13 (p. 173) *Tagus* the river on whose estuary Lisbon stands

14 (p. 174) *Fielding's grave* The novelist Henry Fielding (1782–1837) died in Lisbon and was buried there.

15 (p. 175) *Whistler* James Abbot McNeill Whistler (1834–1903), American artist who painted scenes of the River Thames, which Mrs Dalloway is perhaps recalling in her comparison

16 (p. 177) *'May I be in my grave before a woman has the right to vote in England!'* Women were granted the right to vote in 1918.

17 (p. 178) *Shelley . . . Adonais* Percy Bysshe Shelley (1792–1822) wrote *Adonais* (1821) as an elegy to John Keats.

18 (p. 178) *Matthew Arnold* (1822–88), critic and poet

19 (p. 179) *Antigone* tragedy by Sophocles, *c.*442 BC. The Greek quotation uttered by Mr Pepper is from the chorus of the play.

20 (p. 179) *Plato* (*c.*427–347 BC), Athenian philosopher, pupil of Socrates

21 (p. 180) *a Reynolds or a Romney* Sir Joshua Reynolds (1723–92) and George Romney (1734–1802) were both portrait painters.

22 (p. 180) *Bayreuth* Bayreuth Festival Theatre, founded by Wagner for the production of his operas and site of the Wagner Festival after his death

23 (p. 180) *Parsifal* (1882), opera by Wagner

24 (p. 181) *Watts* George Frederic Watts (1817–1904), painter

25 (p. 181) *Joachim* Josef Joachim (1831–1907), Hungarian violinist who founded the Joachim Quartet

26 (p. 184) *the light burning over the House* the light indicating that Parliament is sitting

27 (p. 184) *from Lord Salisbury to Alfred* The Marquis of Salisbury (1830–1903) was Conservative Prime Minister for three separate spells, totalling fourteen years, between 1885 and 1902. Alfred the Great (849–900) was King of Wessex from 871, and kept East Anglia and Southern England independent from the Danes. Woolf is perhaps ironising Richard Dalloway's corralling Alfred into a continuum of Conservatism.

28 (p. 184) *R. D. loquitur* R. D. speaking

29 (p. 185) *Pascal* Blaise Pascal (1623–62), French scientist and philosopher. The 'little white volume' is probably Pascal's *Pensées* (1844).

Chapter 4

30 (p. 186) *'Full fathom five thy father lies'* Ariel's song from Shakespeare's *The Tempest*

31 (p. 107) *Huxley* probably Thomas Henry Huxley (1825–95), scientist and writer

32 (p. 107) *Herbert Spencer* (1820–1903), philosopher

33 (p. 186) *Henry George* (1839–97), American economist

34 (p. 186) *Emerson* Ralph Waldo Emerson (1803–82), American essayist

35 (p. 186) *Thomas Hardy* (1840–1928), novelist and poet

36 (p. 188) *Here lies the duck that Samuel Johnson sat on* A poem that Dr Samuel Johnson (1709–84) supposedly wrote as a three-year-old memorialises a duck 'whom Samuel Johnson trod on'.

37 (p. 189) *Wuthering Heights* (1847), novel by Emily Brontë

38 (p. 190) *Jane Austen* (1775–1817), novelist

39 (p. 190) *'He has outsoared . . . miscall delight'* various lines from Shelley's *Adonais*

40 (p. 193) *Boars Hill* famed beauty spot near Oxford

41 (p. 193) *Persuasion* (1818), Jane Austen's last novel

42 (p. 195) *Trinity* Trinity College, Cambridge

43 (p. 195) *both universities* Oxford and Cambridge

44 (p. 197) *a vast machine, such as one sees at South Kensington* The South Kensington Museum, which would later become the Science Museum, displayed models of industrial machinery.

Chapter 5

45 (p. 203) *Professor Henry Sidgwick* (1838–1900) Knightsbridge Professor of Moral Philosophy (1883) at Cambridge University

46 (p. 204) *Burke* Edmund Burke (1729–97), politician, political theorist and philosopher. *Reflections on the Revolution in France* was published in 1790; his speeches On American Taxation (1774) and On Conciliation with the American Colonies (1775) were made in Parliament.

47 (p. 205) *Bright* John Bright (1811–82), MP representing various northern cities who espoused a number of reformist causes

48 (p. 205) *Disraeli* Benjamin Disraeli (1804–81), politician; Tory Prime Minister 1874–80

Chapter 8

49 (p. 222) *whether Asquith in or Austen Chamberlain out* Herbert Asquith (1858–1928), Liberal Prime Minister 1908–16; Austen Chamberlain (1863–1937), Conservative politician

50 (p. 224) *the Mall* processional route in London running from Admiralty Arch to Buckingham Palace

51 (p. 224) *a Court*   a reception, sometimes involving royalty, as part of the London season, when debutantes were brought out into society

52 (p. 225) *dahabeeyah*   large sailing boat used by travellers on the Nile

Chapter 9

53 (p. 228) *Wordsworth . . . The Prelude*   William Wordsworth (1770–1850), author of *The Prelude* (1850), a long autobiographical poem

54 (p. 228) *Beowulf*   Anglo-Saxon epic poem, *c.* early eighth century

55 (p. 228) *Swinburne*   Algernon Charles Swinburne (1837–1909), poet

56 (p. 230) *Gibbon's History of the Decline and Fall of Rome*   Edward Gibbon (1737–94), historian whose major work was *The History of the Decline and Fall of the Roman Empire* (1776–88)

57 (p. 232) *teetotum*   small four-sided spinning top with letters inscribed on its various sides

58 (p. 233) *Modern Love*   (1862), sonnet sequence by George Meredith (1828–1909), poet and novelist

59 (p. 233) *John Donne*   (1572–1631), Metaphysical poet. Hewet presumably uses Donne's name to refer to an edition of his poems.

60 (p. 234) *'I speak as one . . . the Curtain'*   final stanza of Thomas Hardy's poem 'He Abjures Love' (1883)

61 (p. 235) *'The poor little Queen of Holland'*   The Queen of Holland gave birth in April 1909.

62 (p. 236) *the Irish members*   Ireland was at this time part of the Union of Great Britain and so had representatives in Parliament

63 (p. 237) *Hannibal*   (247–152 BC), Carthaginian general

64 (p. 237) *Coptic*   an Egyptian language written in the Greek alphabet, the language of the Copts

65 (p. 243) *Wilde*   Oscar Wilde (1854–1900), Irish writer

Chapter 10

66 (p. 244) *The Works of Henrik Ibsen*   Henrik Ibsen (1828–1906), Norwegian dramatist

67 (p. 244) *Diana of the Crossways*   (1885), novel by George Meredith

68 (p. 245) *Defoe*   Daniel Defoe (1660–1731), novelist and journalist

69 (p. 245) *Maupassant*   Guy de Maupassant (1850–93), French writer

70 (p. 247) *Wellington . . . Waterloo* Arthur Wellesley, Duke of Wellington (1769–1852), led British troops to a famous victory over Napoleon at the Battle of Waterloo (June 1815).

71 (p. 250) *Garibaldi* Giuseppe Garibaldi (1807–82), key figure in the movement to achieve the unification of Italy

Chapter 11

72 (p. 259) *Father Damien* Joseph de Veuster (1840–89), Belgian Catholic missionary who ministered to a leper colony in Hawaii

73 (p. 261) *Winchester* Winchester College, English public school

74 (p. 261) *Westminster – King's* Westminster School, a public school in London; King's College, Cambridge

Chapter 12

75 (p. 273) *a strong Protectionist* as against Asquith's Free Trade position

76 (p. 276) *the Barcarolle out of Hoffman* song from the opera *Les Contes d'Hoffmann* (1881) by the French composer Jacques Offenbach (1819–80), based on the short stories of German writer E. T. A. Hoffmann (1776–1822)

77 (p. 278) *Alexander Pope* (1688–1744), poet

Chapter 13

78 (p. 284) *Jorrocks* comic fox-hunting character created by R. S. Surtees (1803–64)

79 (p. 284) *Sophocles* (496–406 BC), Greek dramatist

80 (p. 284) *Swift* Jonathan Swift (1667–1745), satirist and essayist

81 (p. 284) *Balzac* Honoré de Balzac (1799–1850), French novelist

82 (p. 284) *Coleridge* Samuel Taylor Coleridge (1772–1834), poet and philosopher

83 (p. 284) *Addison* Joseph Addison (1672–1719), essayist

84 (p. 284) *Marlowe* Christopher Marlowe (1564–93), playwright

85 (p. 284) *La Cousine Bette* (1846), novel by Balzac

86 (p. 285) *Wedekind* Frank Wedekind (1864–1918), German playwright

87 (p. 285) *Webster* John Webster (?1580–?1625), playwright

Chapter 14

88 (p. 289) *Lloyd George*   David Lloyd George (1863–1945), politician

89 (p. 292) *Some exquisite Greuzes*   Jean-Baptiste Greuze (1725–1805), French painter

Chapter 15

90 (p. 306) *a clever man in London called John*   Augustus John (1878–1961), painter

91 (p. 306) *Arthur Balfour*   (1848–1930), Conservative politician, Prime Minister 1902–06

92 (p. 306) *Symposium*   Plato's *Symposium*, one of his Dialogues, on the nature of love

93 (p. 308) *'Be good, sweet maid'*   from 'A Farewell' (1858) by Charles Kingsley (1819–75), author of *The Water Babies*

Chapter 16

94 (p. 320) *John Stuart Mill*   (1806–73), philosopher

95 (p. 320) *a G.F.S. meeting*   The Girls' Friendly Society, a Church of England organisation

96 (p. 325) *Thackeray*   William Makepeace Thackeray (1811–63), novelist

97 (p. 325) *Aristotle*   (382–24 BC), Greek philosopher

Chapter 17

98 (p. 331) *Man and Superman*   (1903), play by George Bernard Shaw (1856–1950), Irish dramatist

99 (p. 333) *'Be merciful unto me . . . rooted out'*   a mixture of lines from Psalms 56 and 58, *Book of Common Prayer*

100 (p. 334) *the Anabasis*   a work by Xenophon (*c.*430–*c.*355 BC), Athenian writer, recounting a military expedition against the Persians in which Xenophon took part

101 (p. 336) *Sappho*   (b. 612 BC), female lyric poet who gathered female followers around her on the Isle of Lesbos. Some of Swinburne's poems incorporated translations of fragments of her work, but they could not be said to be faithful translations. The 'Ode to Aphrodite' is one of her works.

Chapter 19

102 (p. 352) *Temperance* the Temperance movement encouraged abstinence from alcohol

103 (p. 355) *Chaucer* Geoffrey Chaucer (?1343–1400), author of *The Canterbury Tales*

104 (p. 356) *Dryden* John Dryden (1631–1700), poet and dramatist

105 (p. 356) *Euphues* John Lyly (1554–1606) wrote two narratives, *Euphues, The Anatomy of Wit* (1579) and *Euphues and his England* (1580), which are sometimes seen as the origin of the English novel.

106 (p. 361) *'Toll for the Brave'* first line of a poem by William Cowper whose full title is 'On the Loss of the *Royal George*' (1782)

107 (p. 361) *Lord Curzon* George Nathaniel Curzon (1859–1925), politician, Chancellor of Oxford University 1907–25

Chapter 20

108 (p. 368) *'Whoever you are . . . will be useless'* 'Whoever you are holding me now in hand' is the accurate first line and title of a poem in the 1860 version of *Leaves of Grass* by Walt Whitman (1819–92), American poet.

Chapter 21

109 (p. 378) *my Kodak* The Kodak Brownie, a pocket camera which made photography widely available, was first introduced in 1900.

Chapter 22

110 (p. 391) *a perfect Zany* a clown

Chapter 24

111 (p. 409) *Browning* Robert Browning (1812–89), poet

Chapter 25

112 (p. 418) *'There is a gentle nymph . . . Listen and save!'* lines from the masque *Comus* (1634) by John Milton (1608–1674)

113 (p. 437) *'They wrestled up . . . awhile to rest'* lines from Charles Kingsley's 'A New Forest Ballad' (1847)

114 (p. 438) *'Peor and Baalim . . . Astaroth'* lines from 'On the Morning of Christ's Nativity' (1629) by John Milton